MW00667288

Geometry

Student Text

By Steven P. Demme
Miriam Homer

Math·U·See

1-888-854-MATH (6284)
www.MathUSee.com

Math·U·See

1-888-854-MATH (6284)
www.MathUSee.com

Printed in the United States of America

ok'

LESSON PRACTICE 1A

Match each term to its definition.

1. endpoint	an infinite number of connected points
2. collinear	starting point, or origin, of a ray
3. one-dimensional	contained in the same line
4. line	having length but no width

Fill in the blanks.

5. A ____________ has one definite endpoint.

6. A ____________ ____________ has two definite endpoints.

7. Two amounts or measures that are exactly the same are said to be ____________ .

8. ____________ figures are the same shape but have different sizes.

9. Geometric figures that are ____________ are exactly the same shape and size.

Use the drawing as necessary to tell if each statement is true or false.

10. The common endpoint of $\overrightarrow{BE}$ and $\overrightarrow{BF}$ is E.

11. B is collinear with E and F.

12. $\overline{AB}$ is included in $\overleftrightarrow{BC}$.

13. $\overline{AB}$ is included in $\overrightarrow{BC}$.

14. $\overrightarrow{BC}$ contains point D.

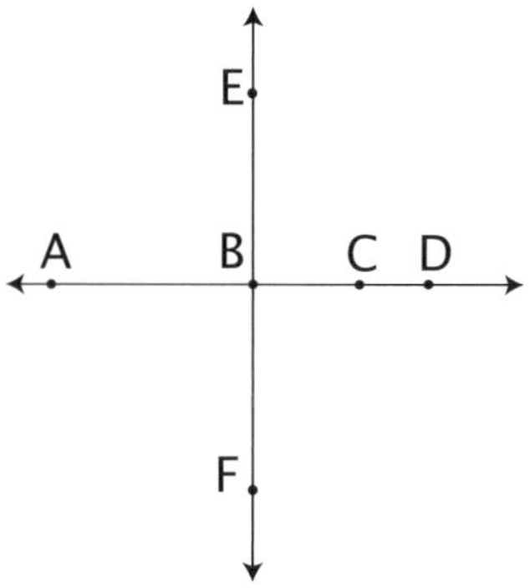

Given: $\overleftrightarrow{AC}$ and $\overleftrightarrow{EF}$ are straight lines and intersect at point B

Assuming the statements are exactly the same on both sides, fill the boxes with = or ≅.

15. 30 $\bigcirc$ 20 + 10

16. angle A $\bigcirc$ angle B

17. measure of rectangle A $\bigcirc$ measure of rectangle B

18. triangle ABC $\bigcirc$ triangle DEF

19. $\overline{AB}$ $\bigcirc$ $\overline{BA}$

20. AB $\bigcirc$ BA

LESSON PRACTICE

1B

Fill in the blanks with the correct geometric term.

1. ___________ means "the measure of the earth."

2. The smallest unit of geometric measure is the ___________ .

3. An infinite number of connected points is referred to as a ___________ .

4. Points contained in the same line are said to be ___________ .

5. A ___________ proceeds infinitely from a definite starting point.

6. A ___________ is a finite, or measurable, piece of a line.

7. Figures that are ___________ have the same shape but are not necessarily the same size.

8. To be ___________ is to have exactly the same length or measure.

9. To be ___________ is to have exactly the same shape and size.

10. The starting point of a line segment or ray is the ___________ .

Match each symbol to its meaning.

11. $\leftrightarrow$ line segment

12. $\rightarrow$ congruent

13. $-$ ray

14. $\cong$ line

Use the drawing to answer the questions.

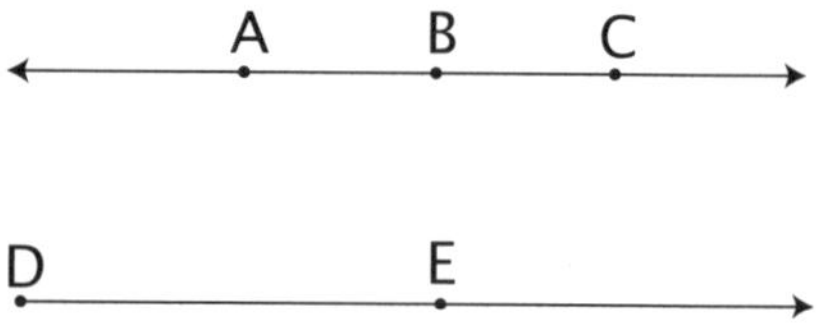

15. What point is collinear with A and B?

16. Point D is the endpoint of ___________.

17. $\overline{BC}$ is contained in line ___________.

18. Give a point contained by $\overrightarrow{CA}$. ___________

19. How many points are contained in $\overleftrightarrow{AC}$?

20. $\overrightarrow{AB}$ travels in the opposite direction from ___________.

SYSTEMATIC REVIEW

Good

1C

Fill in the blanks with the correct word or words.

1. The starting point of a ___________ or ___________ is the endpoint.

2. To be congruent is to have exactly the same ___________ and ___________ .

3. The smallest unit of geometric measure is the ___________ .

4. The symbol ↔ represents a ___________ .

5. An infinite number of connected ___________ is known as a line.

6. The symbol → represents a ___________ .

7. The symbol — represents a ___________ ___________ .

8. $\overleftrightarrow{AB} \cong \overleftrightarrow{BC}$ is read as ___________ AB is ___________ _____ ___________ BC.

9. A ___________ proceeds infinitely from a definite starting point.

10. ___________ means the measure of the earth.

Match each term to its definition.

11. similar	in the same line
12. equal	has same shape but different size
13. collinear	exactly the same shape and size
14. congruent	exactly the same length or measure

Use the drawing to answer the questions.

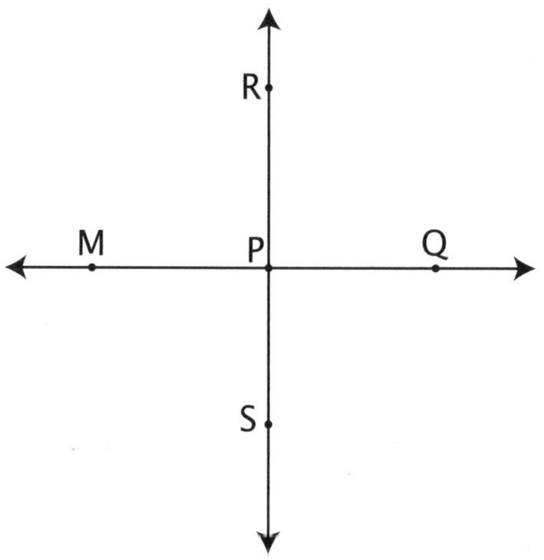

Given: $\overleftrightarrow{MQ}$ and $\overleftrightarrow{RS}$ are straight lines and intersect at point P.

15. What point is collinear with R and P?

16. Point M is the endpoint of ray ______.

17. Point S is contained in line ______.

18. Name three points that are collinear with $\overleftrightarrow{MQ}$.

19. How many points are contained in $\overleftrightarrow{RS}$?

20. How many points are contained in $\overrightarrow{RS}$?

SYSTEMATIC REVIEW

1D

Fill in the blanks with the correct words.

1. A one dimensional figure that extends infinitely in both directions is a ___________ .

2. Two rays contain the ___________ (same/different) number of points.

3. A one-dimensional figure with a measurable length is a ___________ ___________ .

4. Geometric shapes that have the same shape and size are said to be ___________, while numbers that have the same value are said to be ___________ .

5. The endpoint of $\overrightarrow{AB}$ is the point ___________ .

6. Geometry means the ___________ of the ___________ .

7. A geometric figure with no measurable length or width is a ___________ .

8. A geometric figure is said to be ___________ to another figure of the same shape but different size.

9. Points contained in the same line are said to be ___________ .

10. A line is made up of an infinite number of ___________ .

Match each symbol to its meaning.

11. $\overleftrightarrow{AB} \cong \overleftrightarrow{CD}$	line segment AB is congruent to line segment CD
12. $AB = CD$	line AB is congruent to line CD
13. $\overline{AB} \cong \overline{CD}$	ray AB is congruent to ray CD
14. $\overrightarrow{AB} \cong \overrightarrow{CD}$	distance AB is equal to distance CD

Use the drawing as necessary to tell if each statement is true or false.

15. B is collinear with E and A.

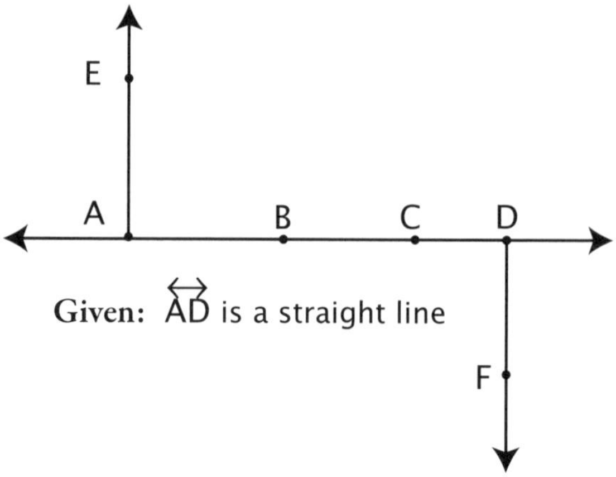

Given: $\overleftrightarrow{AD}$ is a straight line

16. $\overline{BC}$ is contained in $\overleftrightarrow{AD}$.

17. $\overline{AB}$ is included in $\overrightarrow{BD}$.

18. The common endpoint of $\overrightarrow{AB}$ and $\overrightarrow{BC}$ is B.

19. $\overline{DF} \cong \overline{FD}$

20. A straight line could be drawn in which E and F are collinear.

Honors Application Pages

The next page in this book is entitled Honors.

You will find a special challenge lesson after the last systematic review page for each lesson. These lessons are optional, but highly recommended for students who will be taking advanced math or science courses.

In the honors lessons, you will find a variety of problems that do the following:

- Review previously learned material in an unfamiliar context.
- Provide practical application of math skills relating to science or everyday life.
- Challenge the student with more complex word problems.
- Expand on concepts taught in the text.
- Familiarize students with problems that are present in standardized testing.
- Prepare for advanced science courses, such as physics.
- Stimulate logical-thinking skills with interesting or unusual math concepts.

HONORS 4 - STEP APPROACH

Here are four steps to help the student receive the most benefit from the honors pages.

Step 1. Read
Step 2. Think
Step 3. Compare
Step 4. Draw

Step 1. Read

Most of the honors lessons teach new topics or expand on the concepts taught in the regular lessons. Read the explanations carefully. Sometimes you will be led step-by-step to a new concept. When doing word problems, think through what is being described in the problem before trying to work out the math.

Step 2. Think

It has been suggested that one of the major problems with math instruction in the United States is that students do not take enough time to think about a problem before giving up. One of the purposes of the honors pages is to train you in problem-solving skills. Start by deciding what you already know about the concept being studied, and then look for ways to apply what you know in order to solve the problem. Don't be afraid to leave a difficult problem and come back to it later for a fresh look. You will notice that these lessons do not have as many detailed examples as the material in the instruction manual. In real life, individuals must often use what they know in new or unexpected ways in order to solve a problem.

Step 3. Compare

Compare your solution to the one in the back of the instruction manual. If you solved the problem differently, see whether you can follow the given solution. There is often more than one way to solve a problem. The solutions may also give you hints that are not on the lesson pages. If you are not able to solve a problem on your own, do not be upset. Much of this material was purposely designed to stretch your math muscles. You will learn a great deal by giving a problem your best try and then studying the solution.

Step 4. Draw

When in doubt, draw! Often a picture will help you see the big picture and recognize which math skills are necessary to solve the problem.

SCHEDULING HONORS PAGES

Students may not need to do all of the lesson practice pages for each lesson. We do recommend a student finish all of the systematic review pages before attempting the honors page.

If a student needs more time to become comfortable with the new concepts in the text before tackling more advanced problems, he may delay an honors page until he is two or three lessons ahead in the course. The student may also spread one honors section over two or three days while continuing to do the regular student pages. This approach allows time to come back to difficult problems for a fresh look.

Another option is to tackle all the honors pages after finishing the book as a review and preparation for the next level. This approach works especially well if you are continuing your study through the summer months.

Perfect

To be successful in any kind of math, it is very important to be able to think logically. In particular, geometry will require logic and problem-solving skills. This lesson shows you how to use a chart to solve simple logic problems. We will present more logic problems in a later lesson.

For each problem, carefully read the information given. Take one statement at a time, and use the chart to check off choices that will not work. Other impossible choices will also become apparent, and you may want to check them off as well. Study the possibilities that are left and answer the question.

This kind of chart is sometimes called a Carroll diagram.

Solve the logic problems using the charts.

1. Jeff, Tyler, and Madison each have a different favorite food. Tyler and Madison do not like tacos. Madison is allergic to anything made with milk. What is the favorite food of each?

	ice cream	tacos	steak
Jeff			
Tyler			
Madison			

2. Mike, Caitlyn, and Lisa each have a different color of hair. Mike's hair is darker than Lisa's and Caitlyn's. Caitlyn's hair is not as dark as Lisa's. What color is each person's hair?

	black	brown	blonde
Mike			
Caitlyn			
Lisa			

3. Four friends each have a different hobby. Donna's mother thinks she should spend more time outside. George and Adam find their hobbies complement each other very well. Adam is not allowed to use the stove. What is each person's hobby?

	reading	tennis	cooking	eating
George				
Celia				
Donna				
Adam				

4. The four people listed below each have a different favorite season. No person is named after a month in his or her favorite season. None of the girls chose autumn as her favorite season. Linda prefers a season that does not start with "s." What is each person's favorite season?

	spring	summer	autumn	winter
David				
Linda				
Shauna				
April				

LESSON PRACTICE

2A

Fill in the blanks.

1. A plane has both ___________ and ___________ .

2. A plane is said to be ___________ dimensional.

3. Two lines that lie in the ___________ plane are coplanar.

4. ___________-___________ shapes are studied in plane geometry and ___________-___________ shapes in solid geometry.

5. The intersection is where two or more things ___________ .

6. A union is where two or more things are ___________ .

7. A set is a ___________ of things.

8. An empty, or ___________, set means there is no possible answer.

9. A two-dimensional figure that extends infinitely in all directions is a ___________ .

Match each definition to its symbol.

10. subset $\cup$

11. null set $\subset$

12. union $\cap$

13. intersection $\varnothing$

Use the drawing as necessary to tell if each statement is true or false.

14. $\overline{AB} \cup \overline{BC} = \overline{AC}$

15. $\overrightarrow{BE} \cap \overrightarrow{BF} = \overleftrightarrow{EF}$

16. $\overline{AB} \cup \overline{CD} = \varnothing$

17. $\overline{BC} \subset \overleftrightarrow{BC}$

18. $\{A, B, C\} \subset \overleftrightarrow{EF}$

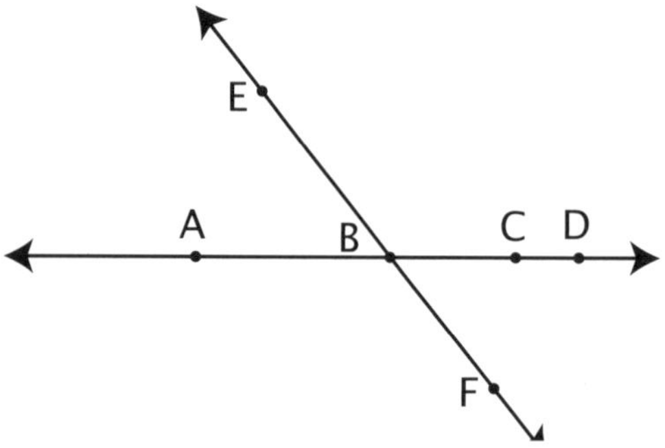

Given: $\overleftrightarrow{AD}$ and $\overleftrightarrow{EF}$ are straight lines and intersect at B.

LESSON PRACTICE

Perfect

2B

Fill in the blanks.

1. A ____________ has neither length nor width.

2. A ____________ has length but not width.

3. A ____________ has both length and width.

4. Two lines that lie in the same plane are ____________.

5. In mathematics, a collection of numbers or things is referred to as a ____________ .

6. A two-dimensional geometric figure that extends infinitely in all directions is a ____________ .

7. A set that contains nothing is called a ____________ set.

8. Solid geometry is the study of objects that have ____________ dimensions.

Match each symbol to its meaning.

9. $A \subset B$	the union of A and B
10. $A \cup B$	the set containing A and B
11. $A \cap B$	A is a subset of B
12. $\{A, B\}$	A is an empty set
13. $A = \varnothing$	the intersection of A and B

Use the drawing as necessary to tell if each statement is true or false.

14. $\overline{QR} \cup \overline{ST} = \varnothing$

15. $\overrightarrow{SQ} \cap \overrightarrow{SV} = \overleftrightarrow{QV}$

16. $\overrightarrow{ST} \cup \overrightarrow{RT} = \overrightarrow{RT}$

17. $\overrightarrow{SV} \subset \overleftrightarrow{WV}$

18. $\{Q, R, S\} \subset \overline{RT}$

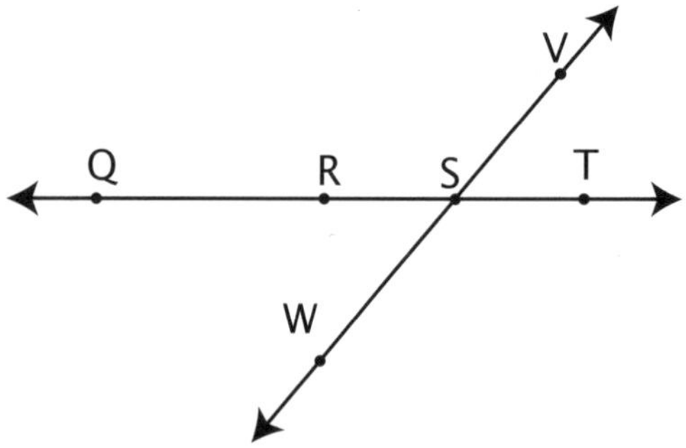

Given: $\overleftrightarrow{QT}$ and $\overleftrightarrow{VW}$ are straight lines and intersect at S.

Fill in the blanks with the geometric terms that match the definitions.

1. An infinite number of connected lines lying in the same flat surface. ___________
2. Two lines that lie in the same plane. ___________________
3. Two points that are contained in the same line. ___________
4. Having the same shape, but not necessarily the same size. __________________
5. Where two or more things meet or overlap. ___________
6. Where two or more things are combined. _________________
7. Exactly the same shape and size. ___________
8. A collection of things. ___________
9. There is no possible answer. ___________
10. Having the same numerical value. ___________

Match each symbol to its meaning.

11.	$\cup$	subset
12.	$\varnothing$	intersection
13.	$\subset$	null, or empty, set
14.	$\cap$	union

Use the drawing to fill in the blanks.

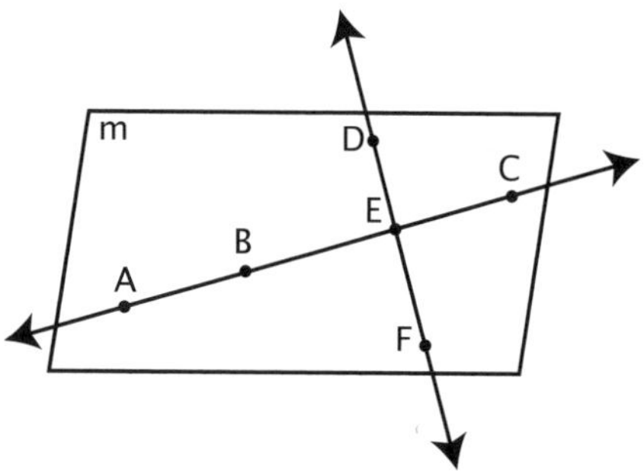

Given: Lines $\overleftrightarrow{AB}$ and $\overleftrightarrow{FD}$ lie in plane m and intersect at point E.

15. $\overline{DE} \subset$ ______

16. $\overrightarrow{EB} \cup \overrightarrow{EC} =$ ______

17. $\overline{EB} \cup \overline{EC} =$ ______

18. $\overrightarrow{EA} \cap \overrightarrow{BC} =$ ______

19. $\overline{AB} \cap \overline{EC} =$ ______

20. $\overleftrightarrow{FE} \cup \overleftrightarrow{ED} =$ ______

SYSTEMATIC REVIEW

2D

Fill in the blanks with the geometric terms that match the definitions.

1. A set that contains no elements. ___________

2. An infinite two-dimensional geometric figure. ___________

3. The starting point of a ray. ___________

4. Term represented by the symbol $\cup$. ___________

5. Term represented by the symbol $\cap$. ___________

6. A subgroup included in a collection. ___________

7. An infinite one-dimensional geometric figure. ___________

8. A geometric figure having no dimensions. ___________

9. Term represented by the symbol $\cong$. ___________

Match each term to its definition.

10.	coplanar	two squares with the same dimensions
11.	collinear	two measurements with the same value
12.	similar	two lines in the same plane
13.	congruent	two points on the same line
14.	equal	two squares with different dimensions

Use the drawing to answer the questions.

15. In $\overrightarrow{LG}$, which point is the starting point?

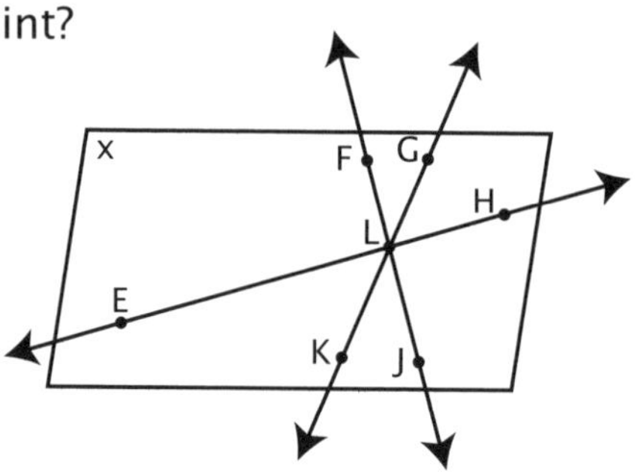

16. $\overline{EL} \cup \overline{LH} =$ ____________

17. $\overrightarrow{EL} \cup \overrightarrow{LH} =$ ____________

Given: All three lines lie in plane x and intersect at point L.

18. How many lines go through both points J and F?

19. $\overrightarrow{LH}$ and $\overrightarrow{LK}$ share a common ____________ .

20. Which labeled points are contained in $\overleftrightarrow{KG}$?

SYSTEMATIC REVIEW 2E

Fill in the blanks with the correct geometric terms or symbols.

1. A collection of numbers or things. ________________
2. The symbol that represents the empty or null set. ________________
3. A one-dimensional figure with a definite starting point, extending infinitely in one direction. ________________
4. A one-dimensional figure with a measurable length. _______ _______
5. The symbol used to represent a subset. ________________
6. The combination of all the items in two given sets. ________________
7. The overlap of all the items in two given sets. ________________
8. Two points that are contained in the same line. ________________

Use the drawing to answer the questions.

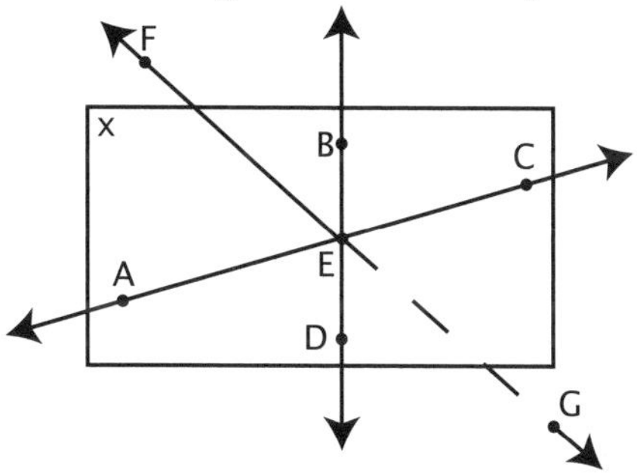

Given: Lines $\overleftrightarrow{AC}$ and $\overleftrightarrow{BD}$ lie in plane x. Line $\overleftrightarrow{FG}$ does not lie in plane x, but passes through it.

9. $\overleftrightarrow{AC}$, $\overleftrightarrow{BD}$, and $\overleftrightarrow{FG}$ appear to intersect at point __________ .
10. How many points are there in plane x?
11. Could another plane be drawn on which $\overleftrightarrow{BD}$ and $\overleftrightarrow{FG}$ would be coplanar?

Use the drawing to answer the questions.

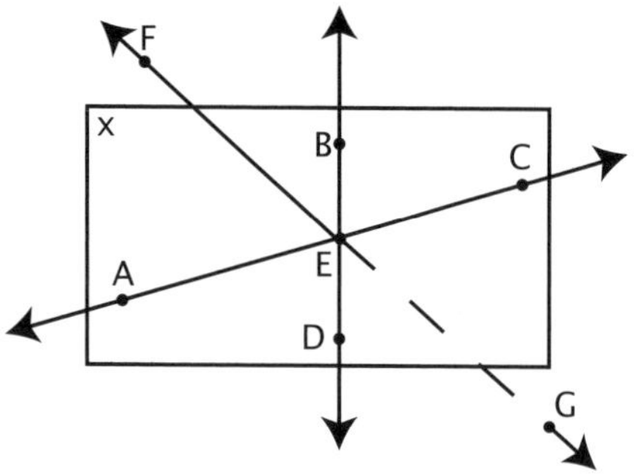

Given: Lines $\overleftrightarrow{AC}$ and $\overleftrightarrow{BD}$ lie in plane x. Line $\overleftrightarrow{FG}$ does not lie in plane x, but passes through it.

12. How many points are there in $\overleftrightarrow{FG}$?

13. How many points are contained in the union of $\overleftrightarrow{FG}$ and plane x?

14. Could a line be drawn in which A and B would be collinear?

15. Could a line be drawn in which A, B, and C would be collinear?

16. Is $\overrightarrow{EF}$ a subset of plane x?

17. $\overline{AE} \cup \overrightarrow{AE} =$ ________

Sharpen your algebra skills!

Order of Operations: parenthesis, exponents, multiply and divide, add and subtract.

EXAMPLE

$$(4 \times 3) + 4^2 - 6 \div 2 =$$
$$12 + 4^2 - 6 \div 2 =$$
$$12 + 16 - 6 \div 2 =$$
$$12 + 16 - 3 = 25$$

18. $(2 \times 5) \times 4^2 - 5^2 =$

19. $42 \times 3 \div (6^2 \div 12) =$

20. $28 \div 2^2 + 6^2 =$

HONORS LESSON 2H

Here is another way to think about set notation. Two or three overlapping figures may be used to illustrate the union and intersections of sets. These are referred to as Venn diagrams.

Study the example, and then answer the questions.

Example: Ten people attended a party and all asked for ice cream. Six of them asked for chocolate ice cream and nine for vanilla. How many asked for both chocolate and vanilla? (Assume no one asked for seconds.) Illustrate the problem with a Venn diagram, and then record the same information using set notation.

Answer: Only 10 people were at the party, but there were 15 requests, so five people must have asked for both chocolate and vanilla. Fill in the overlapping part of the circles first with the number that asked for both kinds. Six asked for chocolate, and 6 - 5 = 1, so one person asked for only chocolate. Nine in all asked for vanilla , and 9 - 5 = 4, so four asked for only vanilla.

chocolate

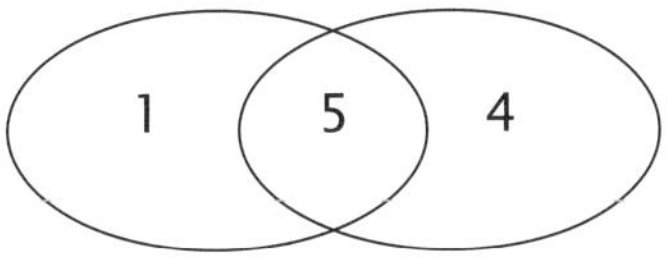

vanilla

For set notation, use C for people who had chocolate and V for people who had vanilla.

$C \cap V = 5$ $\quad$ $C \cup V = 10$

1. During the month of September, 18 days had at least some sunshine. Twenty days had at least some rain. Fill in the Venn diagram to illustrate this, and then record the information with set notation.

sunshine

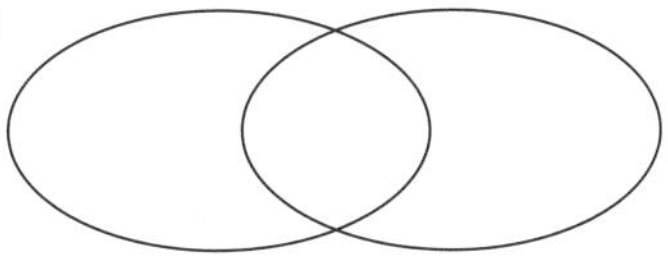

rain

Do you think there are two sides to everything? If so, try this activity.

2. Cut a strip of paper about one inch wide from the long side of a piece of notebook paper. Bring the ends of the paper together, twist one end once, and then tape the ends together. Now pick up your pencil and draw a line down the center of the strip of paper. What happens? How many sides does this loop of paper have?

3. Now use your scissors to poke a hole somewhere on the line you drew, and then cut along the line. Before you do this, try to predict what will happen to your strip of paper. What will happen if you cut the strip a second time in the same way?

Express the word problems using numerals, and then use the correct order of operations to simplify and find the answer to each one.

4. Tom thought of a number. He squared the number and added the result to the starting number. The sum was divided by six, and then 10 was added. If the number Tom thought of was five, what was his final result?

5. Forty-two books were divided evenly among seven shelves. Six more books were added to the last shelf, and then one was taken away. How many books were left on the last shelf?

LESSON PRACTICE

3A

Use the drawing as necessary to answer the questions.

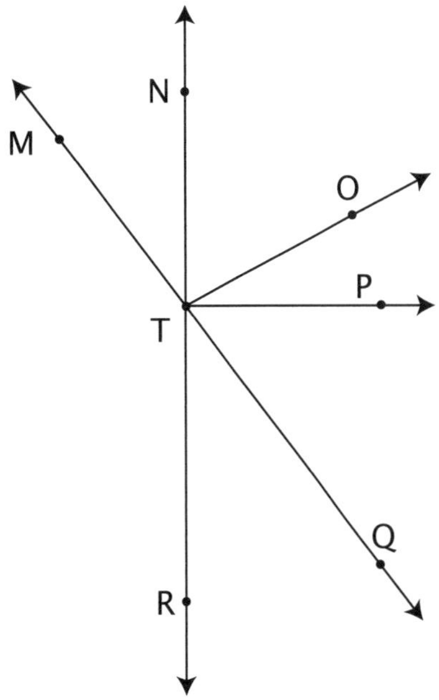

Given: $m\angle PTR = 90°$

$\overleftrightarrow{NR}$ is a straight line.

1. What is the vertex of ∠NTP?

2. What is the vertex of ∠PTO?

3. What is the vertex of ∠ABC? *(not shown)*

4. The common endpoint of $\overrightarrow{TR}$ and $\overrightarrow{TQ}$ is _____.

5. What angle lies between the rays in #4?

6. Points V, X, and W are not collinear. *(not shown)* The common endpoint of $\overrightarrow{WV}$ and $\overrightarrow{WX}$ is _____.

7. What angle is formed by the rays in #6?

8. What is the vertex of the angle described in #7?

Measure the angles to the nearest whole degree.

9. 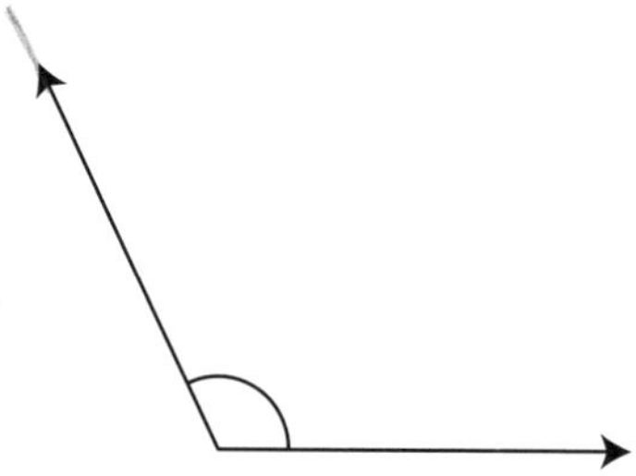

10. 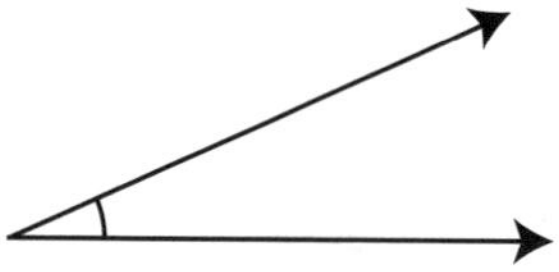

11. 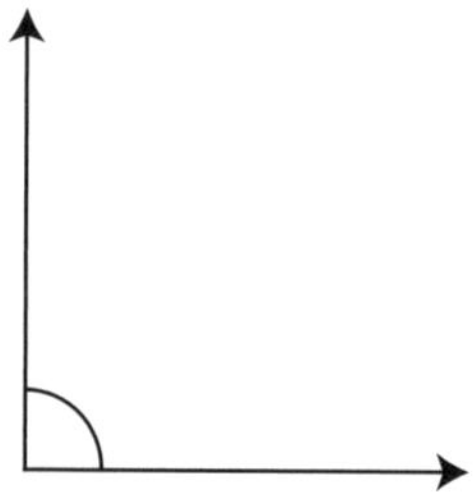

Draw these angles.

12. m∠XYZ = 75°

13. m∠2 = 95°

14. m∠a = 170°

Use the drawing as necessary to answer the questions.

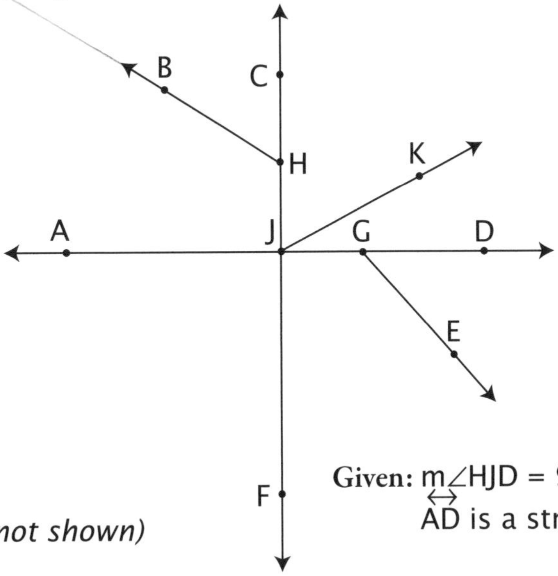

Given: m∠HJD = 90°
$\overleftrightarrow{AD}$ is a straight line.

1. What is the vertex of ∠FJG?

2. What is the vertex of ∠EGA?

3. What is the vertex of ∠RST? *(not shown)*

4. The common endpoint of $\overrightarrow{HB}$ and $\overrightarrow{HC}$ is ______.

5. What angle is formed by the rays in #4?

6. Points X, Y, and M are not collinear. *(not shown)*
   The common endpoint of $\overrightarrow{MX}$ and $\overrightarrow{MY}$ is ______.

7. What angle lies between the rays in #6?

8. What is the vertex of the angle described in #7?

Measure the angles to the nearest whole degree.

9. 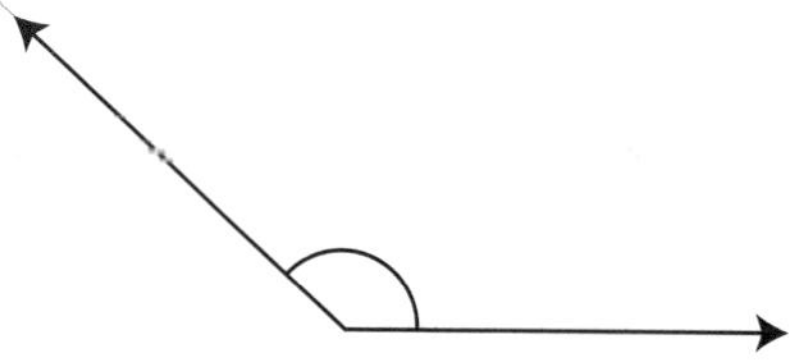

10. 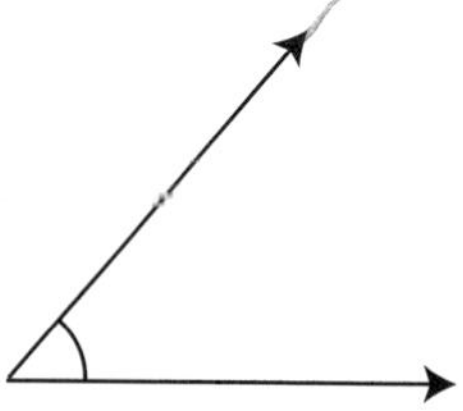

11. 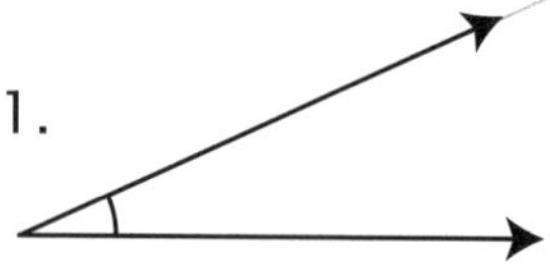

Draw these angles.

12. $m\angle 3 = 15°$

13. $m\angle ABC = 160°$

14. $m\angle \alpha = 110°$

Use the drawing as needed to fill in the blanks.

1. The intersection of two lines forms four ____________.

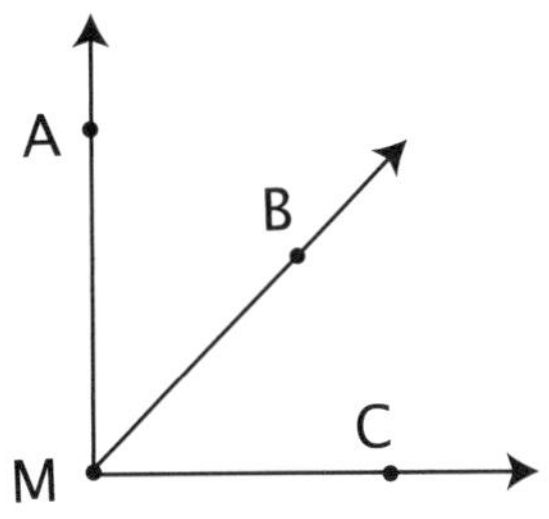

2. The endpoint of two rays forming an angle is called the ____________.

3. The vertex of angle AMB is point ____________.

4. $m\angle 1$ is read "the ____________ of ____________ 1."

5. $\overrightarrow{MB}$ and $\overrightarrow{MC}$ form $\angle$ ____________.

True or False.

6. Angles are measured in degrees.

7. The intersection of two planes is a point.

8. The intersection of two lines is a plane.

9. Two lines that lie in the same plane are coplanar.

Measure the angles to the nearest whole degree.

10.

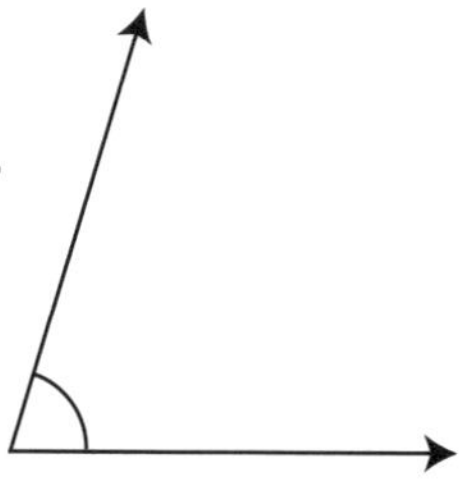

11.

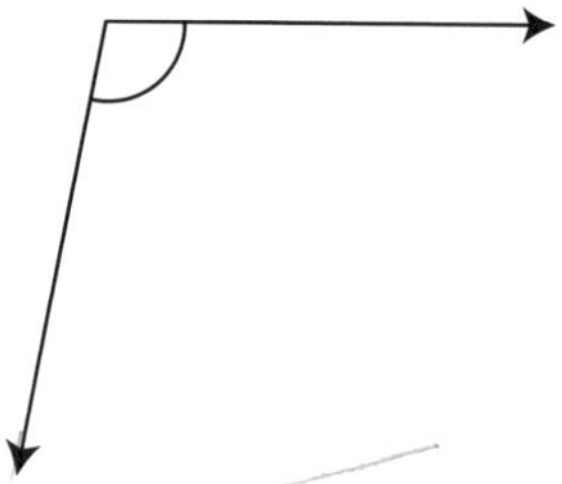

12.

Draw these angles. Use another paper if necessary.

13. $m\angle 1 = 30°$

14. $m\angle \alpha = 25°$

15. $m\angle AHG = 90°$

Use the drawing to fill in the blanks.

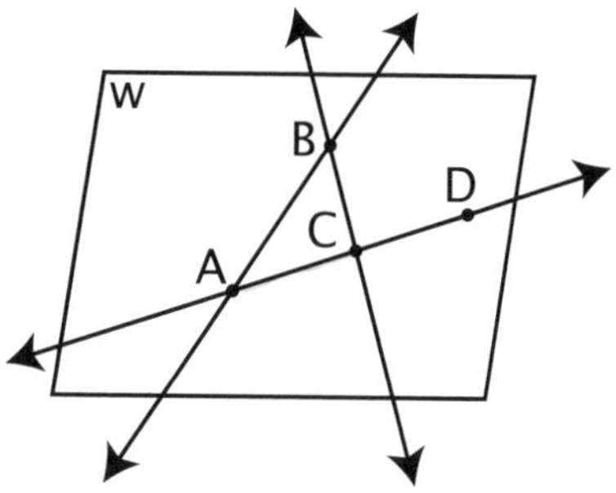

Given: All lines lie in plane w.

16. $\overrightarrow{AB} \cap \overrightarrow{CB} =$ ____________

17. $\overleftrightarrow{AC} \cap \overrightarrow{CD} =$ ____________

18. $\overline{AD} \cup \overrightarrow{CA} =$ ____________

19. $\overline{AD} \cap \overrightarrow{BC} =$ ____________

20. $\overleftrightarrow{AB} \cap \overrightarrow{CD} =$ ____________

SYSTEMATIC REVIEW

3D

Fill in the blanks.

1. Angles are measured in ____________ .

2. The ____________ of ∠XYZ is point Y.

3. Two lines that lie in the same plane are ____________ .

4. m∠α is read "the ____________ of ____________ ____________."

5. A square that is 4" on a side is ______________ to one that is 6" on a side.

Measure the angles to the nearest whole degree.

6. 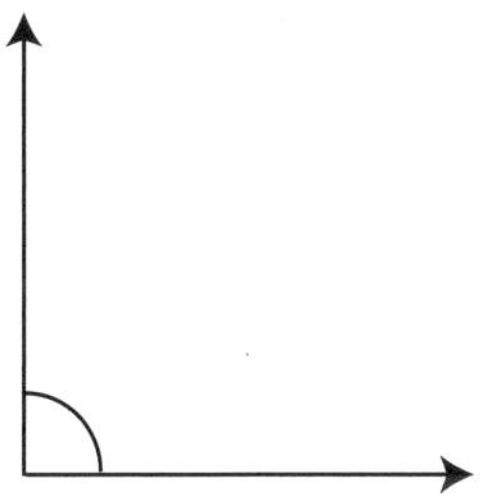

7. 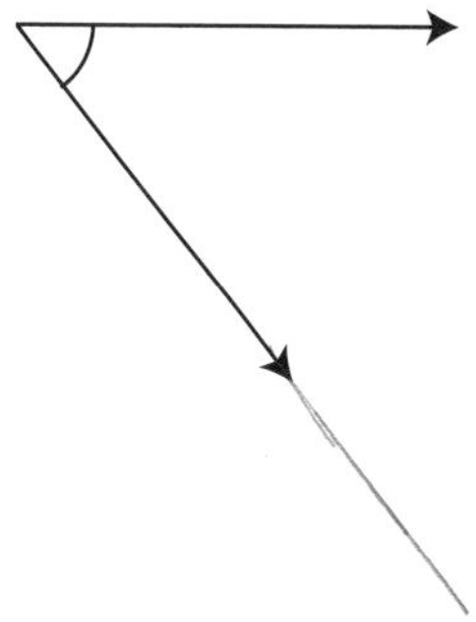

8. 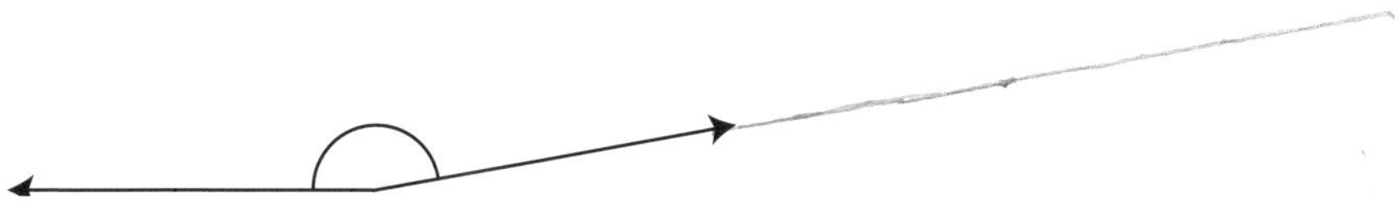

Draw these angles. Use another paper if necessary.

9. $m\angle 3 = 179^\circ$

10. $m\angle \beta = 18^\circ$

11. $m\angle QRS = 88^\circ$

Use the drawing to answer the questions.

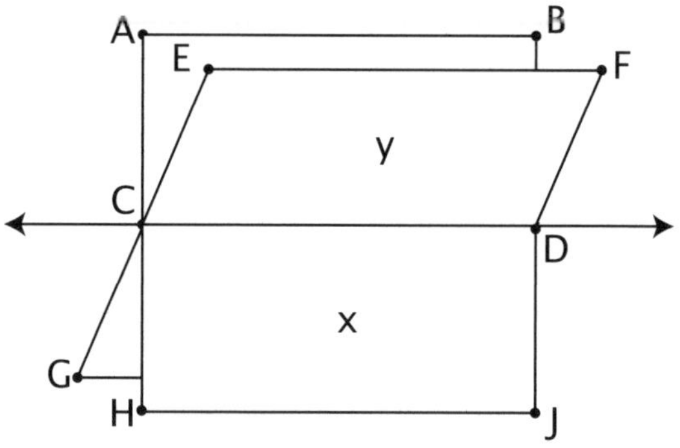

Given: Planes x and y intersect at line $\overleftrightarrow{CD}$.

12. What is the length of $\overleftrightarrow{CD}$?

13. How many dimensions does plane y have?

14. What is the intersection of planes x and y ($x \cap y$)?

15. $\overrightarrow{CE} \cup \overrightarrow{CG} =$

16. $\overrightarrow{CE} \cap \overrightarrow{CG} =$

17. In which plane do points A, B, H, and J lie?

18. How many points are there in plane x?

19. $\overrightarrow{DC} \cap \overrightarrow{CD} =$

20. $\overrightarrow{DC} \cup \overrightarrow{CD} =$

SYSTEMATIC REVIEW

3E

Use the drawing as needed to tell if the statements are true or false.

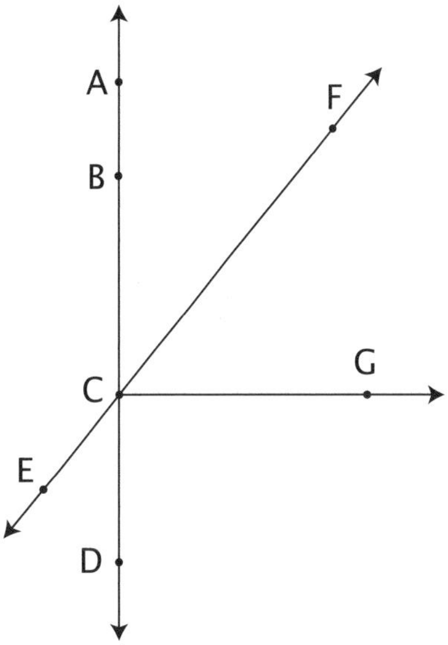

Given: $\overleftrightarrow{AD}$ and $\overleftrightarrow{EF}$ are straight lines. $\overleftrightarrow{AD}$, $\overleftrightarrow{EF}$, and $\overrightarrow{CG}$ all intersect at point C.

1. The vertex of $\angle ECD$ is point C. ____________

2. $\angle ACG \cong \angle BCG$. ____________

3. $\overline{CE} \cup \overline{CF} = \overleftrightarrow{EF}$. ____________

4. The intersection of point A and $\overrightarrow{CD}$ is the null set. ____________

5. Points B, C, and G are collinear. ____________

6. A line could be drawn including points F and G. ____________

7. $m\angle ACF + m\angle FCG = m\angle ACG$. ____________

8. $\overline{CE} \cong \overline{EC}$. ____________

9. $\overrightarrow{BC}$ and $\overrightarrow{DC}$ have a common endpoint which is point C. ____________

Measure the angles to the nearest whole degree.

10. 

11. 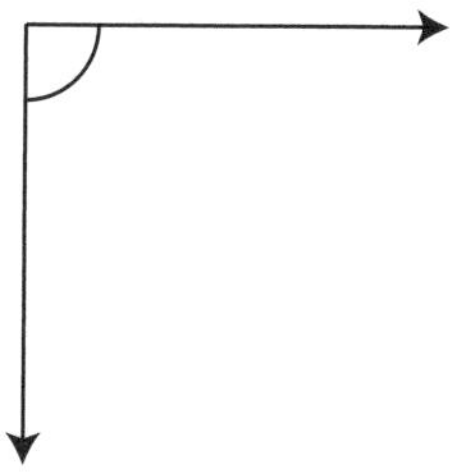

12. 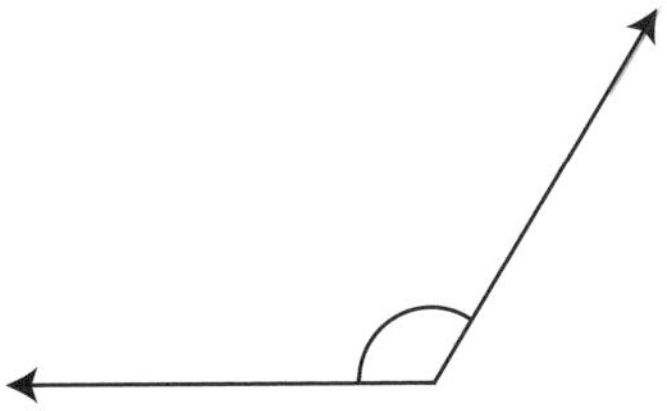

Draw these angles. Use another paper if necessary.

13. $m\angle 1 = 13°$

14. $m\angle \alpha = 125°$

15. $m\angle AHG = 170°$

Sharpen your algebra skills!

Commutative Property: addition and multiplication are commutative; subtraction and division are not.

EXAMPLE 1 $(3 + 4) = (4 + 3)$, but $(3 - 4) \neq (4 - 3)$

EXAMPLE 2 $(2 \times 6) = (6 \times 2)$, but $(2 \div 6) \neq (6 \div 2)$

True or False (for all values of the unknowns).

16. $(X + Y) = (Y + X)$

17. $(2)(A) = (A)(2)$

18. $X \div 6 = 6 \div X$ $(X \neq 0)$

19. $2(A - B) = 2(B - A)$

20. $3(Y + 9) = 3(9 + Y)$

Venn diagrams may have three overlapping circles. When solving this kind of problem, fill in the combined amounts first in the overlapping parts of the circles. Then you can subtract from the totals for each category to fill in the rest of the chart. After you have filled in each chart, answer the questions.

Follow the directions to fill in each chart, and then answer the questions.

The teacher said that the students could collect leaves, flowers, or seeds for a science project. Some students decided to make more than one collection. Eight students collected flowers, 10 collected seeds and seven collected leaves. Of these totals, three collected flowers and leaves, two collected leaves and seeds, and one collected flowers and seeds.

1. How many students collected only leaves?

2. How many students collected only flowers?

3. Use set notation to show how many students collected both leaves and flowers.

4. Use set notation to show how many students collected either leaves or flowers or both.

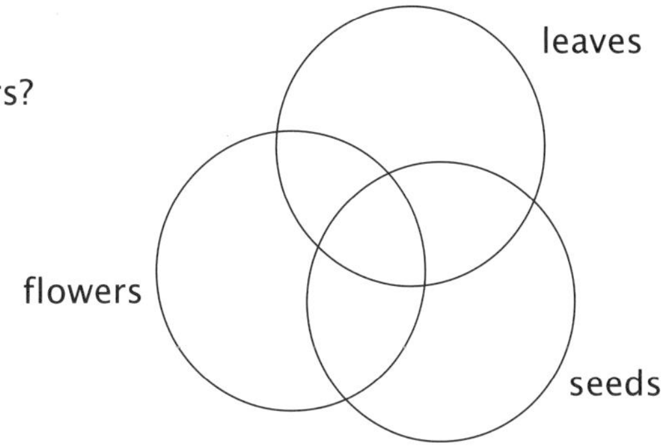

You can also use set notation to show the union of all three circles. The total number of collections is the union of all the different categories. $S \cup F \cup L = 19$

People at the picnic had different ideas about what to put on their hamburgers. Fifteen people used ketchup, eight used mustard and seven used pickles. Of these totals, four put all three on their hamburgers. Two people used ketchup and pickles, and one used ketchup and mustard. No one used just mustard and pickles.

5. How many people used only ketchup?

6. How many people used only mustard?

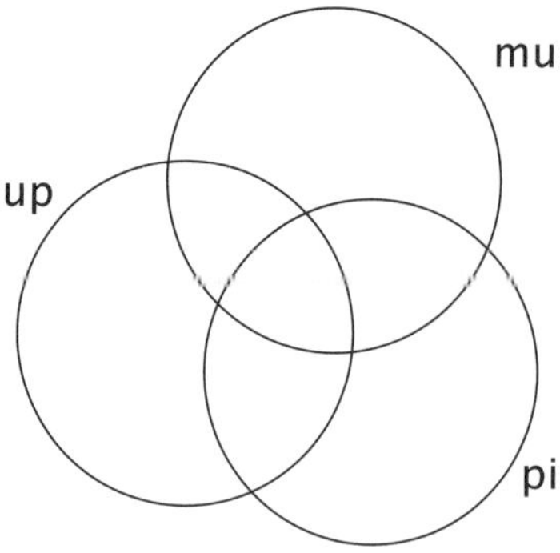

7. Use set notation to show how many people used just ketchup or just mustard or just ketchup and mustard.

8. Use set notation to show the intersection, or the number of people using all three condiments on their hamburgers.

The following examples illustrate either the associative or commutative property. Write each one as an equality or inequality. Tell what property is being illustrated, and whether it is true for the operation being used.

9. Three donuts were placed in each of four bags. Four donuts were placed in each of three bags.

10. Michael took nine steps forward and six steps back. Dylan took six steps forward and nine steps back.

11. Joanne ate two apples and one pear. Later she ate five grapes. Kia ate two apples. Later she ate one pear and five grapes.

12. Two cakes were divided among eight people. Eight cakes were divided between two people.

Try writing your own examples to illustrate how the associative and commutative properties work for each basic operation of arithmetic.

LESSON PRACTICE

4A

Fill in each blank with the type of angle indicated. Each set of points actually defines two different angles. In problems like these, assume the smaller angle is meant unless you are told otherwise.

1. ∠MTN is a(n) __________ angle.

2. ∠NTQ is a(n) __________ angle.

3. ∠PTR is a(n) __________ angle.

4. ∠QTP is a(n) __________ angle.

5. ∠QTR is a(n) __________ angle.

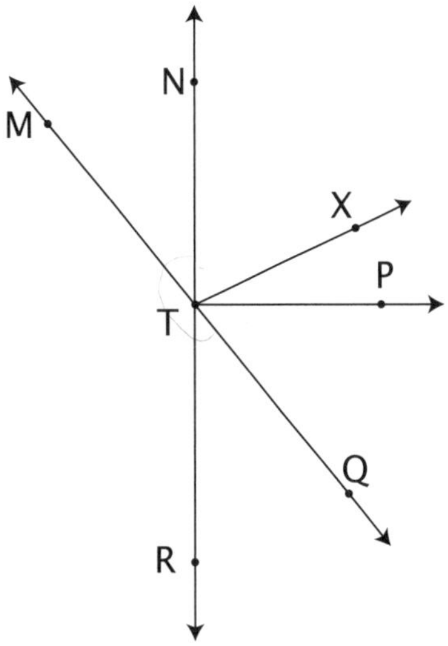

Given: m∠PTR = 90°.
$\overleftrightarrow{NR}$ is a straight line.

Measure the angles. Give the measure, and then tell what kind of angle it is.

6. 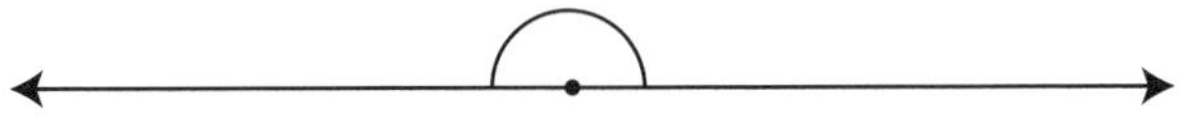

7. 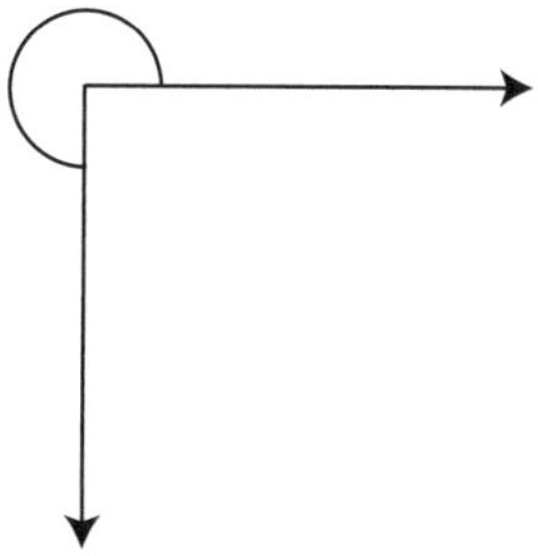

8. 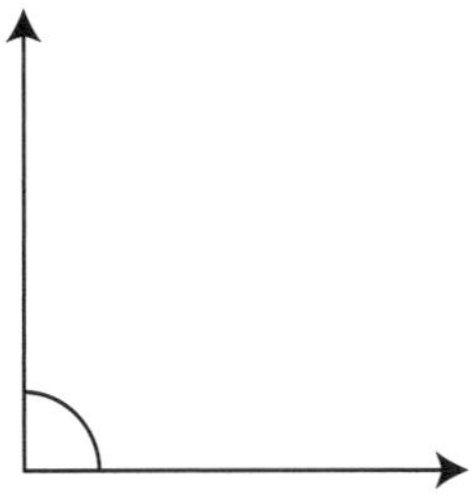

9. Draw a 190° angle. What kind of angle is this?

10. Draw a 10° angle. What kind of angle is this?

11. Draw a 340° angle. What kind of angle is this?

12. Draw a 100° angle. What kind of angle is this?

LESSON PRACTICE

4B

Refer to the drawing and fill in the blanks. Describe the smaller angle named by the given points unless directed otherwise.

1. ∠MRP is a(n) ___________ angle.

2. ∠NRQ is a(n) ___________ angle.

3. ∠NRQ is a(n) ___________ angle.
   (larger angle formed)

4. ∠NRP is a(n) ___________ angle.

5. ∠PRQ is a(n) ___________ angle.
   (larger angle formed)

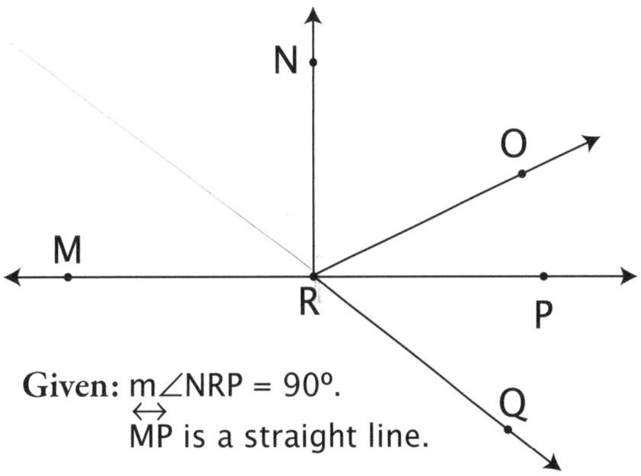

Given: m∠NRP = 90°.
$\overleftrightarrow{MP}$ is a straight line.

Measure the angles. Give the measure, and then tell what kind of angle it is.

6.

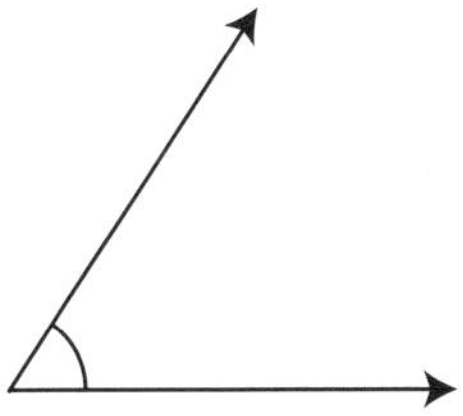

7.

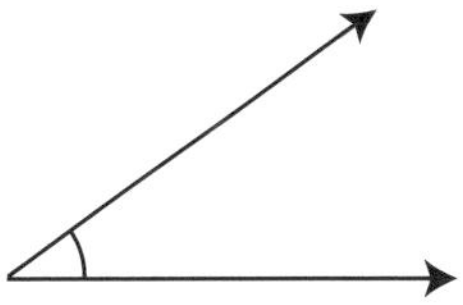

8.

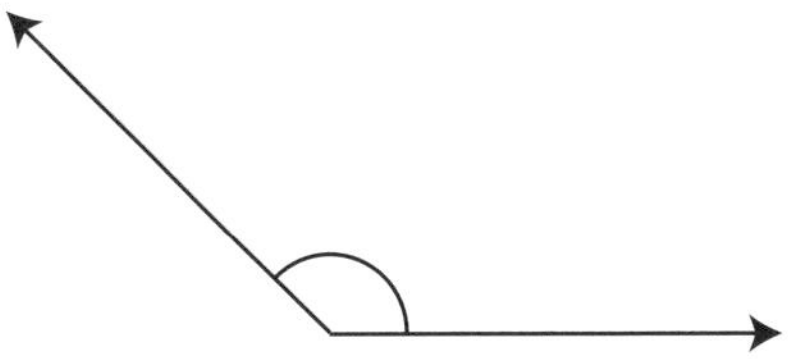

9. Draw a 170° angle. What kind of angle is this?

10. Draw a 5° angle. What kind of angle is this?

11. Draw a 90° angle. What kind of angle is this?

12. Draw a 120° angle. What kind of angle is this?

SYSTEMATIC REVIEW

4C

Use the drawing as needed to fill in the blanks and answer the questions.

1. Another name for $\angle\alpha$ is ____________ .

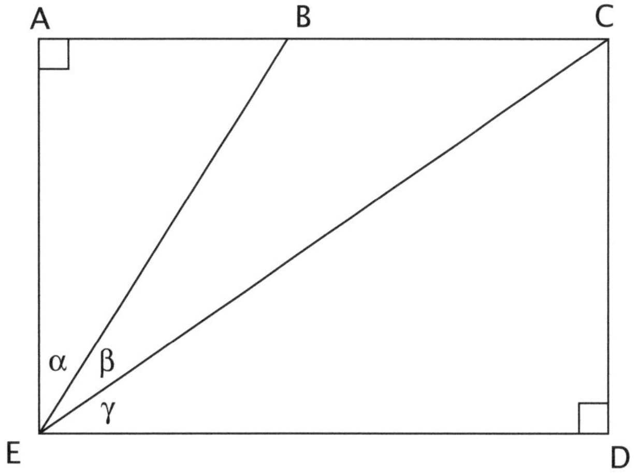

Given: m $\angle$AED = m$\angle$ACD = 90°

2. Name three acute angles.

3. $\angle$AEB + $\angle$BEC ≅ $\angle$_________.

4. m$\angle$AEC + m$\angle$DEC = ______.

5. Name two right angles.

6. The vertex of $\angle\beta$ is ____________.

7. $\angle\beta + \angle\gamma \cong \angle$____________.

8. Name an obtuse angle.

9. Draw a 20° angle. What kind of angle is this?

10. Draw a 45° angle. What kind of angle is this?

11. Draw a 135° angle. What kind of angle is this?

12. Two points that lie in the same line are ____________.

13. "Geo" means ____________ and "metry" means ____________.

14. Two figures exactly the same shape and size are said to be ____________.

15. $\overline{AE} \cap \overline{CD}$ = ____________ (refer to the drawing on the previous page).

True or False.

16. $\{a, b, c\} \cup \{c, d\} = \{a, b, c, d\}$.

17. A point has two dimensions.

18. A plane has one dimension.

19. An angle with a measure of 170° is an obtuse angle.

20. A line segment is infinite in length.

SYSTEMATIC REVIEW

4D

Use the drawing as needed to fill in the blanks. Describe the smaller angle named by the given points unless directed otherwise.

1. ∠PTM is a(n) ____________ angle.

2. ∠PTS is a(n) ____________ angle.

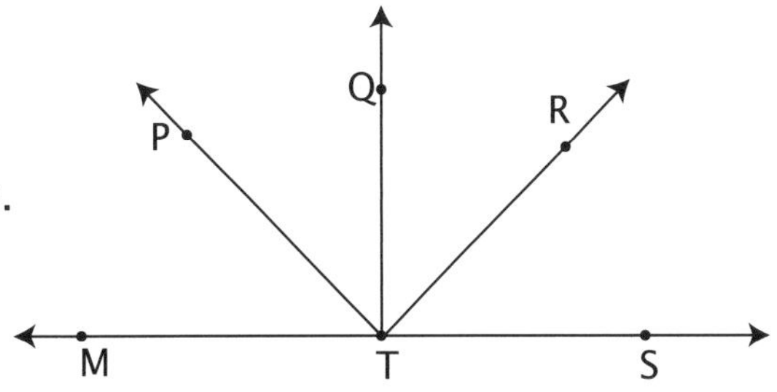

Given: $\overleftrightarrow{MS}$ is a straight line.
m∠MTQ = 90°.

3. ∠RTM is a(n) ____________ angle.
(larger angle formed)

4. ∠MTQ is a(n) ____________ angle.

5. m∠MTQ + m∠QTS = ____________.

6. $\overrightarrow{TR}$ and $\overrightarrow{TP}$ form ∠ ____________.

7. An acute angle is greater than 0° and less than ____________.

8. An obtuse angle is greater than ____________ and less than 180°.

9. The vertex of ∠QTR is ____________.

10. $\overrightarrow{TM} \cup \overrightarrow{TS} \cong$ ____________.

Draw these angles and tell what kind they are. Use another paper if necessary.

11. $m\angle\beta = 90^\circ$ 12. $m\angle\alpha = 35^\circ$ 13. $m\angle ABC = 175^\circ$

14. $m\angle JKL = 180^\circ$ 15. $m\angle 2 = 5^\circ$

Make your own drawing.

16. Draw $\overleftrightarrow{AB}$ and $\overleftrightarrow{CD}$ that intersect in plane X.

17. How long is $\overrightarrow{AB}$?

18. Label the intersection of your two lines E.

19. Name one angle formed by the intersection of the two lines.

20. What is the vertex of your angle?

Use the drawing as needed to fill in the blanks and answer the questions. Describe the smaller angle named by the given points unless directed otherwise.

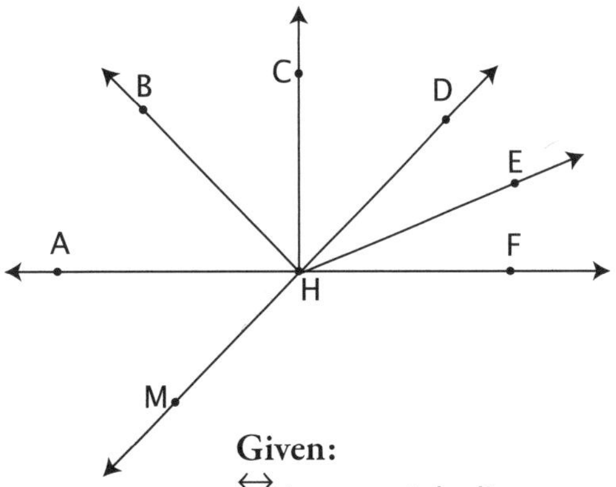

Given:
$\overleftrightarrow{AF}$ is a straight line.
m∠FHC = 90°.

1. ∠AHC is a(n) ____________ angle.

2. ∠AHE is a(n) ____________ angle.

3. ∠CHD is a(n) ____________ angle.

4. ∠AHF is a(n) ____________ angle.

5. ∠FHM is a(n) ____________ angle. *(larger angle formed)*

6. What is the vertex of ∠CHD?

7. What is the vertex of ∠QZW? *(not shown)*

8. What is the common endpoint of $\overrightarrow{HB}$ and $\overrightarrow{HE}$?

9. What angle is formed by the two rays in #8?

10. What angle lies between the two rays $\overrightarrow{PS}$ and $\overrightarrow{PY}$? *(not shown)*

11. Draw a 95° angle. What kind of angle is this?

12. A right angle plus an acute angle equals a(n) ____________ angle.

13. A right angle plus a right angle equals a(n) ____________ angle.

14. A straight angle plus an acute angle equals a(n) ____________ angle.

True or False.

15. A line is a two-dimensional figure.

16. A ray extends infinitely in one direction only.

17. A point has width but not length.

18. An angle with a measure of 270° is a reflex angle.

Sharpen your algebra skills!
Solve for one unknown by performing the same operations on both sides of an equation.

EXAMPLE

$$\begin{array}{rcr} 4X - 16 & = & 24 \\ +16 & & +16 \\ \hline 4X & = & 40 \\ \div 4 & & \div 4 \\ \hline X & = & 10 \end{array}$$

19. $30 = 42Y + 18$

20. $15 = -45M - 30$

A compass rose is a design used on maps to indicate directions. The directions can be indicated by names like northeast (NE) and south southwest (SSW), or they may be indicated by angles. In navigation, these are referred to as bearings. A compass rose is shown below.

Try answering the questions by looking at the diagram, and then use your protractor to check your answers. You may want to draw lines from point to point across the center of the circle to make it easier to measure the angles.

1. A ship sailed east, and then changed its bearing to northeast. How many degrees had the ship's direction, or heading, changed?

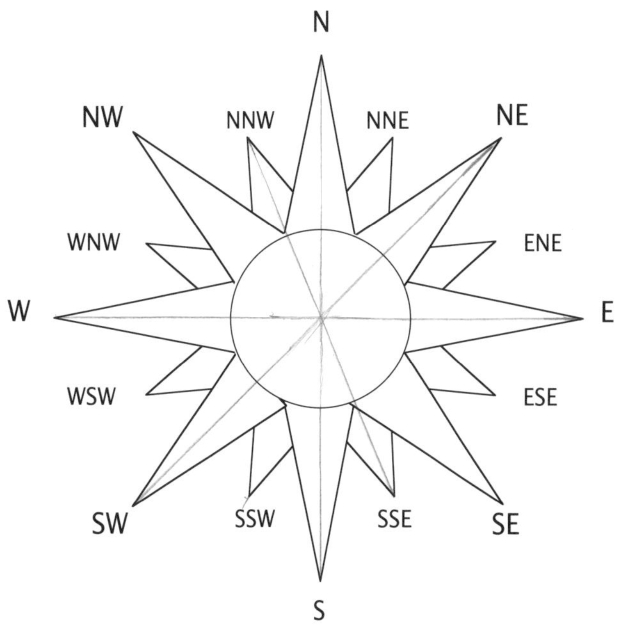

2. An airplane was headed north. After changing its bearing 22° toward the west, in what direction was it flying?

3. A hiker walked SSW for five miles and then used his compass to turn 180°. Now in what direction is he walking?

4. A ship that was sailing SW was blown off course, so that it was sailing SSE. The captain corrected his course back 50° toward the south and west. Is the ship back on its original bearing?

Write an equation for each word problem. Solve for the unknown and answer the questions.

5. Five times the unknown minus six is equal to two times the unknown plus eighteen. What is the unknown?

6. If 10 is added to twice the cost, the result is the same as it would be if the cost were subtracted from 43. Let C be the cost and find the value of C.

7. A sandwich and a drink together cost $3.25. The sandwich costs $1.75 more than the drink. How much does each one cost? Let D stand for the drink. Write the cost of the sandwich in terms of D. Can you write an equation now?

8. Aaron and Isaac have paper routes. Aaron has twice as many customers as Isaac. Together they have 105 customers. How many customers does each one have?

9. Jim has a piece of lumber 18 feet long. He wants to cut it into two pieces, one twice as long as the other. How long will each piece be?

10. Lisa bought 144 apples in two boxes. One box had 20 more apples than the other box. How many apples were in each box?

LESSON PRACTICE 5A

Fill in the blanks.

1. Two lines in the same plane that never intersect are ________________ lines.

2. Two lines that intersect and form a right angle are ________________ lines.

3. A line that cuts an angle or a line segment in half is a ________________ .

4. A bisector that forms a 90° angle with the original line is a ________________ .

5. If AB = BD, then B is the ________________ of $\overline{AD}$.

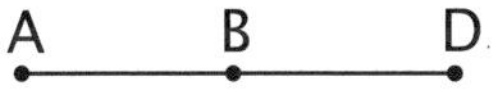

Use your straightedge and compass to find the midpoint of each segment and draw the perpendicular bisector.

6. 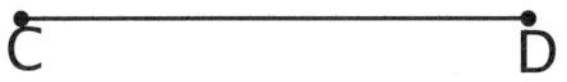

7. 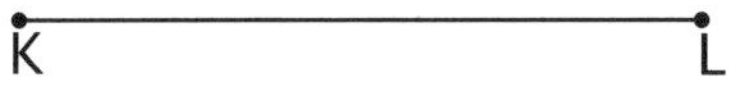

Use your straightedge and compass to draw the bisector of each angle.

8. 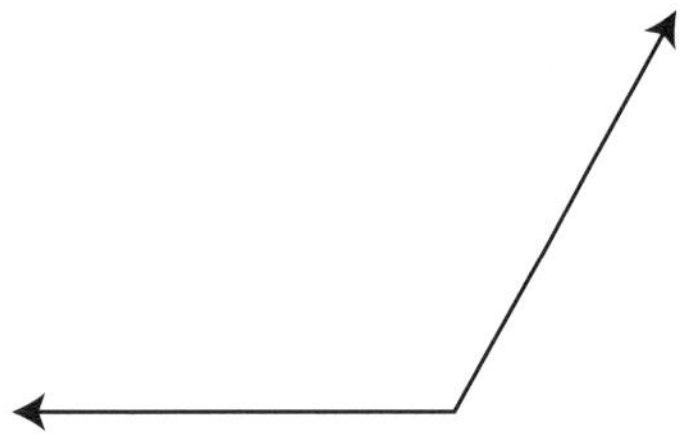

9. 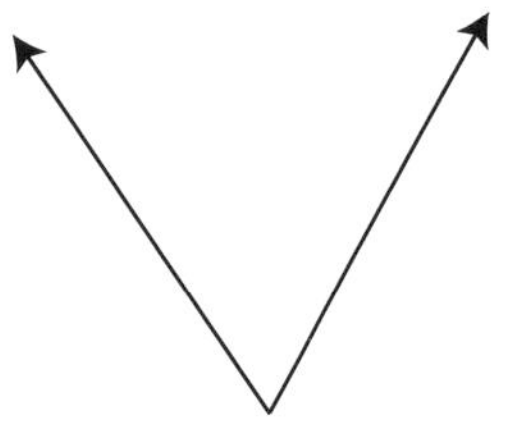

LESSON PRACTICE 5B

Fill in the blanks.

1. Two lines that intersect and form a ________________ angle are perpendicular lines.

2. Two lines in the same plane that never ________________ are parallel lines.

3. A line that cuts an ________________ or a ________________ in half is a bisector.

4. A bisector that forms a ________________ angle with the original line is a perpendicular bisector.

5. If XY = YZ, then Y is the midpoint of ________________.

Use your straightedge and compass to find the midpoint of each segment and draw the perpendicular bisector.

6. 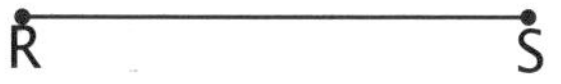

7. 

Use your straightedge and compass to draw the bisector of each angle.

8. 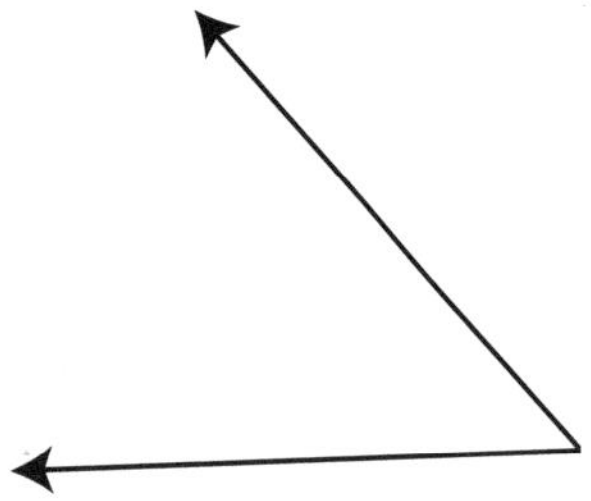

9. 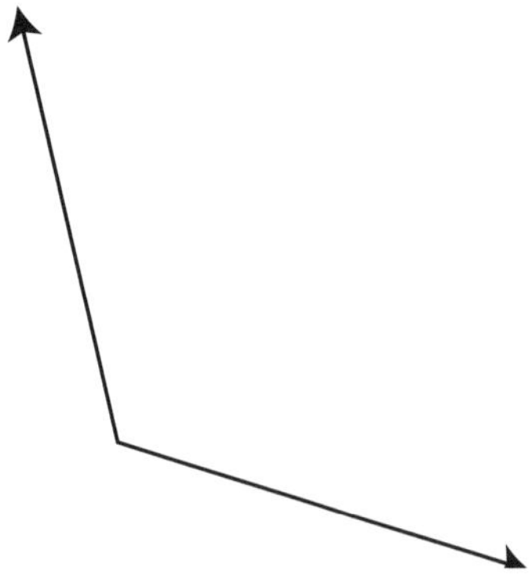

5C

Use the letters to match each term with an example.

___1.	parallel lines	a.	three dots drawn on the kitchen table by your baby sister
___2.	perpendicular lines	b.	line cutting an angle into two equal parts
___3.	bisector	c.	double yellow lines on a straight highway
___4.	union	d.	the set that includes only subsets from two other sets
___5.	intersection	e.	set combining the set of boys and the set of girls in my family
___6.	coplanar	f.	in a building, a column and the beam resting on it

Answer the questions.

7. What is the vertex of $\angle DEC$?

8. What is the degree measure of a straight angle?

9. Which two tools can be used to bisect an angle or a line?

10. Give an example of a reflex angle.

11. Give another name for the empty set.

Use another paper for your drawings if necessary.

12. Draw a line segment $2\frac{1}{2}$" long.

13. Draw the perpendicular bisector of the line segment you drew for #12. Do not measure to find the midpoint.

14. Draw and label ∠DEF with a measure of 68°.

15. Using your compass, draw a ray through point G that bisects ∠DEF. Check your work with your protractor.

Identify the five kinds of angles.

16. 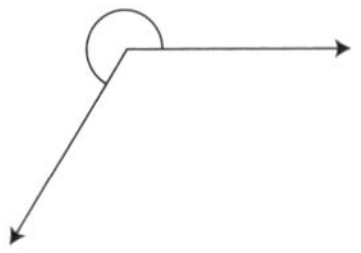

17. 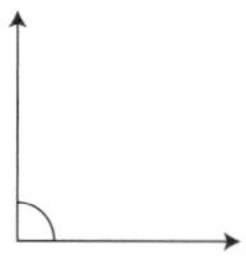

18. 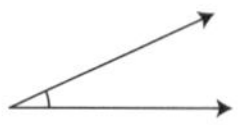

19. 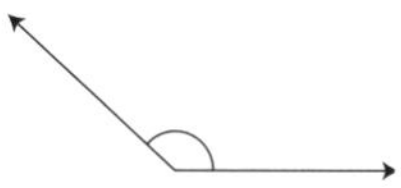

20. 

Fill in the blanks.

1. A line that cuts an angle or line segment into two congruent parts is a ________________.

2. Two lines in the same plane that never intersect are ______________.

3. An angle with a measure between 180° and 360° is called a(n) ________________ angle.

4. Two lines that intersect and form a right angle are______________.

5. Two figures with the same shape but different sizes are _____________.

6. Two figures with exactly the same shape and size are ________________.

Use the drawing to answer the questions.

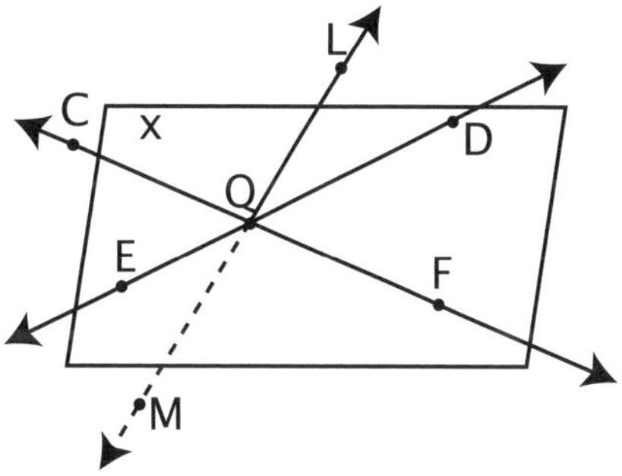

Given: $\overleftrightarrow{CF}$ and $\overleftrightarrow{ED}$ lie in plane x.
$\overleftrightarrow{LM}$ intersects plane x at Q.

7. What is the union of $\overrightarrow{QD}$ and $\overrightarrow{QE}$?

8. What is the intersection of $\overrightarrow{QD}$ and $\overrightarrow{QE}$?

9. Could a line be drawn making points L and F collinear?

10. What is the intersection of $\overleftrightarrow{LM}$ and plane x?

11. Is there a plane in which $\overleftrightarrow{LM}$ and $\overleftrightarrow{CF}$ would be coplanar?

12. Draw a line segment 3" long.

13. Draw a perpendicular bisector for the line segment in #12. Do not measure to find the mid-point.

14. Draw and label ∠ABC with a measure of 46°.

15. Using your compass, draw a ray through point G that bisects ∠ABC. Check your work with your protractor.

Sketch an example of each of the five kinds of angles.

16. straight

17. reflex

18. right

19. acute

20. obtuse

5E

Use the letters to match each term with an example.

___1. collinear	a. sheets of computer paper from the same package
___2. parallel lines	b. relationship between the vertical and horizontal lines of an upper case "T"
___3. perpendicular lines	c. the set of orange trees native to Antarctica
___4. null set	d. the ages of each of a pair of twins
___5. coplanar	e. the lines on a piece of writing paper
___6. congruent	f. points A, B, and C on $\overleftrightarrow{AC}$
___7. equal	g. any two lines drawn on a chalkboard

True or False.

8. The midpoint of a line segment can be found *only* by measuring with a ruler.

9. The bisector of an angle divides the angle into two angles with equal measures.

10. The bisector of a line segment divides the segment into two parts that are not necessarily congruent.

11. All lines passing through the midpoint of another line segment are perpendicular to that line segment.

12. Parallel lines extend to infinity without meeting.

13. Draw a line segment $1\frac{3}{4}$" long.

14. Draw a perpendicular bisector for the line segment in #12. Do not measure to find the midpoint.

15. Draw and label ∠XYZ with a measure of 20°

16. Using your compass, draw a ray through point G that bisects ∠XYZ. Check your work with your protractor.

Sharpen your algebra skills!

Equations may be simplified using the distributive property.

EXAMPLE

15Y + 30X = 10,
so 5(3Y + 6X) = 5(2).
Divide both sides by 5 to get 3Y + 6X = 2.

Simplify using the distributive property.

17. 24Q + 18Y = 30

18. -14Q - 21D = -42

Simplify and solve for X.

19. 16X - 8 = 56

20. 22X + 33 = 44

5H

Bisecting the angles or sides of geometric figures can lead to some interesting patterns. Practice your bisecting skills as directed below. To see the patterns clearly, don't let the line segments you draw go outside the lines of each figure.

1. Inside the triangle, draw the perpendicular bisector of each line.

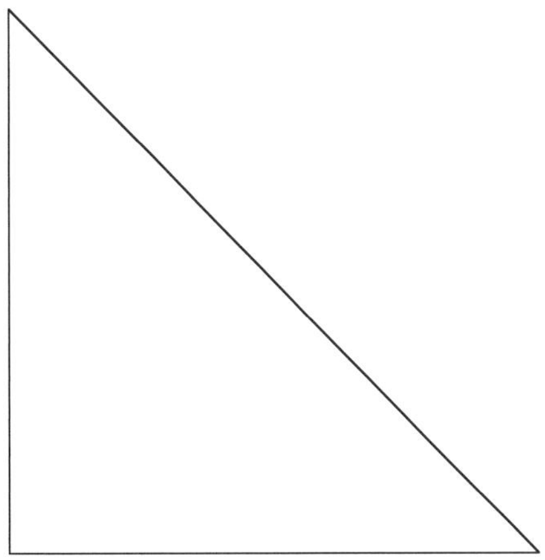

2. Including the triangle you started with, how many different triangles can you count in your drawing?

3. Now use your compass and straightedge to bisect each angle of this triangle.

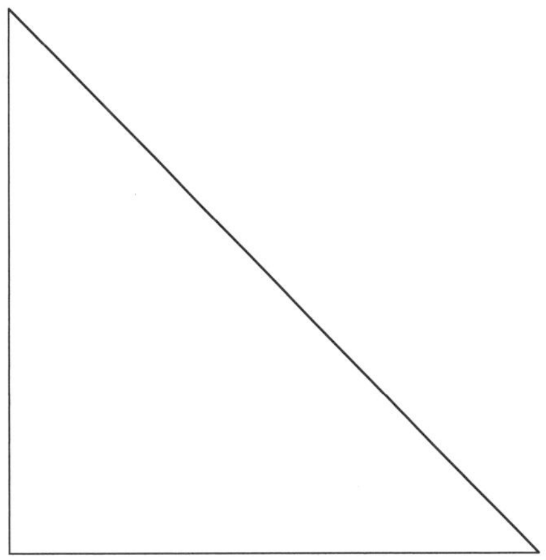

4. Including the triangle you started with, how many different triangles can you count in your drawing?

5. Draw the perpendicular bisectors of each line inside the rectangle below.

6. Using dotted lines or a different colored pencil, bisect each angle in the original rectangle.

Use the drawing to fill in the blanks.

1. ∠AHC is adjacent to ∠______ and ∠______.

2. ∠BHD is adjacent to ∠______ and ∠______.

3. ∠FHB and ∠______ are vertical angles.

4. ∠FHC and ∠______ are vertical angles.

5. ∠LFJ and ∠______ are supplementary angles.

6. ∠FHC and ∠______ are complementary angles.

7. ∠JFH and ∠______ are supplementary angles.

8. ∠BHD and ∠______ are complementary angles.

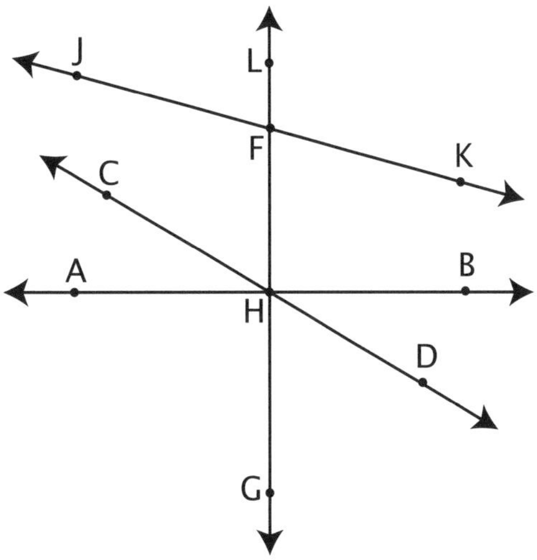

Given: $\overleftrightarrow{AB}$, $\overleftrightarrow{CD}$, $\overleftrightarrow{LG}$, and $\overleftrightarrow{JK}$ are straight lines. m∠FHB = 90°.

The drawing is a sketch and not necessarily to scale. Don't make any assumptions about the lines and angles other than what is actually given.

9. If m∠CHA = 40°, then m∠BHD = ______.

Use the drawing from the previous page to fill in the blanks.

10. If $m\angle JFL = 65^\circ$, then $m\angle KFH =$ _______.

11. If $m\angle FHB = 90^\circ$, then $m\angle FHA =$ _______.

12. If $m\angle CHA = 40^\circ$, then $m\angle FHC =$ _______.

13. If $m\angle LFJ = 65^\circ$, then $m\angle LFK =$ _______.

14. If $m\angle FHB = 90^\circ$, then $m\angle AHG =$ _______.

Use the letters to match each term to the best answer.

15. β ___

16. adjacent angles ___

17. supplementary angles ___

18. α ___

19. complementary angles ___

20. vertical angles ___

a. share a common ray

b. alpha

c. always have the same measure

d. add up to 90°

e. add up to 180°

f. beta

LESSON PRACTICE

6B

Use the drawing to fill in the blanks.

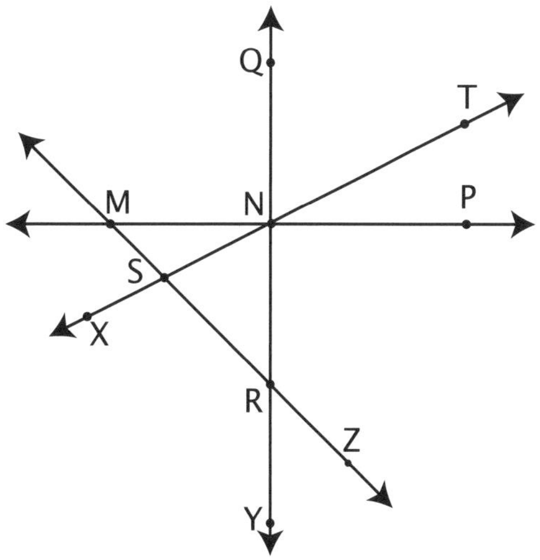

Given: All lines that appear to be straight lines are straight lines. m∠QNP = 90º.

The drawing is a sketch and not necessarily to scale. Do not make any assumptions about the lines and angles other than what is actually given.

1. ∠MNS is adjacent to ∠______ and ∠______.

2. ∠QNT is adjacent to ∠______ and ∠______.

3. ∠SRN and ∠______ are vertical angles.

4. ∠MNS and ∠______ are vertical angles.

5. ∠QNP and ∠______ are supplementary angles.

6. ∠QNT and ∠______ are complementary angles.

7. ∠NRZ and ∠______ are supplementary angles.

8. ∠MNS and ∠______ are complementary angles.

Use the drawing from the previous page to fill in the blanks.

9. If m∠MNS = 35°, then m∠SNR = ______.

10. If m∠MNS = 35°, then m∠TNP = ______.

11. If m∠QNP = 90°, then m∠PNR = ______.

12. If m∠MSN = 95°, then m∠NSR = ______.

13. If m∠SRN = 40°, then m∠YRZ = ______.

14. If m∠XNY = 55°, then m∠QNT = ______.

Fill in the blanks with the correct terms.

15. The name of the Greek letter α is ________________.

16. Two angles whose measures add up to 90° are called ________________.

17. Two angles whose measures add up to 180° are called ________________.

18. The name of the Greek letter γ is ________________.

19. Intersecting lines form two pairs of ________________ angles.

20. The name of the Greek letter δ is ________________.

Use the drawing to fill in the blanks.

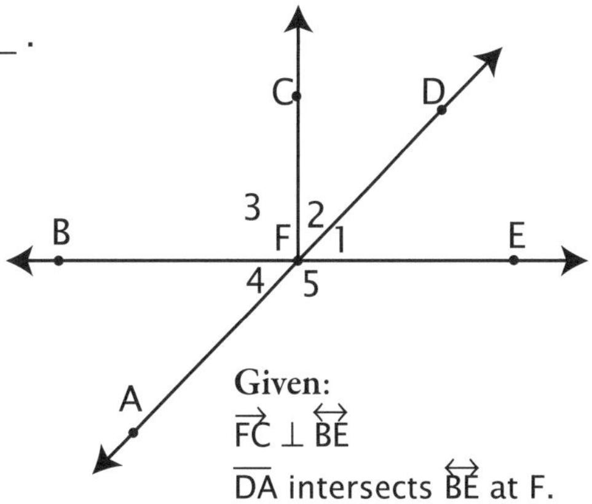

Given:
$\overrightarrow{FC} \perp \overleftrightarrow{BE}$
$\overline{DA}$ intersects $\overleftrightarrow{BE}$ at F.

From now on, we will assume lines that look straight to be straight lines. Do not make any assumptions about the size of the angles.

1. ∠1 is adjacent to ∠______ and ∠______ .

2. ∠1 and ∠______ are vertical angles.

3. ∠AFE and ∠______ are vertical angles.

4. ∠______ is a straight angle.

5. ∠______ is an obtuse angle.

6. ∠2 and ∠______ are complementary angles.

7. If m∠2 = 50°, then m∠1 = ______. Why?

8. If m∠2 = 50°, then m∠4 = ______. Why?

9. ∠5 and ∠______ are supplementary angles.

10. If m∠4 = 40°, then m∠5 = ______. Why?

11. Name two acute angles.

12. Name two right angles.

Follow the directions.

13. Draw a line segment $1\frac{1}{2}$ inches long. Then draw its perpendicular bisector using compass and straightedge.

14. Draw a 52° angle and bisect it.

Fill in the blanks with the correct terms.

15. Two lines forming a right angle are said to be __________________ to each other.

16. A right angle has a measure of ______$^\circ$.

17. A straight angle has a measure of ______$^\circ$.

18. The measures of two complementary angles add up to______$^\circ$.

19. The measures of two supplementary angles add up to ______$^\circ$.

20. The intersection of two sets with no elements in common is the __________________ set.

SYSTEMATIC REVIEW

6D

Use the drawing to tell if each statement is true or false.

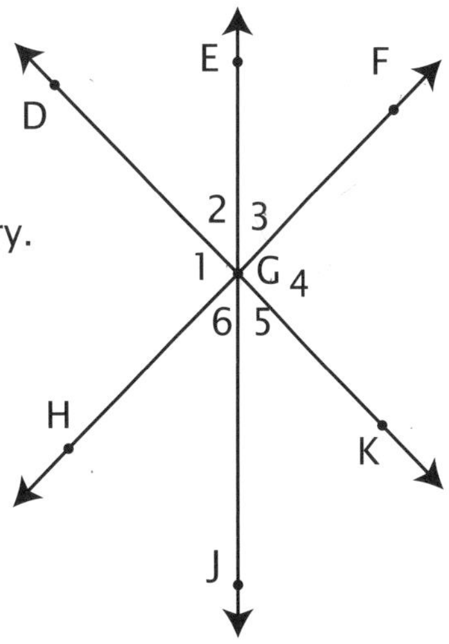

Given:
$\overleftrightarrow{DK}$, $\overleftrightarrow{EJ}$, and $\overleftrightarrow{FH}$ intersect at G.

Lines that look straight are straight. Do not make any other assumptions.

1. ∠2 and ∠5 are vertical angles.

2. If $\overleftrightarrow{FH} \perp \overleftrightarrow{DK}$, then ∠2 and ∠3 are supplementary.

3. ∠3 and ∠4 are adjacent angles.

4. ∠FGK is known to be a right angle.

5. $\overrightarrow{GJ}$ is the common side for ∠JGK and ∠KGF.

6. ∠2, ∠3 and ∠5 appear to be acute.

Use the drawing to fill in the blanks.

7. If m∠3 = 39º, then m∠6 = _______. Why?

8. If $\overleftrightarrow{FH} \perp \overleftrightarrow{DK}$ and m∠3 = 39º, then m∠2 = _______. Why?

9. If $\overleftrightarrow{FH} \perp \overleftrightarrow{DK}$, then m∠1 and m∠4 are each _______. Why?

10. If m∠1 is 90º, then it is a(n) ______________ angle.

11. If the measures of ∠4 and ∠1 add up to 180º, they are called ___________________ angles.

12. m∠1 + m∠2 + m∠3 + m∠4 + m∠5 + m∠6 = _______º.

Use the letters to match each description to the correct term.

13.	Greek letter beta ________	a.	α
14.	less than 90° ________	b.	complementary
15.	measures add up to 90° ________	c.	δ
16.	Greek letter alpha ________	d.	obtuse
17.	Greek letter gamma ________	e.	acute
18.	between 90° and 180° ________	f.	β
19.	measures add up to 180° ________	g.	γ
20.	Greek letter delta ________	h.	supplementary

Use the drawing to fill in the blanks or answer the questions.

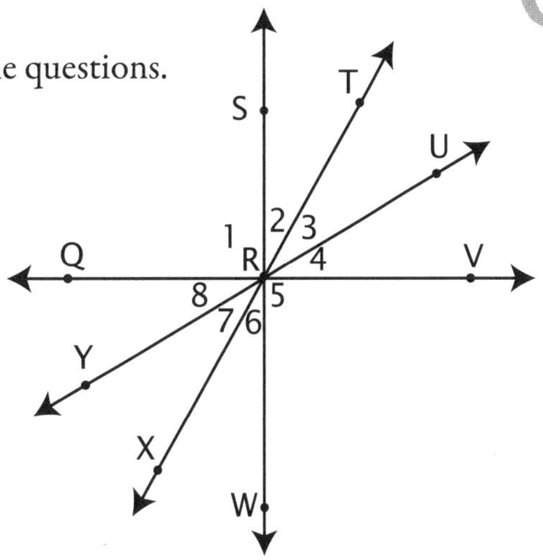

Given: $\overleftrightarrow{SW} \perp \overleftrightarrow{QV}$

All four straight lines intersect at R.

Remember the drawing is a sketch.

Use the measurements given in the questions, even if the drawing appears to be different.

1. Name a line containing $\overrightarrow{RV}$.

2. Name a line segment contained in $\overleftrightarrow{RT}$.

3. If all eight angles were congruent, rather than as given, what would the measure of each be?

4. Since m∠1 is 90°, what is m∠2 + m∠3 + m∠4?

5. ∠4 + ∠5 is a(n) ________________ angle.

6. Are ∠1 and ∠5 supplementary?

7. Are ∠1 and ∠5 complementary?

8. Are ∠1 and ∠5 vertical angles?

9. If ∠2 ≅ ∠3 ≅ ∠4, then m∠8 = ______°.

10. ∠6 ≅ ∠______.

11. ∠2 and ∠3 are ________________ angles (size).

12. If m∠2 = 25°, and m∠4 = 35°, then m∠3 =______.

13. If m∠2 = 25°, and m∠4 = 35°, then m∠YRX =______.

14. Which ray is the common side for ∠SRQ and ∠QRX?

15. Draw the perpendicular bisector of the given line segment.

16. Draw a ray that bisects the given angle.

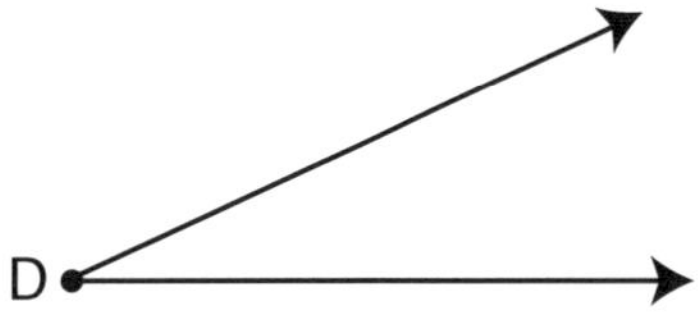

Sharpen your algebra skills!
Be very careful when squaring negative numbers.

EXAMPLE 1 $(-5)^2 = (-5)(-5) = +25$

EXAMPLE 2 $-(8)^2 = -(8)(8) = -64$

EXAMPLE 3 $-6^2 = -(6)(6) = -36$

17. $(-7)^2 =$

18. $-(15)^2 =$

19. $-12^2 =$

20. $-(9)^2 =$

SYSTEMATIC REVIEW

6H

Here are some more figures you may use to practice your bisection skills.

1. Draw the perpendicular bisectors of each line inside the square.

2. Using dotted lines or a different colored pencil, bisect each angle in the original square.

3. Draw the perpendicular bisectors of each side of the triangle. You have marked off two line segments on each side of the triangle. Now construct a perpendicular bisector for each of those line segments. What kinds of shapes do you see inside the large triangle?

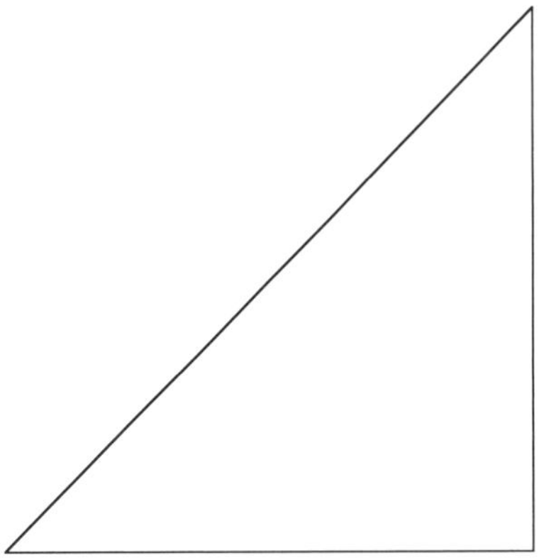

4. If you wish, draw other shapes and construct bisectors as you did above. Try parallelograms, trapezoids, octagons, and other kinds of triangles for interesting results.

Read and follow the directions.

5. Lindsay's base pay is X dollars an hour. For every hour of overtime she works, she gets her base pay plus .5X. Last week she worked six hours of overtime. Let P be her total overtime pay for the week, and write an equation to find P.

6. Lindsay's base pay is $8 an hour. Use the equation you wrote in #9 to find her total overtime pay for the week.

Fill in the blanks.

1. A straight line that intersects two other straight lines is called a(n) ________________ .

2. ________________ angles lie outside parallel lines crossed by a transversal.

3. ________________ angles lie inside parallel lines crossed by a transversal.

4. Given two parallel lines crossed by a transversal, corresponding angles are ________________ .

5. Corresponding interior angles on the opposite sides of the transversal are called ________________ interior angles.

6. If corresponding angles are congruent, the lines crossed by the transversal must be ________________ .

7. Given parallel lines cut by a transversal, the measures of two alternate exterior angles are always ________________ (the same / different).

8. Given parallel lines, any pair of alternate interior angles are ________________ .

Use the drawing to answer the questions.

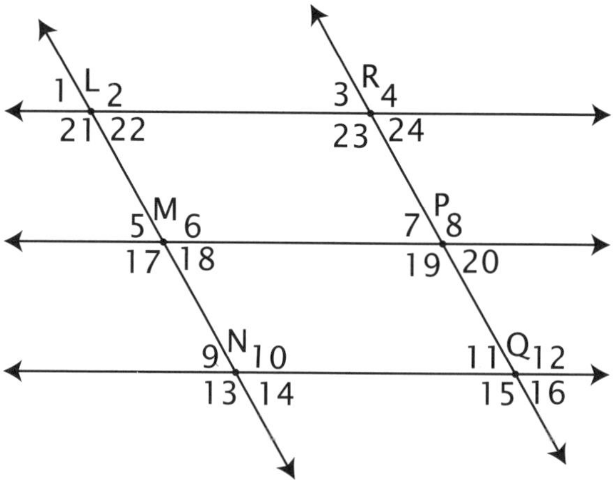

Given: $\overleftrightarrow{LR}$, $\overleftrightarrow{MP}$, and $\overleftrightarrow{NQ}$ are ||.

The drawing is a sketch and not necessarily to scale. Do not make any assumptions about the lines and angles other than what is actually given. (Lines are assumed to be straight lines.)

9. If $m\angle 1 = 60°$, then $m\angle 22 =$ _______°.

10. If $m\angle 1 = 60°$, then $m\angle 5 =$ _______°.

11. If $m\angle 1 = 70°$, then $m\angle 6 =$ _______°.

12. If $m\angle 1 = 70°$, then $m\angle 9 =$ _______°.

13. If $m\angle 8 = 120°$, then $m\angle 12 =$ _______°.

14. If $m\angle 8 = 120°$, then $m\angle 19 =$ _______°.

15. Are $\angle 1$ and $\angle 17$ supplementary angles?

16. Are $\angle 2$ and $\angle 13$ alternate exterior angles?

17. Are $\angle 20$ and $\angle 11$ alternate exterior angles?

18. Assuming neither is a right angle, are $\angle 6$ and $\angle 9$ congruent ?

19. Are $\angle 1$ and $\angle 9$ congruent?

20. If $\angle 12 \cong \angle 13$, are $\overleftrightarrow{LN}$ and $\overleftrightarrow{RQ}$ parallel? (Think of $\overleftrightarrow{NQ}$ as the transversal.)

True or False.

1. Two lines that look parallel in a drawing should always be considered parallel.

2. If two parallel lines are cut by a transversal, then alternate interior angles are congruent.

3. The converse of #2 is true.

4. Given two parallel lines crossed by a transversal, corresponding angles are never congruent.

5. If a pair of alternate exterior angles are congruent, none of the lines forming the angles are parallel.

6. If corresponding angles are congruent, then the lines crossed by the traversal must be parallel.

7. Interior angles lie in the space between two lines.

8. Given parallel lines cut by a transversal, any pair of alternate interior angles have the same measure.

Use the drawing to answer the questions.

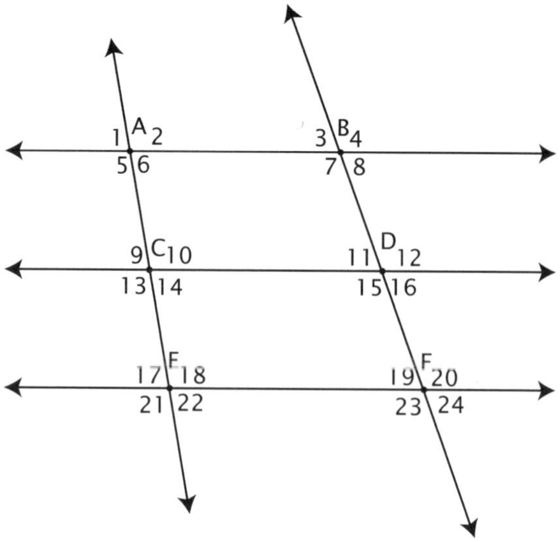

Given: $\overleftrightarrow{AB}$, $\overleftrightarrow{CD}$, and $\overleftrightarrow{EF}$ are ||.

The drawing is a sketch and not necessarily to scale. Don't make any assumptions about the lines and angles other than what is actually given.

9. If m∠7 = 110º,
   then m∠12 = ______º.

10. If m∠7 = 110º,
    then m∠15 = ______º.

11. If m∠1 = 85º,
    then m∠9 = ______º.

12. If m∠1 = 80º,
    then m∠9 = ______º.

13. If m∠1 = 80º,
    then m∠22 = ______º.

14. If m∠9 = 85º,
    then m∠14 = ______º.

15. Are ∠1 and ∠5 supplementary angles?

16. Are ∠2 and ∠13 alternate exterior angles? (In relation to the top two horizontal lines.)

17. Are ∠4 and ∠8 vertical angles?

18. Are ∠11 and ∠19 congruent angles?

19. As given, do you know if ∠1 and ∠3 are congruent? (Think of $\overleftrightarrow{AB}$ as the transversal.)

20. If it were given that ∠1 and ∠3 are congruent, what would you know about $\overleftrightarrow{AE}$ and $\overleftrightarrow{BF}$? (Remember to go by what is given and not by how the drawing looks.)

Use the drawing to answer the questions.

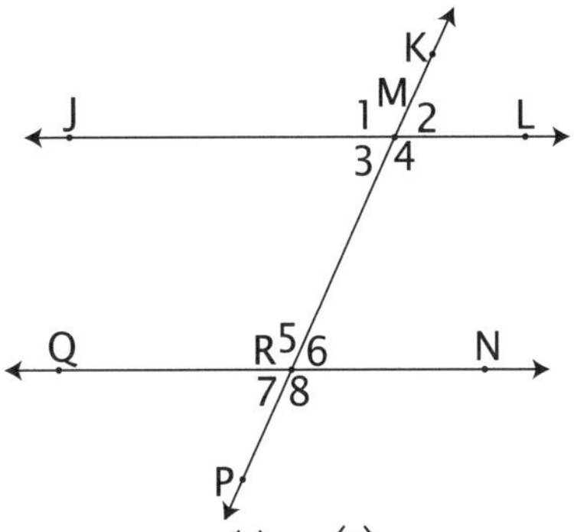

Given: $\overleftrightarrow{JL} \parallel \overleftrightarrow{QN}$
$\overleftrightarrow{KP}$ intersects $\overleftrightarrow{JL}$ and $\overleftrightarrow{QN}$ at M and R.

1. Name four interior angles.

2. Name four exterior angles.

3. Name two pairs of alternate interior angles.

4. Name two pairs of alternate exterior angles.

5. Name four pairs of corresponding angles.

6. Which angle corresponds to $\angle 5$?

7. If $m\angle 1$ is 115°, what is $m\angle 8$?

8. Give the reason for your answer to # 7.

9. If $m\angle 1$ is 115°, what is $m\angle 5$?

10. Give the reason for your answer to # 9.

True or False. Refer to the drawing on the previous page.

11. $\angle 1$ and $\angle 3$ are complementary angles.

12. $\overleftrightarrow{KR}$ contains $\overleftrightarrow{RQ}$.

13. $\overleftrightarrow{QN}$ contains $\overleftrightarrow{RN}$.

14. $\angle 3 \cong \angle 6$. Tell why it is true or false.

Answer each question.

15. If two lines crossed by a transversal are parallel, then the alternate interior angles are congruent. State the converse:

    If alternate interior angles are congruent, then ________________

    ____.

16. If two lines are perpendicular, then they form right angles. State the converse:

    If two lines form right angles, then ____________________________.

17. How many points are in a line?

18. An angle whose measure is less than 90° is called a(n) ________________ angle.

19. An angle whose measure is between 90° and 180° is called a(n) ________________ angle.

20. An angle whose measure is between 180° and 360° is called a(n) ________________angle.

Use the drawing to answer the questions.

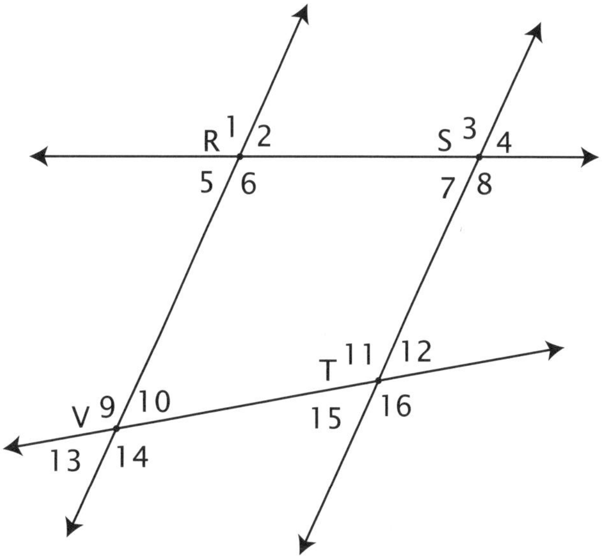

Given:
$\overleftrightarrow{RS}$ is not parallel to $\overleftrightarrow{VT}$.
$\angle 1 \cong \angle 3$

1. If $\angle 1 \cong \angle 3$, then $\overleftrightarrow{RV}$ _____ $\overleftrightarrow{ST}$.

2. $\angle 5$ is congruent to and corresponds to $\angle$ _____.

3. $\angle 6 \cong \angle$ _____ because alternate interior angles are congruent.

4. $\angle 5 \cong \angle$ _____ because alternate exterior angles are congruent.

5. If m$\angle 2$ is 70º, what is m $\angle 1$? Why?

6. $\angle 1$ and $\angle 2$ are _______________ angles.

7. $\angle 7$ and $\angle 4$ are _______________ angles.

8. If m$\angle 7$ is 72º, what is m$\angle 6$? Why?

9. If m$\angle 1$ is 110º, what is m$\angle 8$?

10. Give the reason for your answer to #9.

True or False. Refer to the drawing on the previous page.

11. $\angle 1$ and $\angle 4$ are supplementary angles.

12. $\angle 2$ is known to be congruent to $\angle 10$.

13. $\angle 11$ and $\angle 15$ are supplementary angles.

14. $\angle 10$ is known to be congruent to $\angle 13$.

Answer each question.

15. If corresponding angles are congruent, then the two lines cut by a transversal are parallel. State the converse:

    If the two lines cut by a transversal are parallel, then ______________

    ____.

16. If the measure of two angles adds up to 180°, then the angles are supplementary. State the converse:

    If two angles are supplementary, then ___________________________

    ____.

17. If the measures of two angles add up to 90°, then the angles are said to be ____________________ .

18. Two angles that share one ray as a common side are ______________________ to each other.

19. The symbol β stands for the Greek letter ____________________ .

20. The symbol δ stands for the Greek letter ____________________ .

SYSTEMATIC REVIEW

Use the drawing to answer the questions.

1. If m∠1 is 100°, what is m∠11? Why?

2. If m∠1 is 100°, what is m∠14? Why?

3. If m∠1 is 100°, what is m∠4? Why?

4. If m∠1 is 100°, what is m∠5? Why?

5. ∠10 and ∠ ______ are vertical angles.

6. Are ∠6 and ∠10 supplementary?

7. Are ∠7 and ∠10 congruent?

8. Are ∠12 and ∠8 congruent?

True or False. Refer to the drawing.

9. ∠1 and ∠6 are vertical angles.

10. ∠1 ≅ ∠16

11. $\overleftrightarrow{BD}$ contains $\overrightarrow{DC}$.

12. $\overleftrightarrow{AC} \cap \overleftrightarrow{BD} = \varnothing$

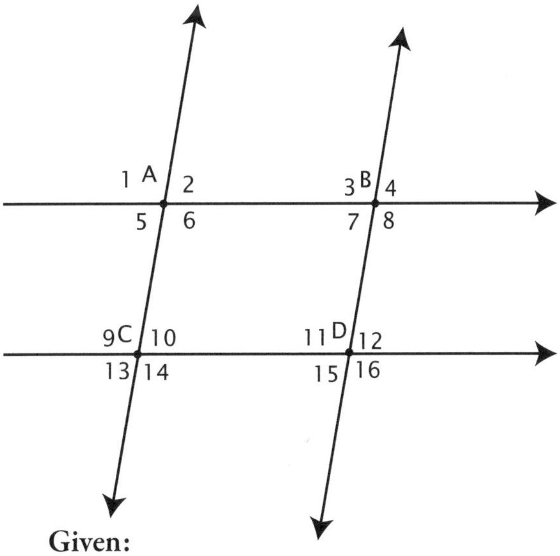

Given:
$\overleftrightarrow{AB} \parallel \overleftrightarrow{CD}$ and $\overleftrightarrow{AC} \parallel \overleftrightarrow{BD}$.
Line AB is not ⊥ line AC.

Answer each question.

13. If two lines are parallel and cut by a transversal, then alternate interior angles are congruent. State the converse:

    If alternate interior angles are congruent, then ____________________

    ____.

14. If two lines lie in the same plane, then they are coplanar. State the converse:

    If two lines are coplanar, then ____________________________

    ____.

15. The symbol γ stands for the Greek letter _____ .

16. The symbol α stands for the Greek letter _____.

Sharpen your algebra skills!
The slope of a line on a graph is the $\frac{\text{up dimension}}{\text{over dimension}}$. A line that moves to the right two spaces while moving up four spaces has a slope of 4/2, or 2. Lines that move down to the right have a negative slope.

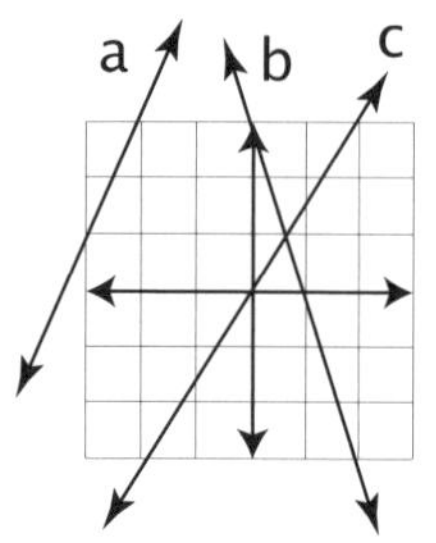

EXAMPLE
slope a = $2/1$ = 2
slope b = $-3/1$ = -3
slope c = $3/2$

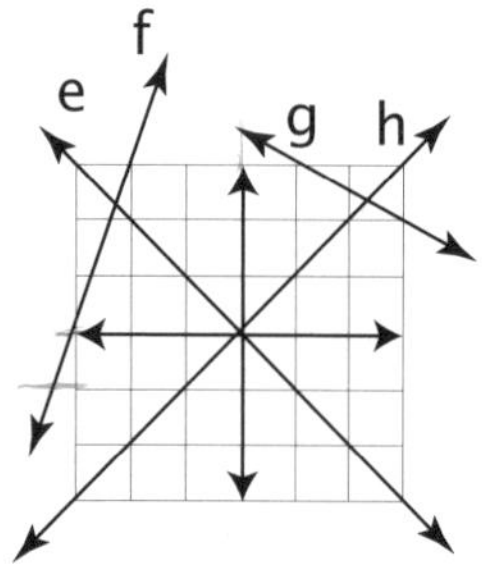

17. slope e =

18. slope f =

19. slope g =

20. slope h =

Use the information you have learned so far about angles and lines to answer each question. You may want to extend some line segments beyond the edges of the figures to see transversals more clearly. Some of these may be challenging. Don't give up too quickly!

1. Study the figure below. Which line segments are parallel? How do you know?

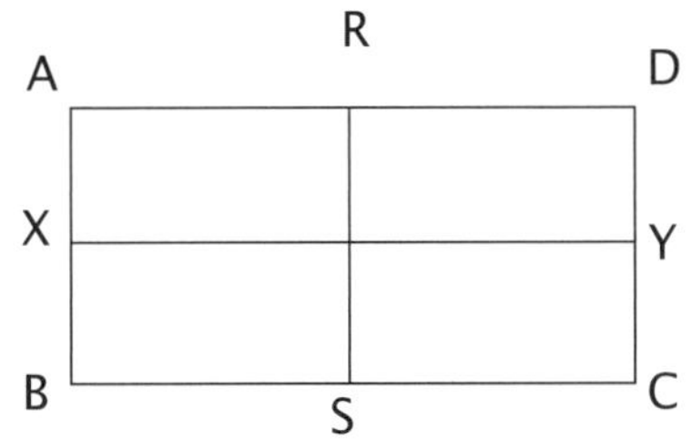

Given:

m∠A, B, C, and D = 90°

$\overline{XY}$ and $\overline{RS}$ are perpendicular bisectors of the sides of the rectangle.

2. Are $\overline{BC}$ and $\overline{DF}$ parallel? How do you know?

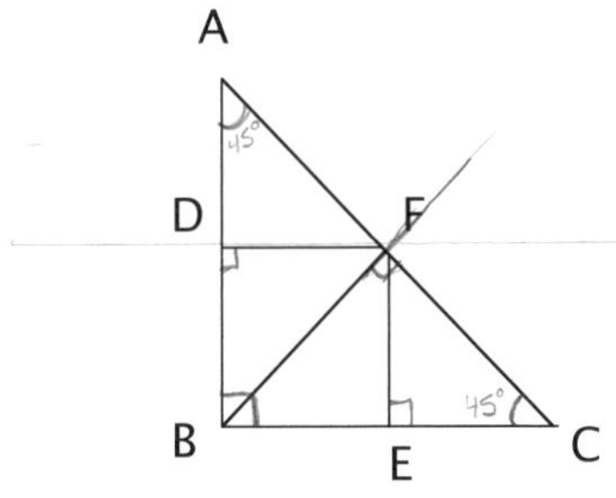

Given:

m∠ABC = 90°
$\overline{DF}$ is a perpendicular bisector of $\overline{AB}$.

m∠BAC = 45°
$\overline{FB}$ is a perpendicular bisector of $\overline{AC}$.

m∠ACB = 45°
$\overline{EF}$ is a perpendicular bisector of $\overline{BC}$.

3. Find the measure of ∠EDF and ∠DEF.

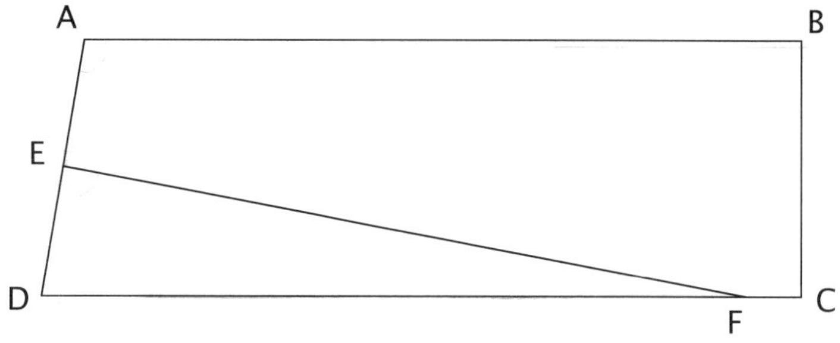

Given:

m∠A = 100°
$\overline{AB}$ is parallel to $\overline{DC}$.

$\overline{EF}$ is a perpendicular bisector of $\overline{AD}$.

4. The octagon (eight-sided figure) is inscribed, or drawn, inside a square. (You will learn more about inscribed figures in lesson 12.) What is the measure of each of the angles inside the octagon?

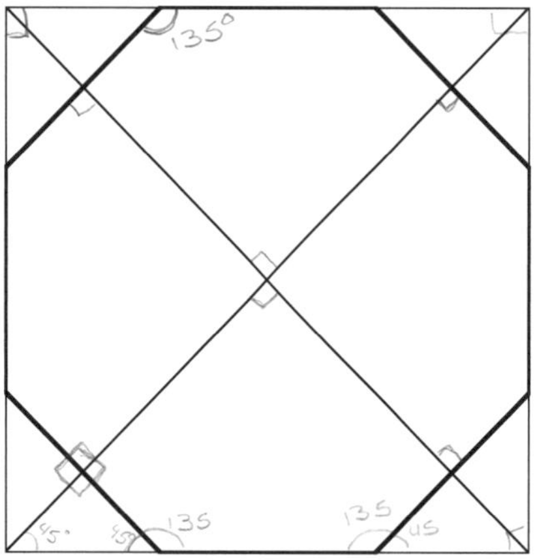

Given:

The measure of each corner of the square is 90°.

The diagonal lines are bisectors of the angles they intersect and perpendicular bisectors of the lines they cross.

If two angles in a triangle are 90° and 45°, the third angle is also 45°.

Identify the shapes.

1. 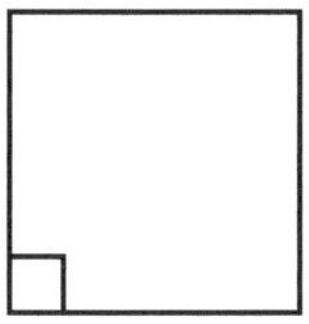

____

2. 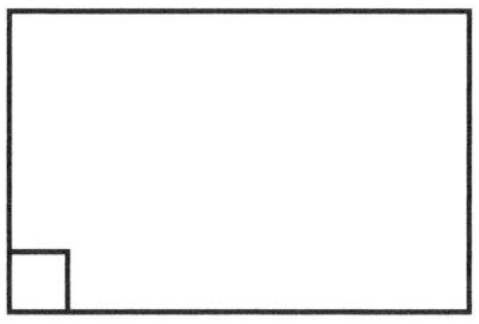

____

3. 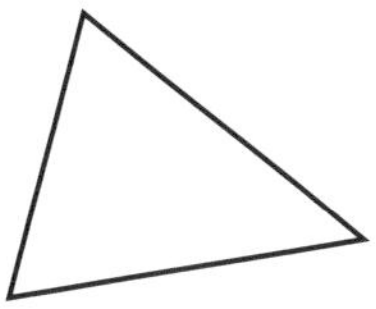

____

4. 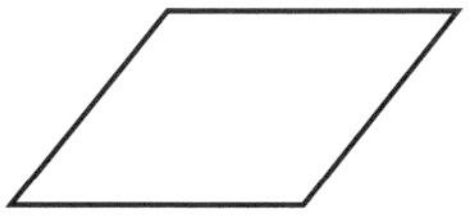

____

5. 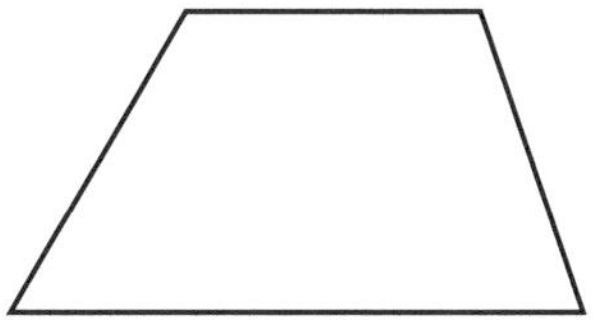

____

6. 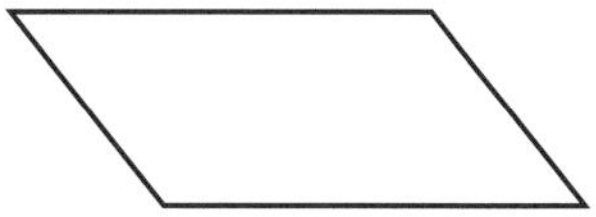

____

Find the perimeter.

7. 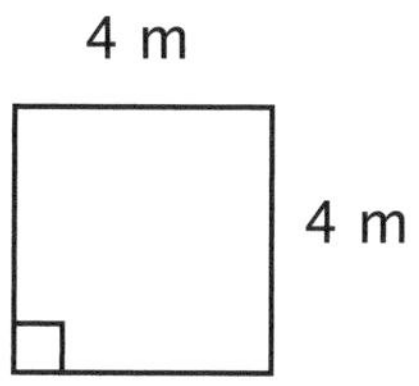

P = ______________

8. 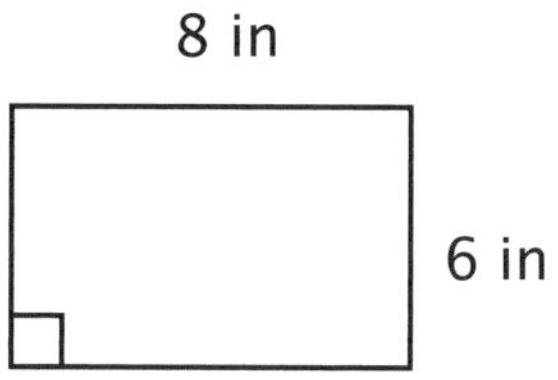

P = ______________

9. 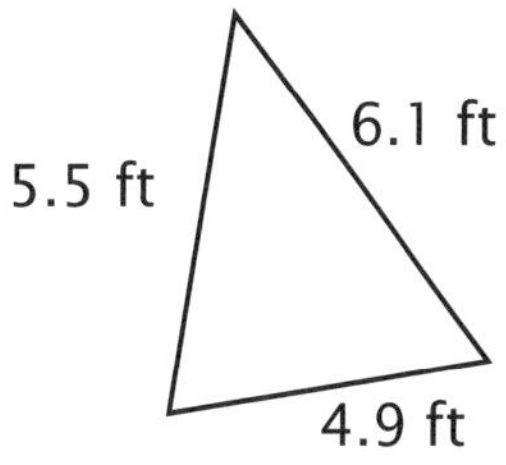

P = ______________

10. 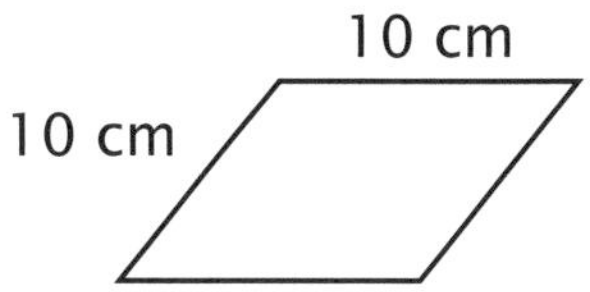

P = ______________

11. 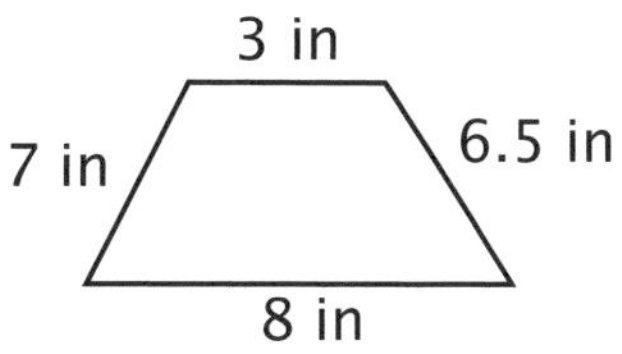

P = ______________

12. 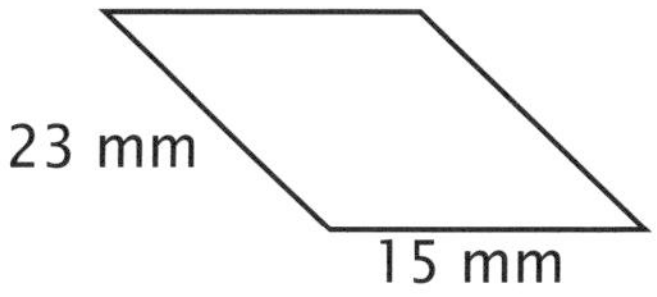

P = ______________

True or false.

13. Perimeter is the distance around a shape or figure.

14. Any four-sided figure can be called a quadrilateral.

15. The sum of the interior angles of a quadrilateral add up to 180°.

16. A square is a rhombus with four right angles.

17. A trapezoid always has at least one right angle.

18. The sum of the interior angles of a triangle add up to 180°.

19. A rectangle has only one pair of parallel sides.

20. A square is a rectangle with all four sides equal.

Identify the shapes.

1. 

____

2. 

____

3. 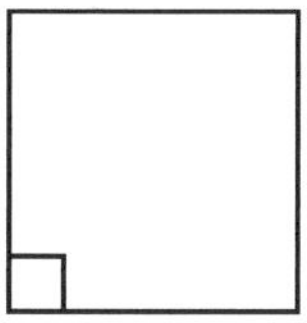

____

4. 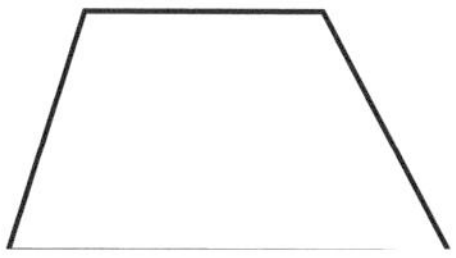

____

5. 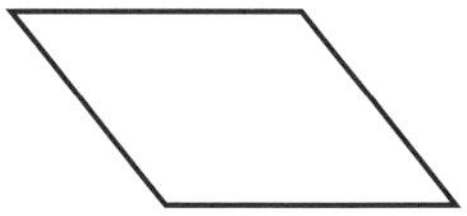

____

6. 

____

Find the perimeter.

7. 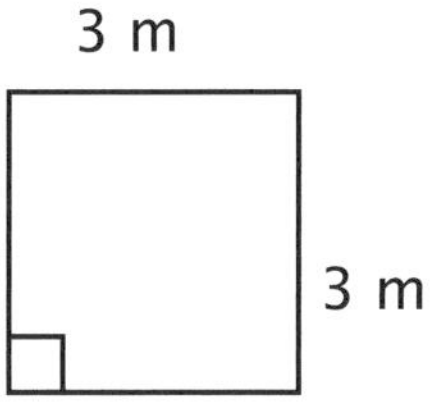

P = ______________

8. 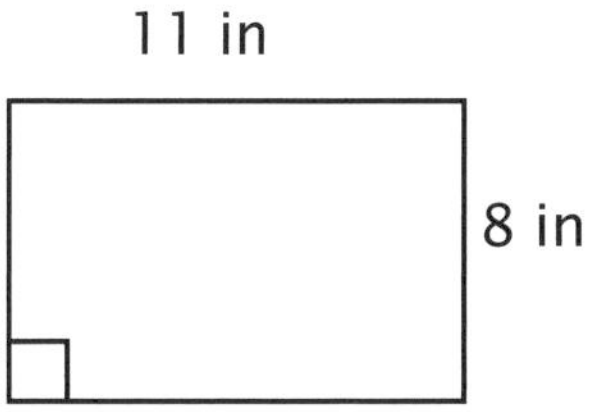

P = ______________

9. 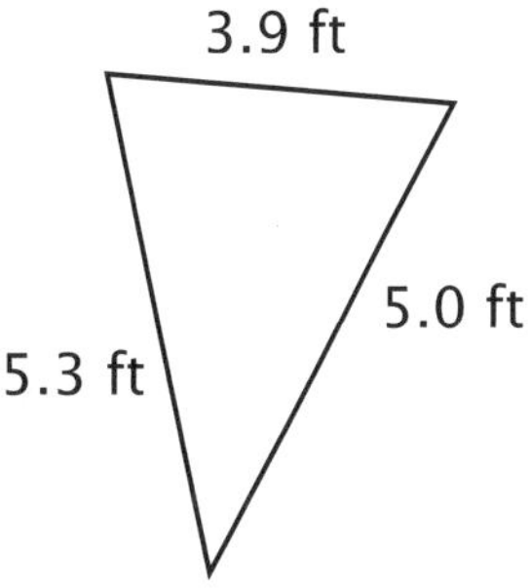

P = ______________

10. 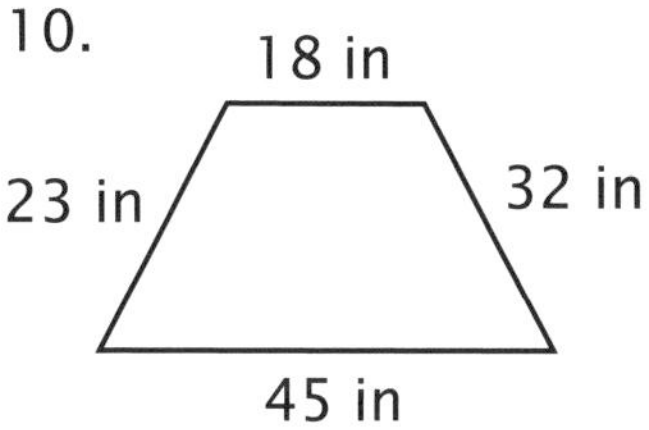

P = ______________

11. 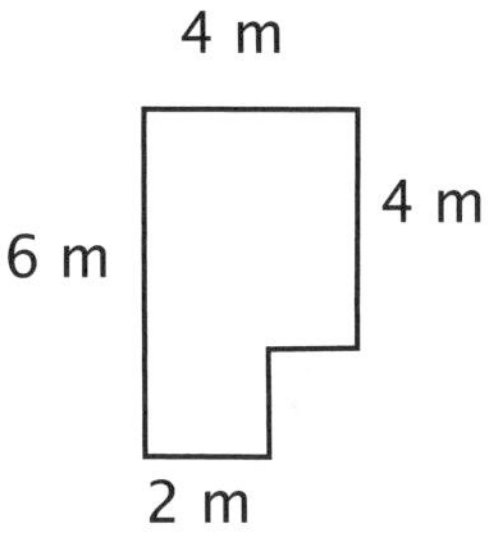

P = ______________

12. 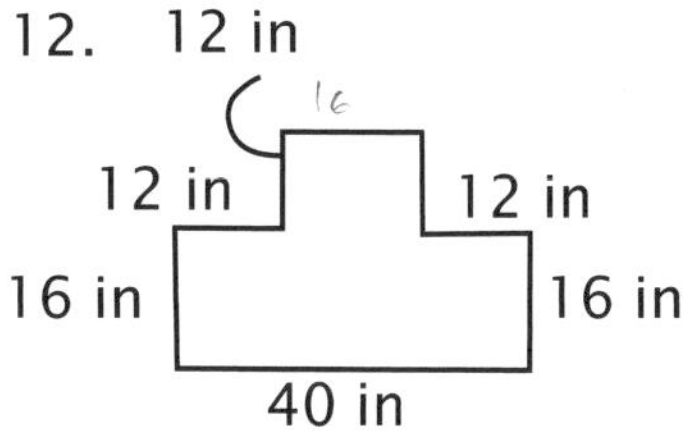

P = ______________

Hint for #11 and #12: Use what is given to find the missing measurements. Then add all the sides to find the perimeter. All angles are 90° angles.

Name each figure (some answers may be used more than once).

13. The sum of the interior angles is 180°. ____________________

14. Any four-sided figure. ____________________

15. Has four equal sides and four right angles. ____________________

16. Has four equal sides; angles may or may not be right angles.

____

17. Any three-sided figure. ____________________

18. The sum of the interior angles is 360° (most inclusive answer).

____

19. Has only one pair of parallel sides and no right angles.

____

20. Has two pairs of parallel sides; angles may or may not be right angles.

____

Match each shape with its best description.

1. quadrilateral
2. rectangle
3. square
4. parallelogram
5. trapezoid
6. rhombus

a. four right angles and two pairs of parallel sides
b. any four-sided polygon
c. four congruent sides; angles may not be right angles
d. two pairs of parallel sides; may or may not have right angles
e. any quadrilateral with only one pair of parallel sides
f. four congruent sides and four right angles

Find the perimeter of each figure.

7.
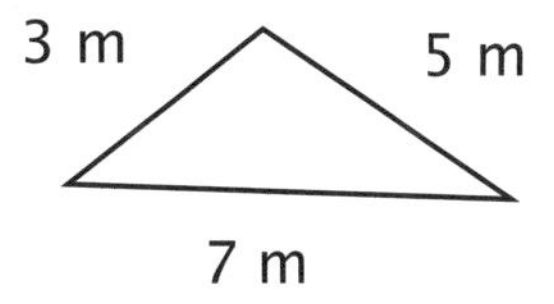

P = ______________

8.
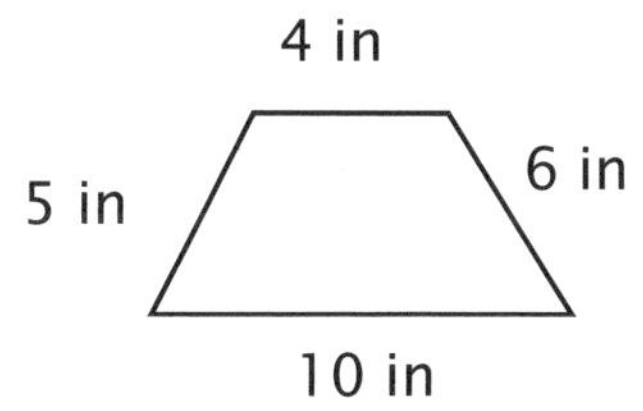

P = ______________

9. What is the sum of the interior angles of a triangle?

10. What is the sum of the interior angles of a quadrilateral?

Use the drawing to answer the questions.

11. If $\angle 1 \cong \angle 5$, then $\overleftrightarrow{AC}$ __________ $\overleftrightarrow{DF}$.

12. What statement proves #11?

13. What is the converse of the statement in #12?

14. If $\angle 5 \cong \angle 12$, then $\overleftrightarrow{DF}$ __________ $\overleftrightarrow{GJ}$.

15. What statement proves #14?

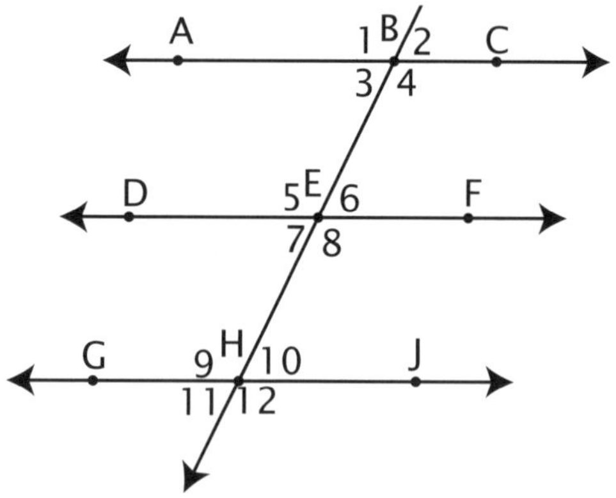

16. If $\angle 1 \cong \angle 5$, and $\angle 5 \cong \angle 12$, then $\angle 1 \cong \angle$__________.

Given:
$\angle 1 \cong \angle 5$ and $\angle 5 \cong \angle 12$.

17. If m $\angle 3$ is 74°, what is m $\angle 8$?

18. Give the reason for your answer to #17.

19. If m $\angle 3$ is 74°, what is m $\angle 11$?

20. Give the reason for your answer to #19.

Fill in the blanks.

1. A square has four congruent sides and four ________________ angles.

2. All four-sided polygons are included under the term ________________.

3. Only a ________________ has four congruent sides and four right angles.

4. A figure with four congruent sides whose angles are not necessarily right angles is a ________________.

5. A ________________ has only one pair of parallel sides.

6. Any quadrilateral with two pairs of parallel sides can be called a ________________.

Find the perimeter of each figure.

7.

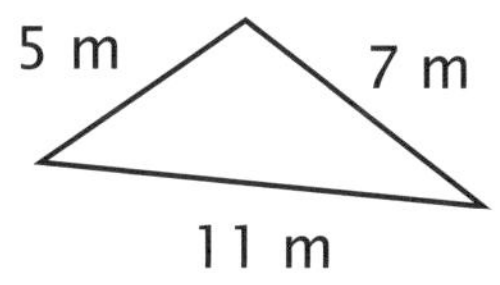

P = ________________

8.

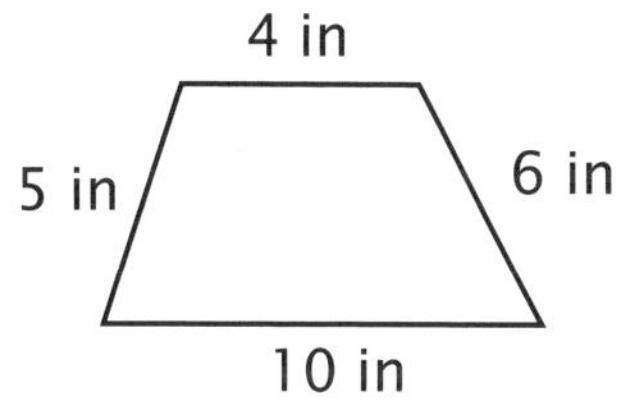

P = ________________

9. **Given:** Figure is a rhombus.

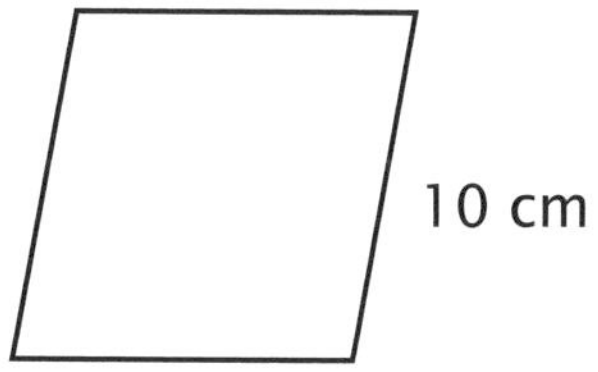

P = ________________

10. **Given:** All angles are right angles.

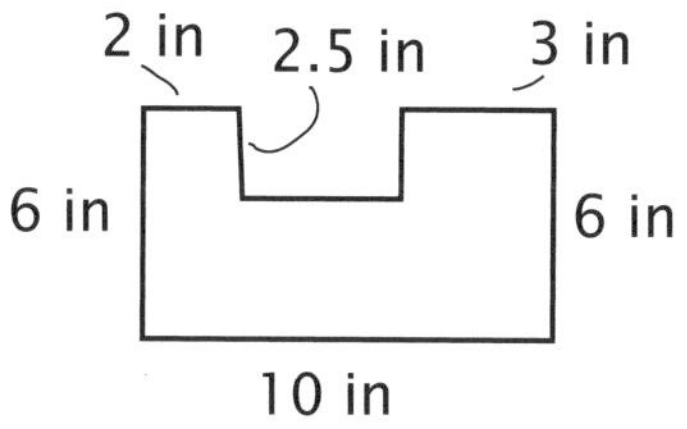

P = ________________

Use the drawing to answer the questions.

11. $\overleftrightarrow{DG}$ is a __________ because $\overline{DE}$ is __________ to $\overline{FG}$.

12. What is m∠g? Why?

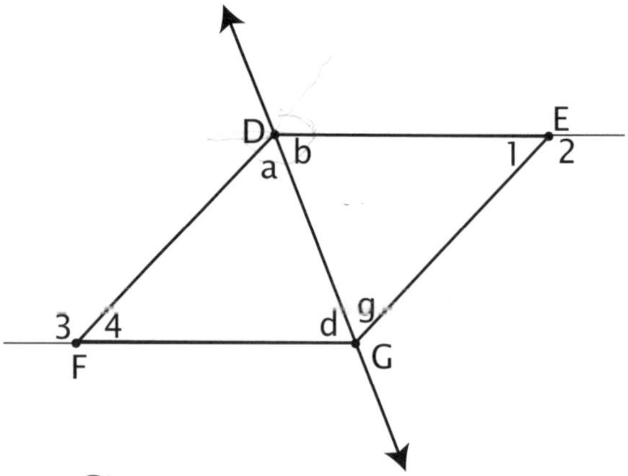

13. What is m∠d? Why?

14. What is m∠1? Why?

Given:
▭ DEFG is a parallelogram
m∠a and m∠b each equals 54°.

15. What kind of angles make up ΔDEG?

16. What is m∠2?

17. What is the relationship between ∠1 and ∠2?

18. Name an obtuse angle.

19. Which pair of angles correspond to ∠2?

20. If two lines intersect and form a right angle, then they are perpendicular. State the converse.

True or False.

1. Perimeter measures the distance around a geometric figure.

2. The measures of the interior angles of a triangle add up to 360º.

3. A square is a rhombus with four right angles.

4. A trapezoid has two pairs of parallel sides.

5. A parallelogram could have four interior angles with measures of 100º, 80º, 100º, 80º.

6. A trapezoid must have at least one right angle.

Find the perimeter of each figure.

7.

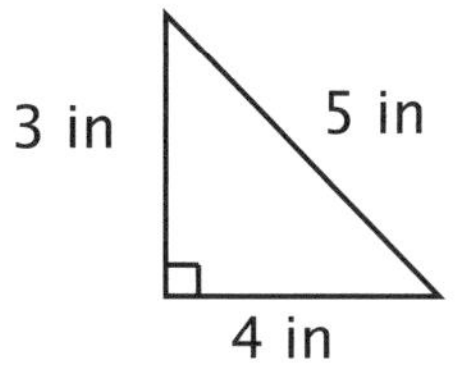

P = ______________

8.

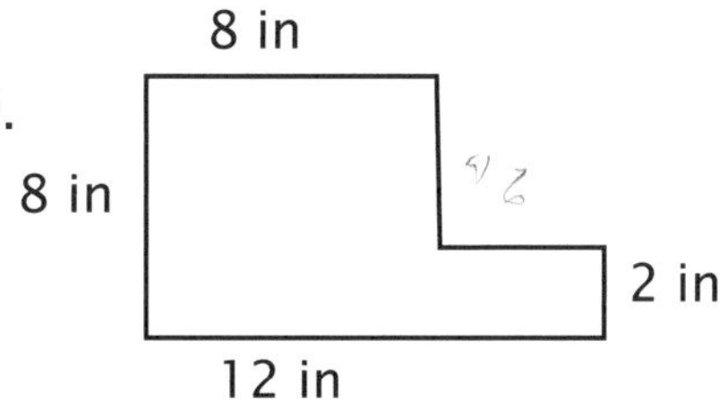

P = ______________

Use the drawing to answer the questions.

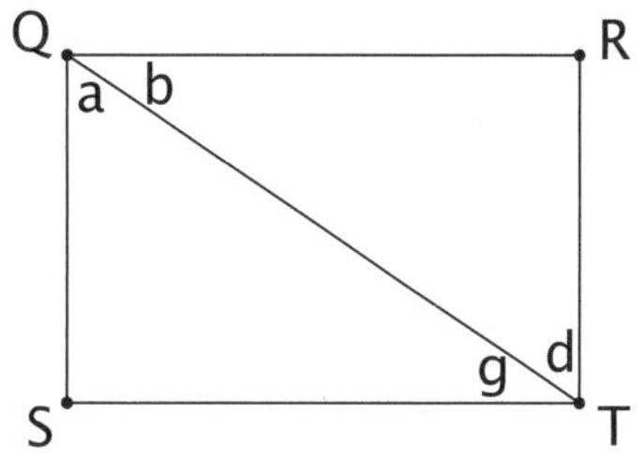

Given: ▭ QRTS is a rectangle.

9. Name a transversal.

10. $\overline{QS}$ _____ $\overline{ST}$

11. $\overline{QS}$ _____ $\overline{RT}$

12. ∠a and ∠b are adjacent and ______________.

Use the drawing to answer the questions.

13. $\angle a$ and $\angle d$ are ______________ interior angles.

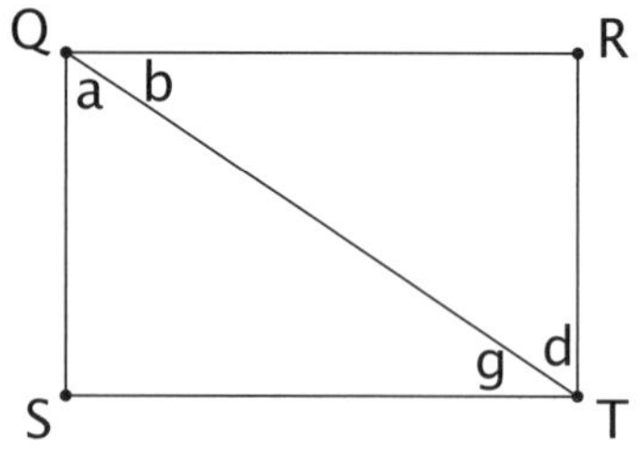

Given: ▭ QRTS is a rectangle.

14. Are $\angle a$ and $\angle d$ congruent?

15. If $m\angle b$ is 43°, is $\overline{QT}$ a bisector of $\angle RQS$?

16. If $m\angle b$ is 43°, what is $m\angle d$?

17. Is $\overline{RT} \perp$ to $\overline{QS}$?

18. If point A is the middle point of line segment DP, then A is the midpoint. State the converse.

Sharpen your algebra skills!

In the slope-intercept form Y = mX + b, *m* indicates the slope of a line, and *b* indicates the Y-intercept, or the place where the line crosses the Y axis.

EXAMPLE 1	Y = 3X + 1	The slope is 3 and the Y-intercept is 1.
EXAMPLE 2	Y = -X - 5	The slope is -1 and the Y-intercept is -5.

19. What are the slope and intercept of Y = -2X + 4?

20. What are the slope and intercept of Y = X - 2?

You can find out a surprising amount about a geometric drawing using what you have learned about bisectors, vertical angles, and supplementary and complementary angles. To answer the questions on this page, remember that the three angles of any triangle always add up to 180°.

Without measuring, write the size of each angle on the figures below. Start with what you can deduce easily from the information given, and then use the rules you have learned to find other angles. You may need to look at the larger triangles within the figure first. Even though we are not doing formal proofs at this stage, you should be able to give a reason for each of your answers.

1.

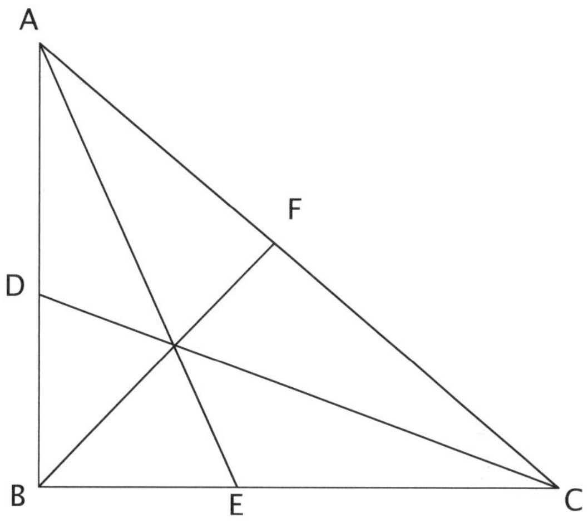

Given:

m∠ABC = 90°

m∠BAC = 50°

m∠ACB = 40°

Line segments AE, BF, and CD bisect angles A, B, and C.

Give yourself plenty of time to do #1 on your own. If you have trouble, study the solution before trying the next question.

2.

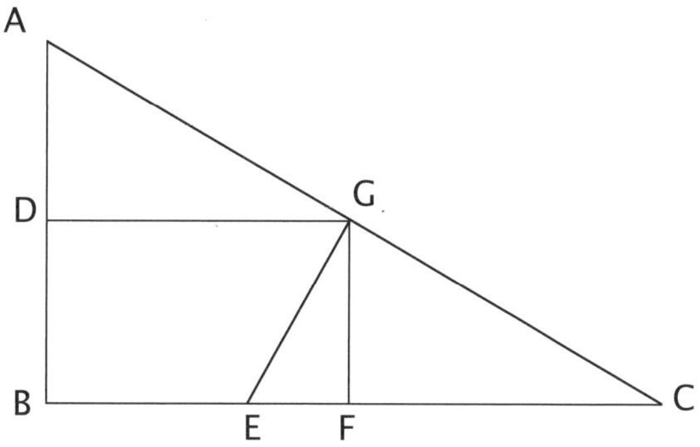

Given:

m∠ABC = 90°
$\overline{DG}$ is a perpendicular bisector of $\overline{AB}$.

m∠BAC = 60°
$\overline{GE}$ is a perpendicular bisector of $\overline{AC}$.

m∠ACB = 30°
$\overline{FG}$ is a perpendicular bisector of $\overline{BC}$.

3.

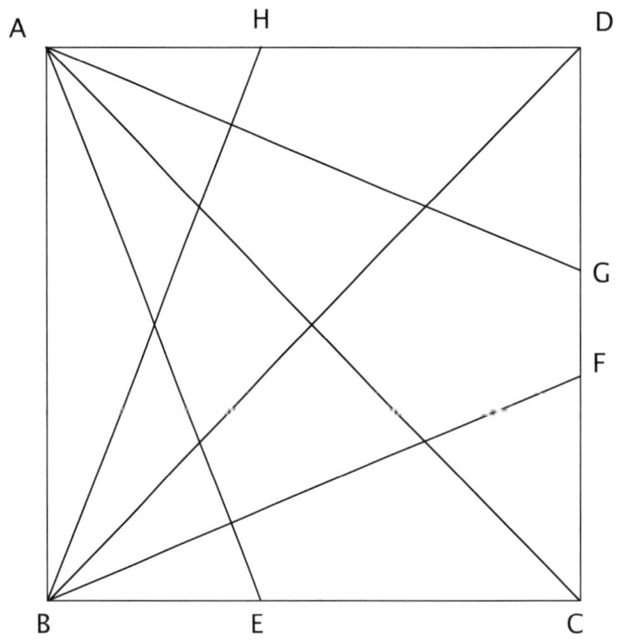

Given:

The measure of each corner of the square is 90°.

∠BAD and ∠ABC have each been bisected. Each of the resulting angles have also been bisected.

Find the area of each figure.

1.

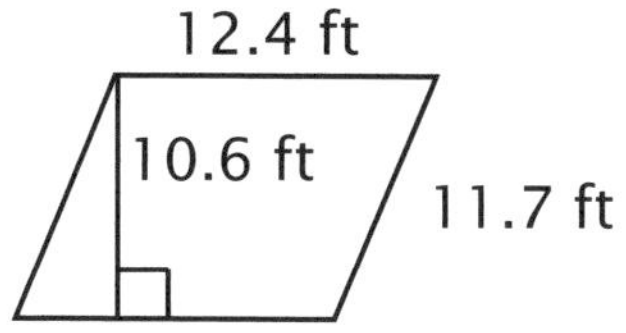

A = ________________

2.

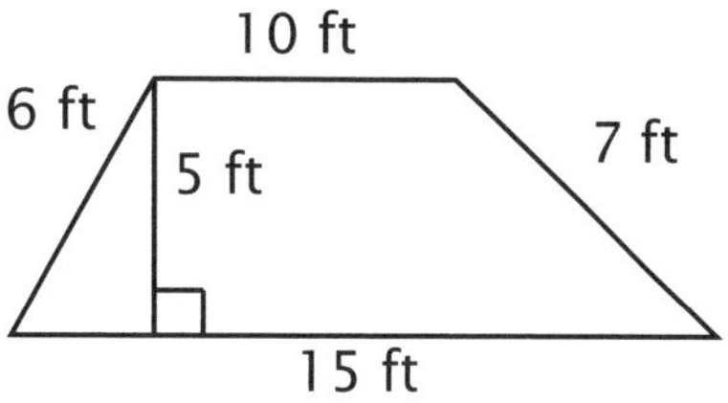

A = ________________

3.

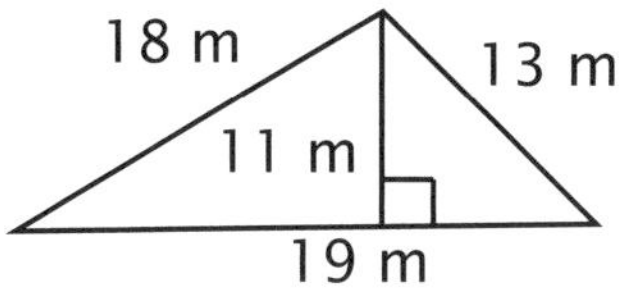

A = ________________

4.

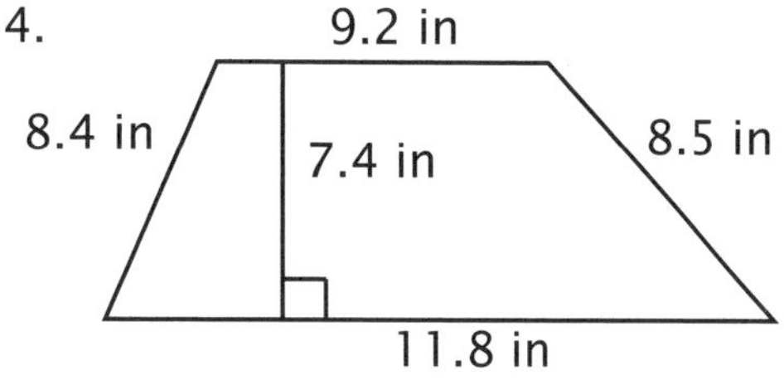

A = ________________

5.

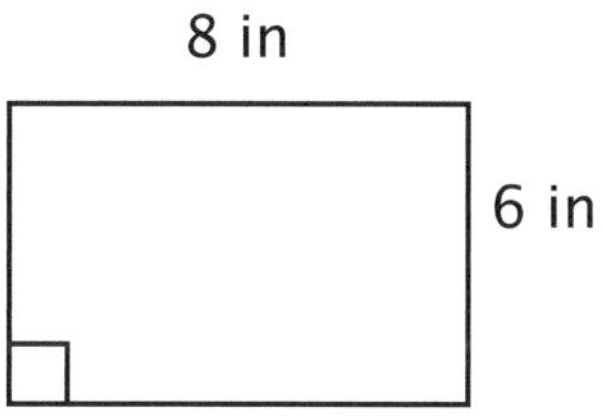

A = ________________

6.

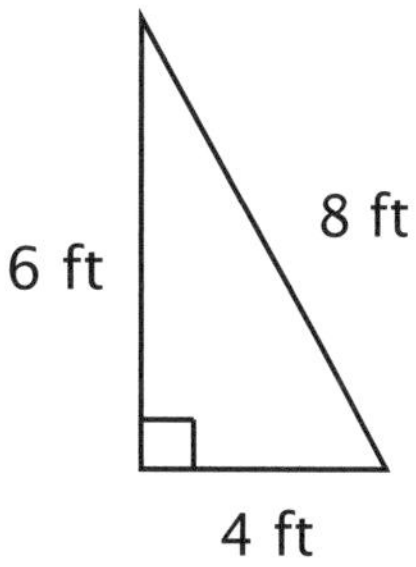

A = ________________

7.

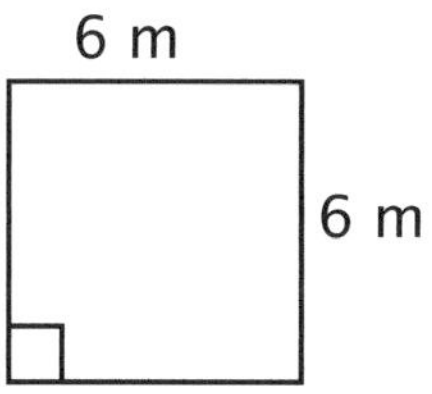

A = ________________

8.

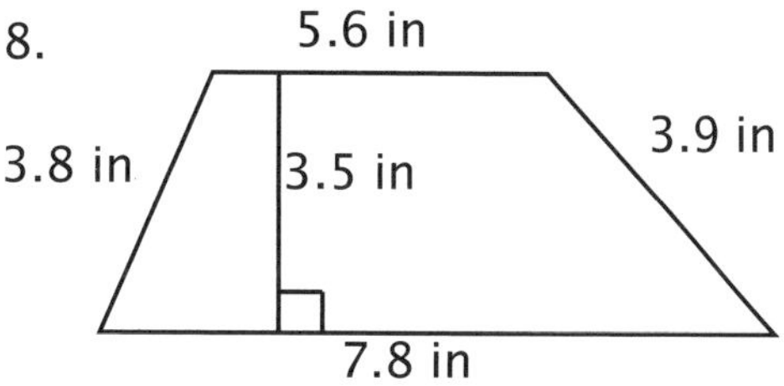

A = ________________

9.

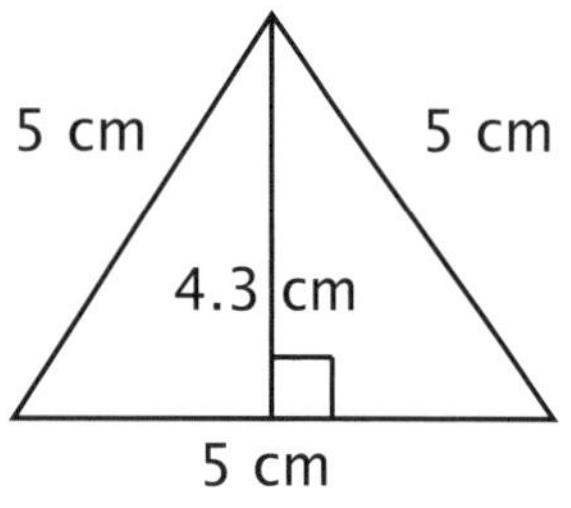

A = ______________

10.

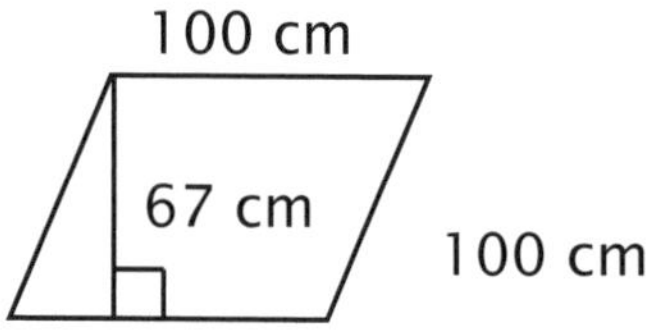

A = ______________

11.

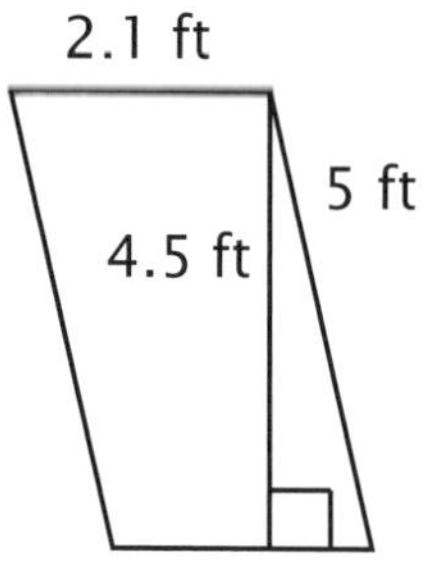

A = ______________

12.

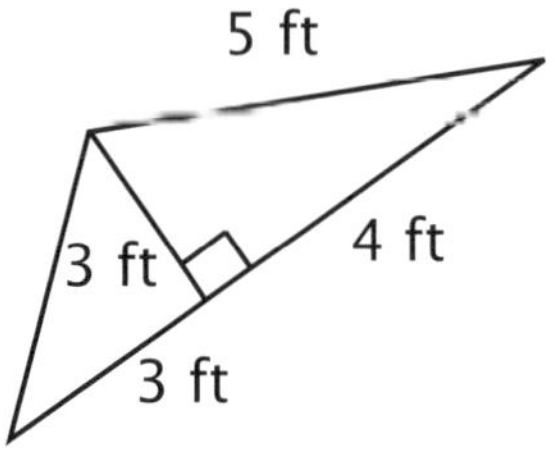

A = ______________

13. The area of a parallelogram is found by multiplying the ______________ by the ______________ .

14. In order to find the area of a trapezoid, it is first necessary to find the ______________ base.

15. The area of a triangle is ______________ the area of a rectangle with the same base and height.

Find the area of each figure.

1.

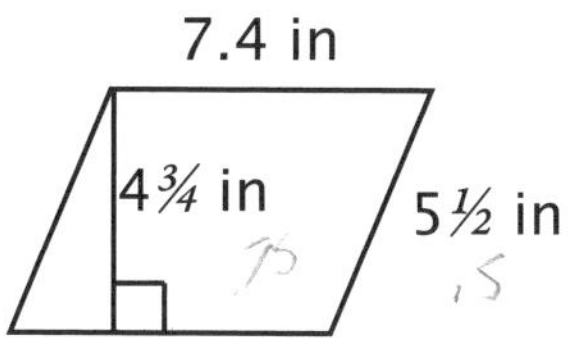

A = ________________

2.

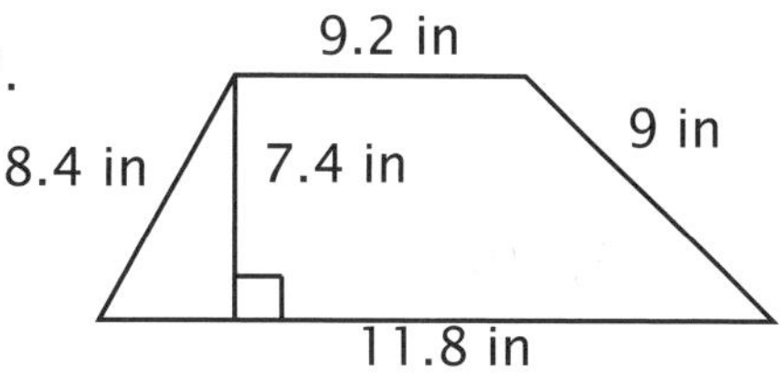

A = ________________

Hint for #1: First change all numbers to either decimals or fractions.

3.

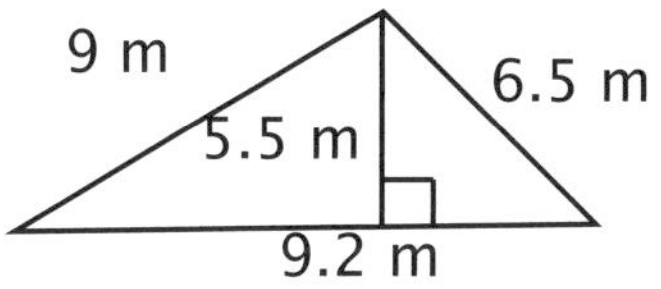

A = ________________

4.

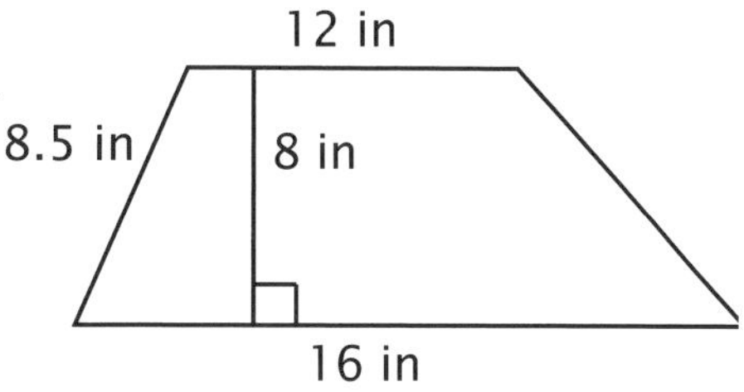

A = ________________

5.

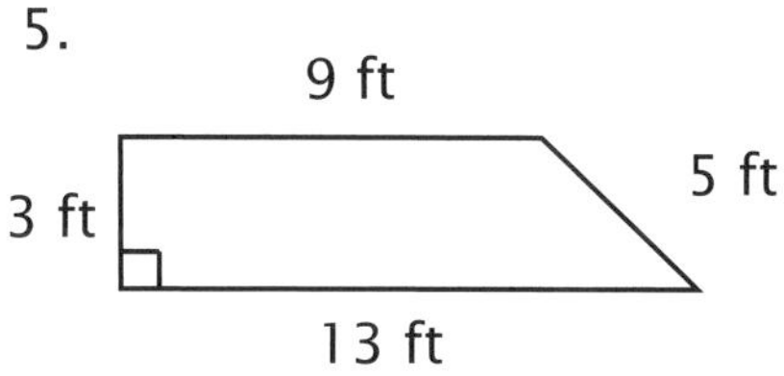

A = ________________

6.

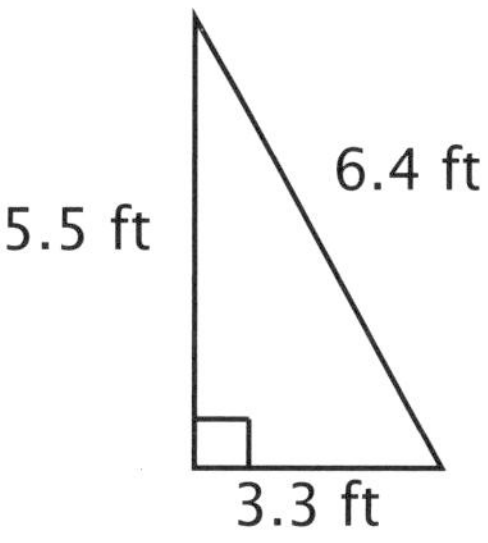

A = ________________

7.

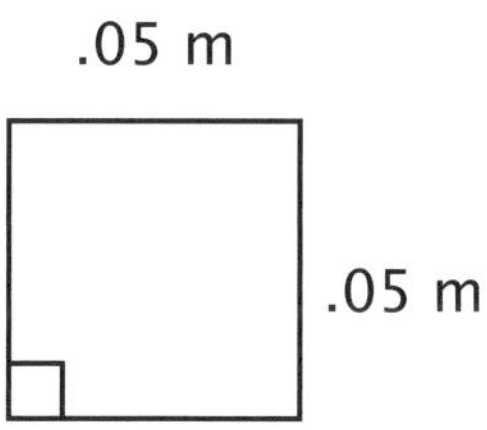

A = ________________

8.

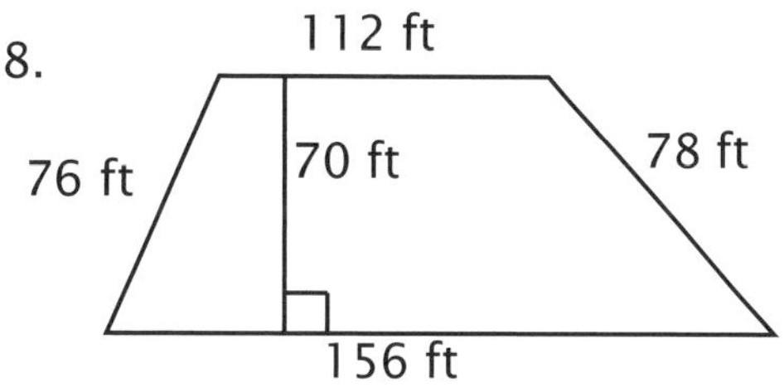

A = ________________

9.

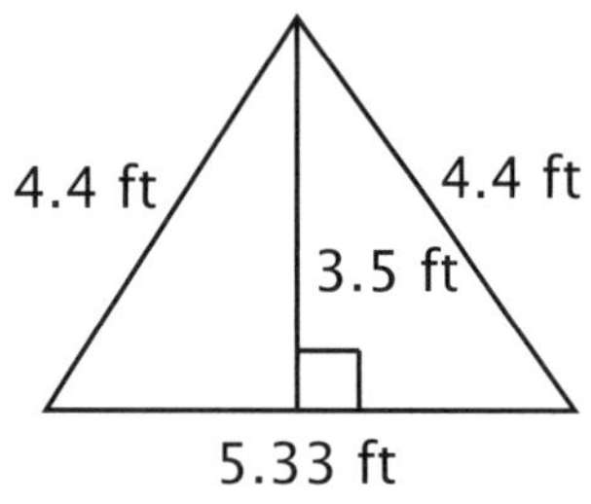

A = ______________

10.

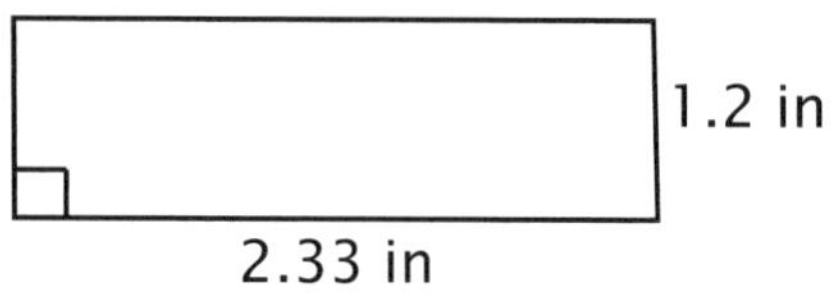

A = ______________

11.

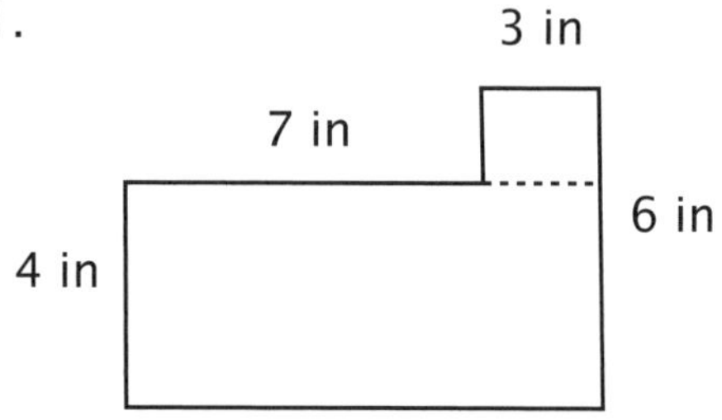

A = ______________

Hint for #11: Draw a dotted line and find the area of each rectangle; then add.

12.

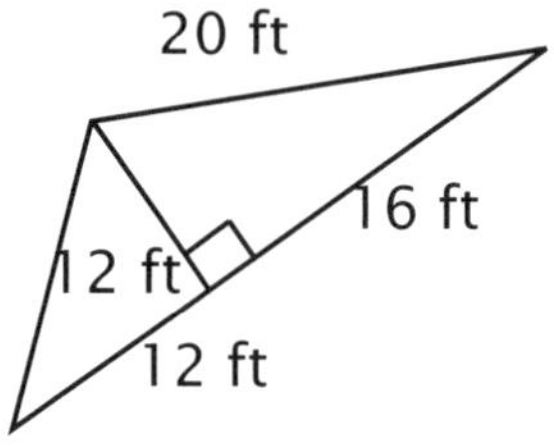

A = ______________

13. The height of a quadrilateral is always ______________ to the base.

14. In order to find the area of a ______________, it is first necessary to find the average base.

15. The area of a triangle is one-half the area of a ______________ with the same base and height.

Find the area of each figure.

1.

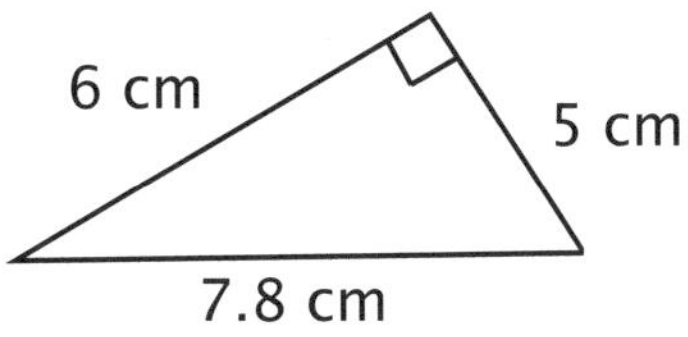

A = _______________

2.

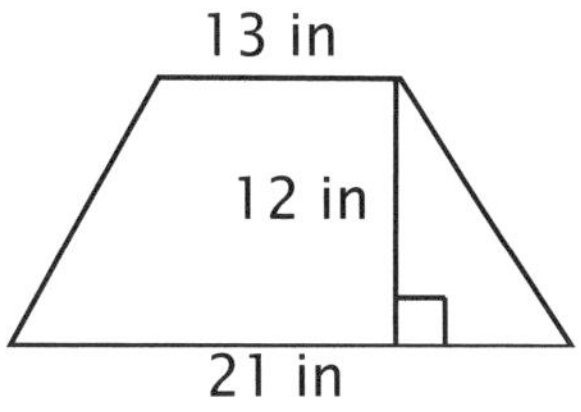

A = _______________

3.

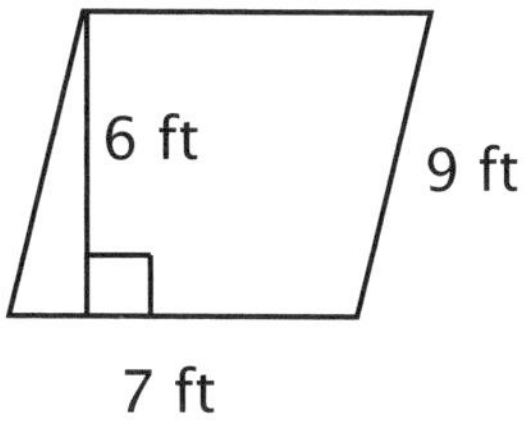

A = _______________

4.

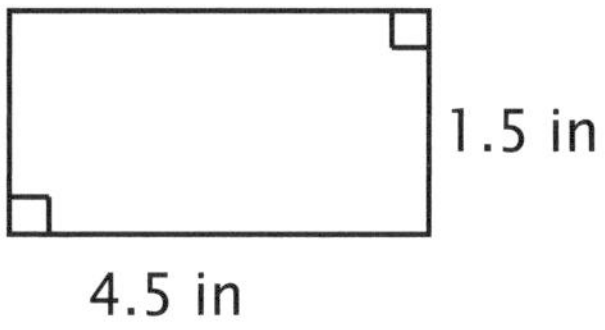

A = _______________

Name all the quadrilateral(s) that fit each description.

5. four right angles ______________________

6. two pairs of parallel sides ______________________

7. four right angles and four congruent sides ______________________

8. one pair of parallel sides ______________________

Describe the polygon as exactly as possible.

9. parallelogram

10. square

Use the drawing to answer the questions. Then give the reason for each answer.

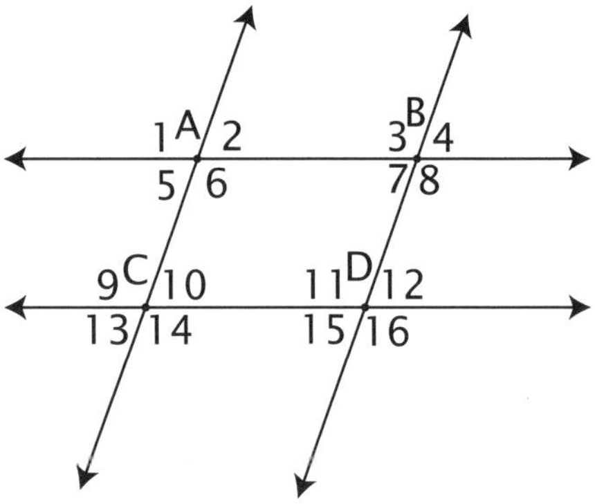

Given:
$\overleftrightarrow{AB} \parallel \overleftrightarrow{CD}$ and $\overleftrightarrow{AC} \parallel \overleftrightarrow{BD}$.

11. Is $\angle 6 \cong \angle 14$?

12. Is $\angle 6 \cong \angle 9$?

13. Is $m\angle 5 = m\angle 15$?

14. If $m\angle 5 = 84°$, what is $m\angle 10$?

15. If $m\angle 5 = 84°$, what is $m\angle 11$?

16. If $m\angle 5 = 84°$, what is $m\angle 12$?

17. If $m\angle 5 = 75°$, what is $m\angle 14$?

18. If $m\angle 5 = 75°$, what is $m\angle 7$?

19. If $m\angle 5 = 75°$, what is $m\angle 4$?

20. Find the perimeter.

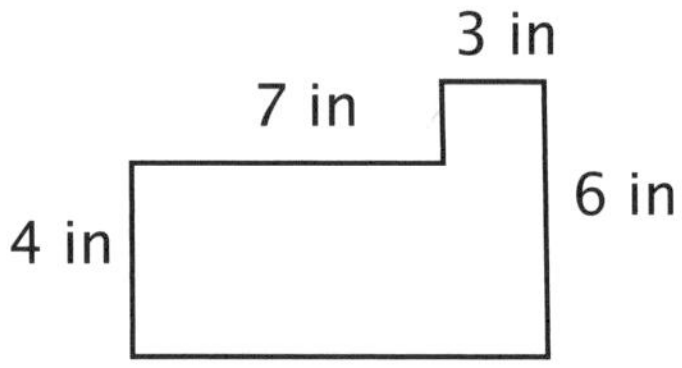

Given:
All angles are right angles.

Find the area of each figure.

1.

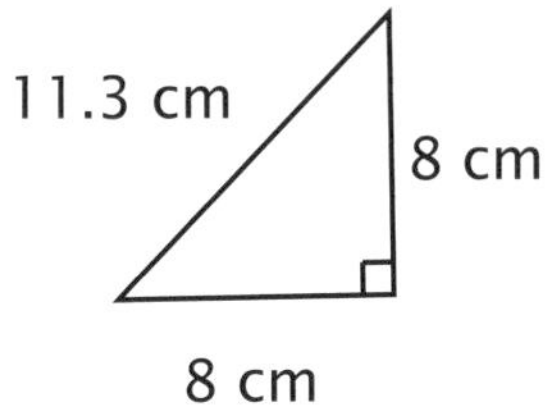

A = ______________

2.

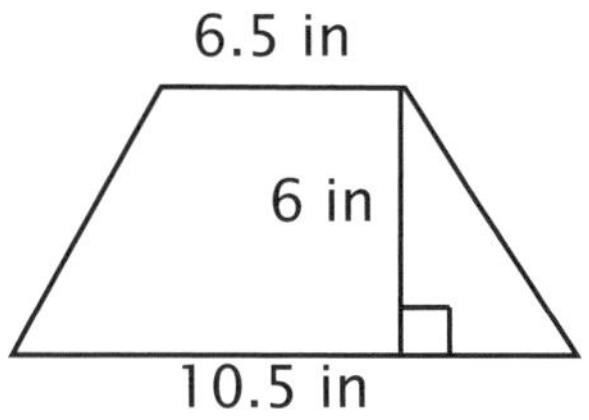

A = ______________

3.

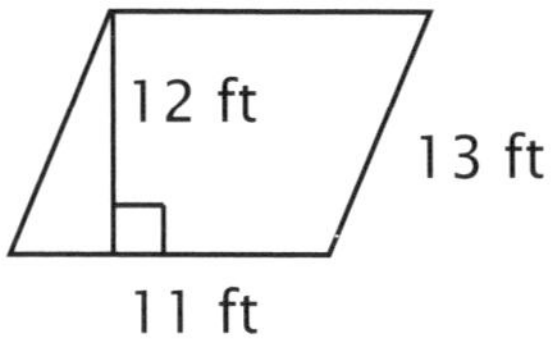

A = ______________

4.

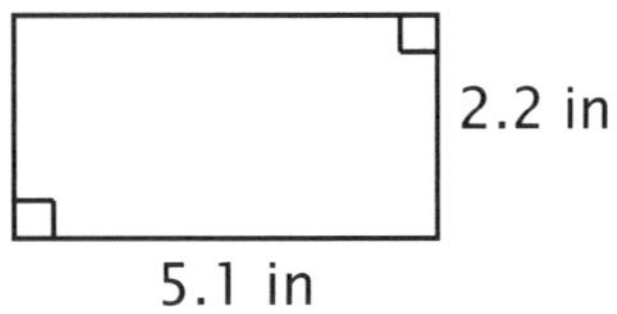

A = ______________

True or false.

5. Both squares and rhombuses have four equal sides.

6. The Greek symbol for gamma is γ.

7. 175° is the measure of a reflex angle.

8. A parallelogram always has at least one right angle.

9. The height of a figure is always perpendicular to the base.

10. The interior angles of a four-sided polygon add up to 180°.

Use the drawing to answer the questions.

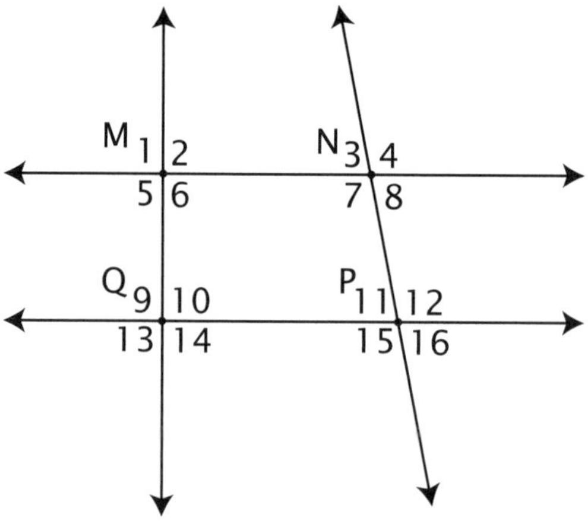

Given: In quadrilateral MNPQ, $\overleftrightarrow{MN} \parallel \overleftrightarrow{QP}$ and $\overleftrightarrow{MQ} \perp \overleftrightarrow{QP}$.

11. Are angles 9, 10, 13, and 14 all congruent? Why or why not?

12. If $m\angle 3 = 79°$, what is $m\angle 8$? Why?

13. If $m\angle 3 = 79°$, what is $m\angle 11$? Why?

14. If $m\angle 3 = 79°$, what is $m\angle 7$? Why?

15. Given your answers above, are $\angle 7$ and $\angle 11$ supplementary?

16. Which angle is congruent to and corresponds to $\angle 8$?

17. Name two pairs of congruent alternate interior angles.

18. Name two pairs of congruent alternate exterior angles.

19. $\angle 4$ and $\angle 7$ are ____________ angles, as are $\angle 3$ and $\angle 8$.

20. If a quadrilateral has only one pair of parallel sides, then it is a trapezoid. State the converse.

Find the area and perimeter of each figure.

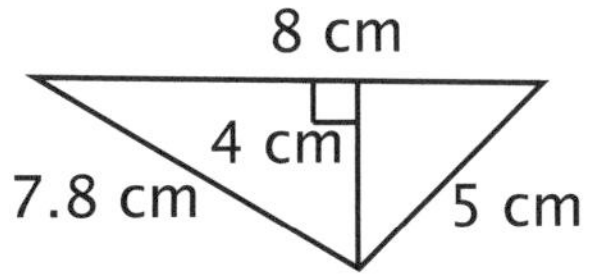

1. A = ______________

2. P = ______________

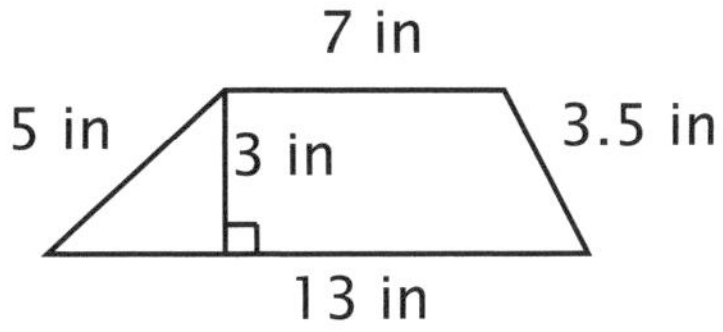

3. A = ______________

4. P = ______________

Given:
All angles are right angles.

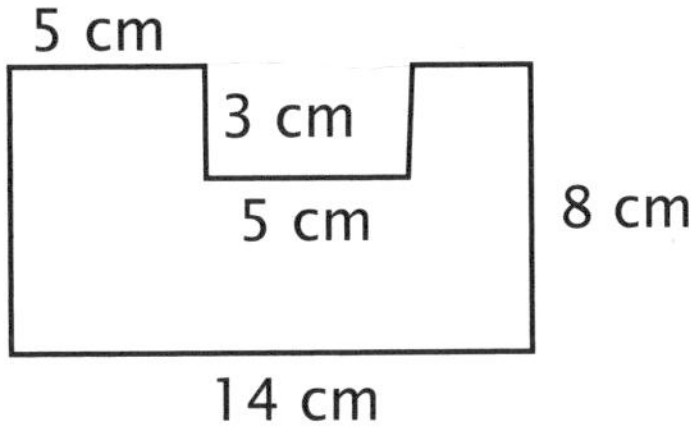

5. A = ______________

6. P = ______________

Use the drawing to answer the questions.

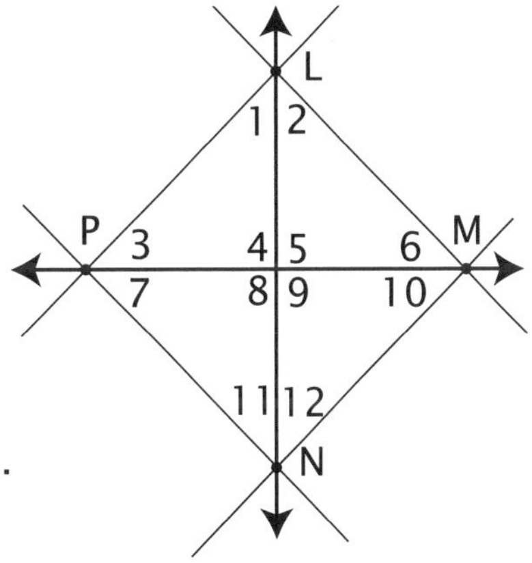

Given: $\overleftrightarrow{MP} \perp \overleftrightarrow{LN}$
PLMN is a parallelogram.

7. m∠5 = ________°. Why?

8. ∠1 and ∠3 are complementary angles. Why?

9. If ∠1 ≅ ∠2, then $\overleftrightarrow{LN}$ is a ______________ of ∠PLM.

10. If $\overleftrightarrow{LN}$ is ⊥ and a bisector, then it is a ______________ ______________.

Answer the questions.

11. What is the first step in finding the area of a trapezoid?

12. What do we call two geometric figures that have exactly the same size and shape?

13. What is the sum of the interior angles of a rectangle?

14. What is the sum of the interior angles of a trapezoid?

15. Draw a line segment with a measure of 3½" and label it AB.

16. On line segment AB (#15), draw a perpendicular line through the midpoint and label the line CD.

Sharpen your algebra skills!
You can use algebra skills to express the perimeter and area of a figure whose dimensions include unknowns.

EXAMPLE 1
square

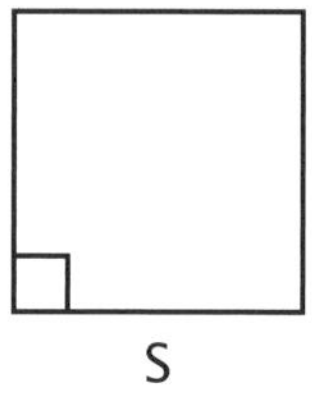

$P = 4S$
$A = S^2$

EXAMPLE 2
triangle

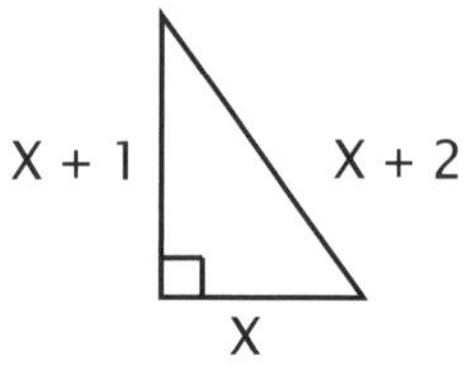

$P = X + (X + 1) + (X + 2) = 3X + 3$ units

$A = \frac{X(X+1)}{2}$ or $\frac{X^2+X}{2}$ units^2

Express the area and perimeter in simplest form.

17.

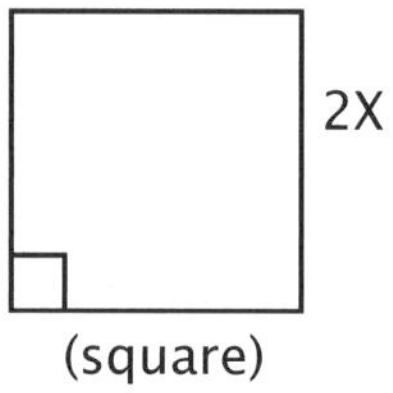

18.

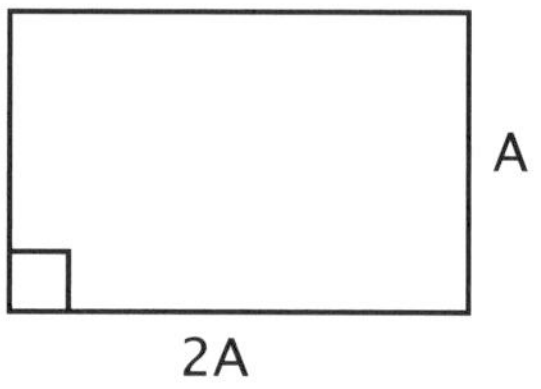

19.

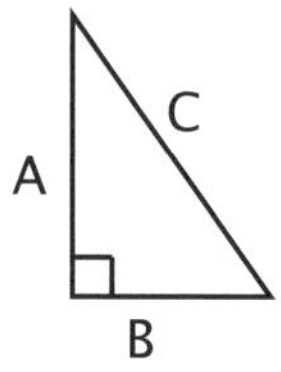

20.

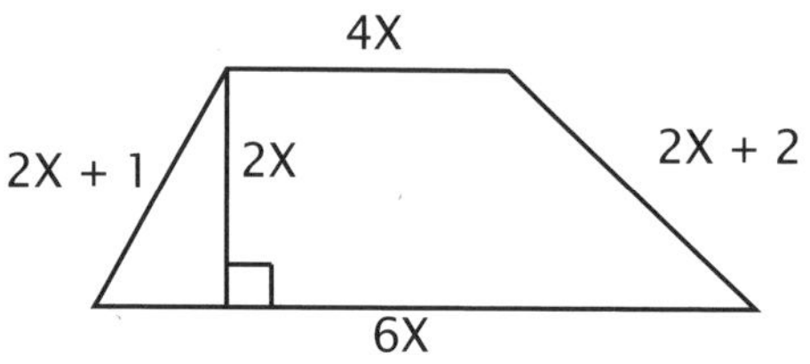

Find the area of each figure. Lines that appear to be perpendicular may be assumed to be so.

1.

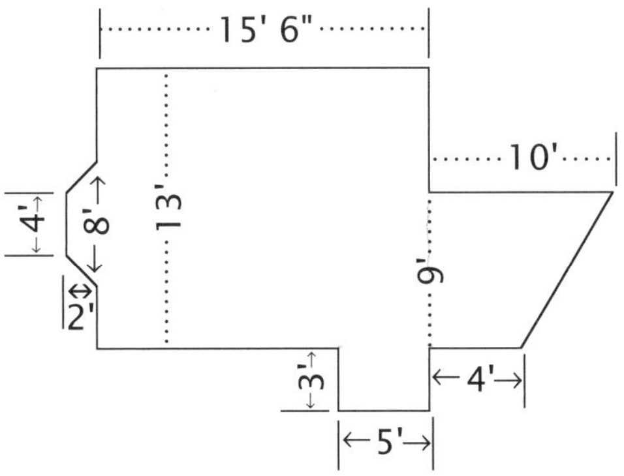

2.

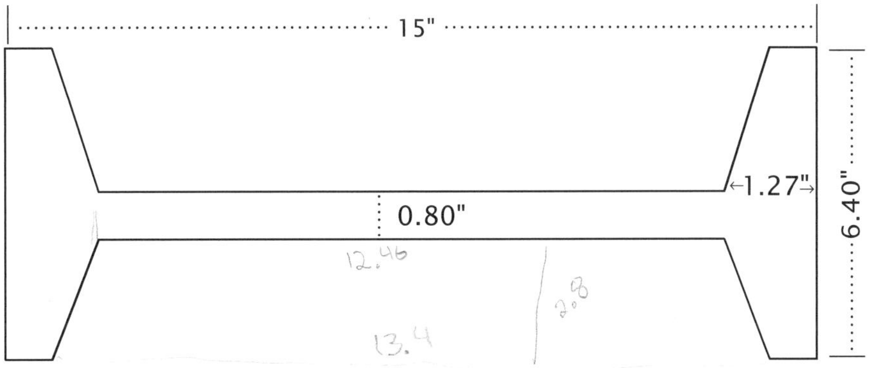

Both ends of the figure have the same measures, as do the top and bottom of the figure.

Follow the directions.

3. Sketch a rectangle, and label the two dimensions *a* and *b*. What is the area of the rectangle?

4. Sketch another rectangle, and label the two dimensions to indicate that each is twice the length of the rectangle in #3. What is the area of the new rectangle?

5. Label a third rectangle to indicate that each side is *n* times the length of the rectangle in #3. What is the area of this rectangle?

6. A rectangular garden is planned with dimensions of four feet and five feet. It is then decided to make each side of the garden five times as long as the original plan. Use your answer to #5 to find the area of the new garden.

7. Sketch two triangles, and write an algebraic expression showing what happens to the area when the base and height of a triangle are both doubled.

8. Sketch two squares, and write an algebraic expression showing what happens to the area when the length of each side is squared.

Describe each triangle according to the sides.

1. 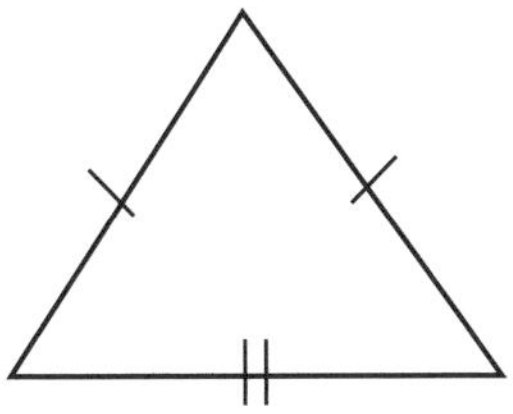

2. 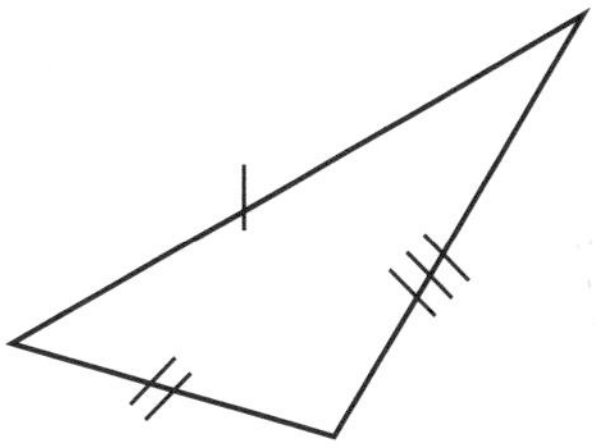

3. 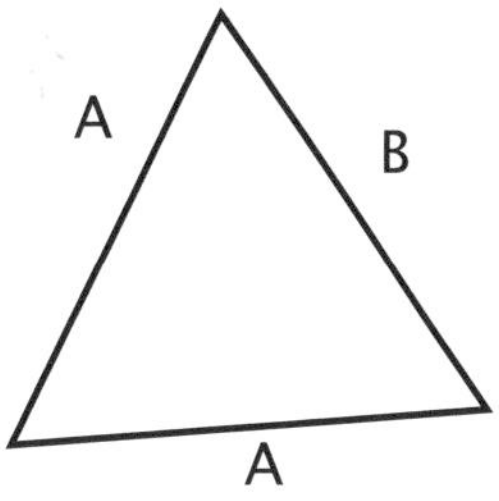

Describe each triangle according to the angles.

4. 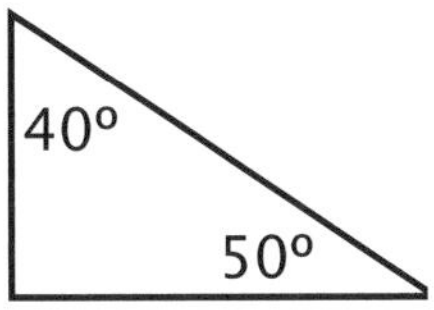

5. 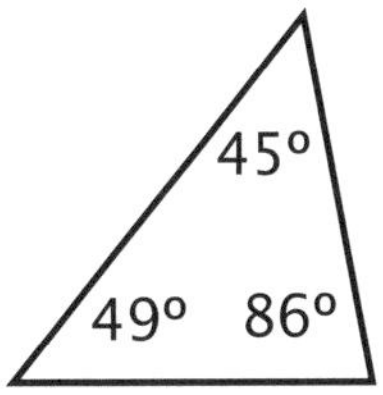

6. 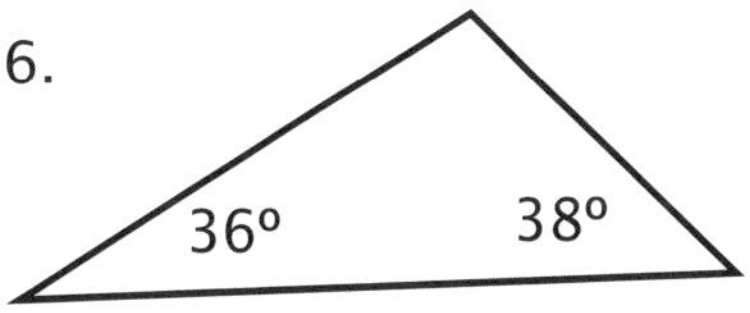

7. Can there be an isosceles right triangle?

8. Explain the reason for your answer to #7.

9. Can you have a triangle with sides 5, 7, and 15?

10. Can you have a triangle with sides 8, 9, and 11?

Fill in the blanks.

11. A triangle with only two sides congruent is called a(n) ____________________ triangle.

12. A triangle with all sides congruent is called a(n) ____________________ triangle.

13. If a triangle is equiangular, all of its ____________________ have the same measure.

14. A triangle with all of its angles greater than 0° and less than 90° is a(n) ____________________ triangle.

15. A triangle with one angle greater than 90° is a(n) ____________________ triangle.

16. A triangle with no sides congruent is called a(n) ____________________ triangle.

17. If one angle in a triangle is equal to 90°, the triangle is a(n) ____________________ triangle.

Construct each of the following triangles and label the size of each angle. Use another paper if necessary.

18. right triangle.

19. acute triangle.

20. isosceles triangle.

Describe each triangle according to the sides.

1.
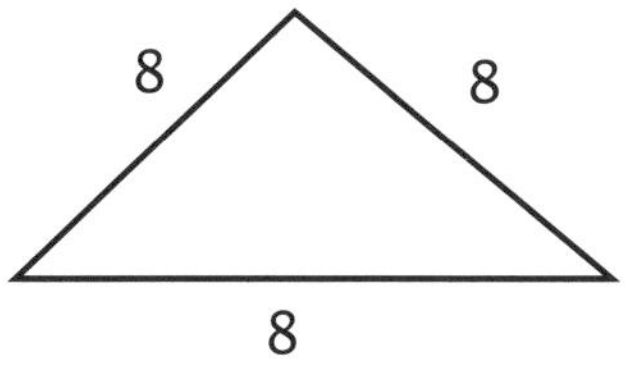

2.
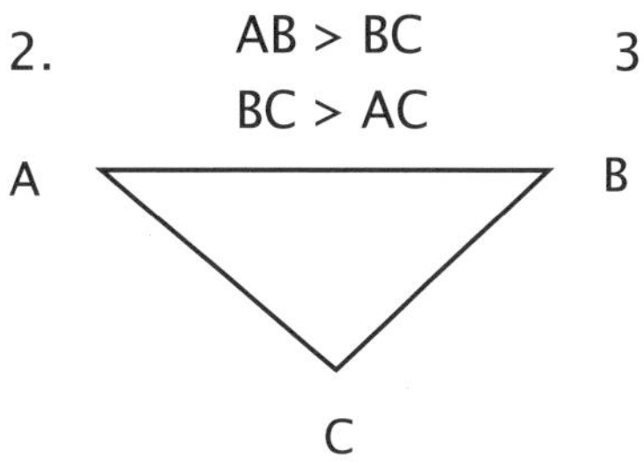

3.
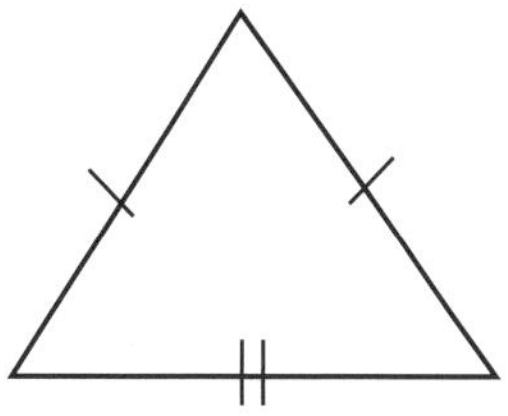

> means "greater than" and
< means "less than."

Describe each triangle according to the angles.

4.
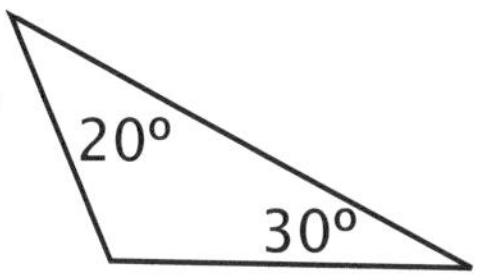

5.
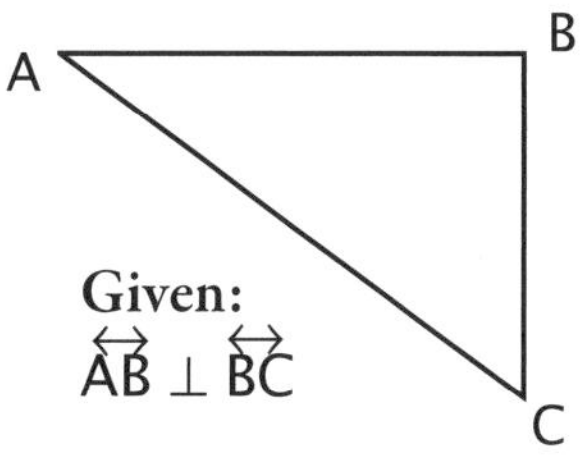

6.
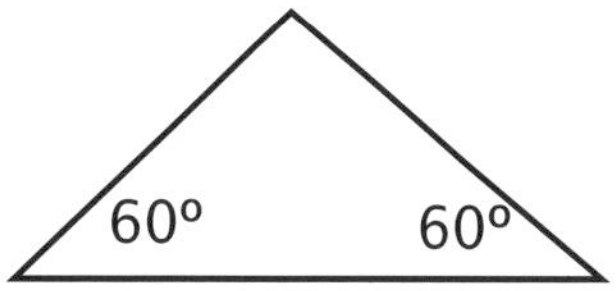

7. Can there be a right obtuse triangle?

8. Explain the reason for your answer to #7.

9. Can you have a triangle with sides 10, 11, and 12?

10. Can you have a triangle with sides 6, 7, and 2?

Fill in the blanks.

11. A triangle with only ____________________ sides congruent is called an isosceles triangle.

12. A triangle with ____________________ sides congruent is called an equilateral triangle.

13. A triangle with ____________________ sides congruent is a scalene triangle.

14. A right triangle has one angle whose measure is equal to ____°.

15. The measurements of the angles of an acute triangle are each less than ____°.

16. If the two short sides of a triangle have measures of 10 and 8, the measure of the long side must be less than ____.

17. If one angle in a triangle is greater than 90°, the triangle is a(n) ____________________ triangle.

Construct each of the following triangles and label the size of each angle. Use another paper if necessary.

18. scalene triangle

19. obtuse triangle

20. equiangular triangle
(Hint: if the measures of the angles of a triangle add up to 180°, what is the measure of each angle of an equiangular triangle?)

Follow the directions.

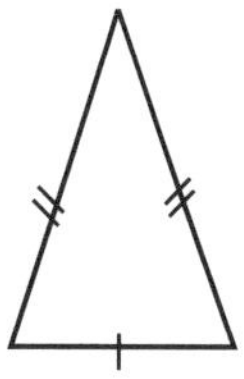

1. Describe the triangle according to the sides.

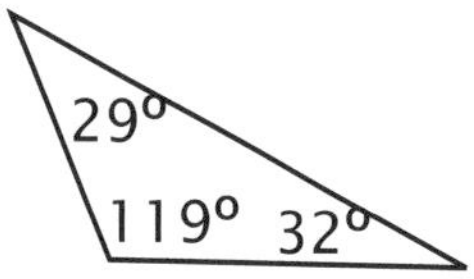

2. Describe the triangle according to the angles.

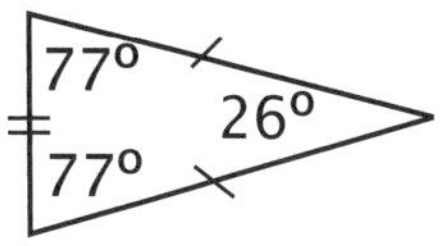

3. Describe the triangle according to the sides and the angles.

4. Construct an isosceles right triangle.

5. Can there be an equilateral right triangle?

6. Give the reason for your answer to #5.

Find the area and perimeter of each figure.

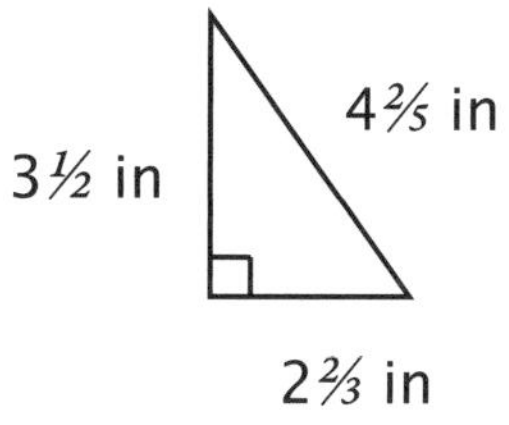

Given: All angles are right angles.

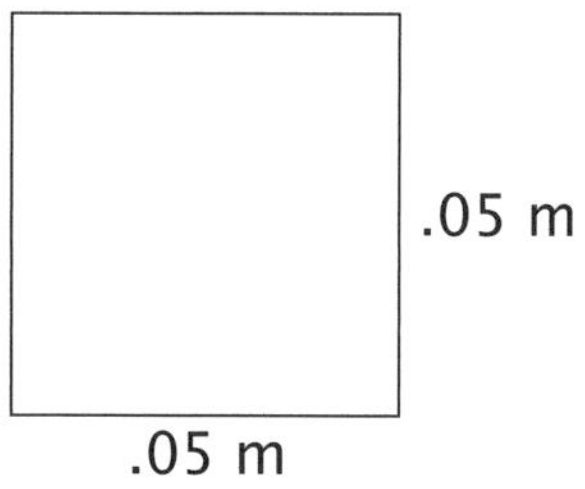

7. A = ________________ 8. A = ________________

9. P = ________________ 10. P = ________________

True or False.

11. The sum of the measures of two complementary angles equals 90°.

12. The sum of the measures of two supplementary angles equals 360°.

13. An angle with a measure of 89.6° is acute.

14. If corresponding angles are congruent, then the two lines are parallel.

15. If two lines lie in the same plane, they are collinear.

16. If two parallel lines are cut by a transversal, corresponding angles are congruent.

17. The symbol for the Greek letter beta is α.

18. Vertical angles are not congruent.

19. A reflex angle has a measure greater than 180° and less than 360°.

Find the area.

20. A = _______________

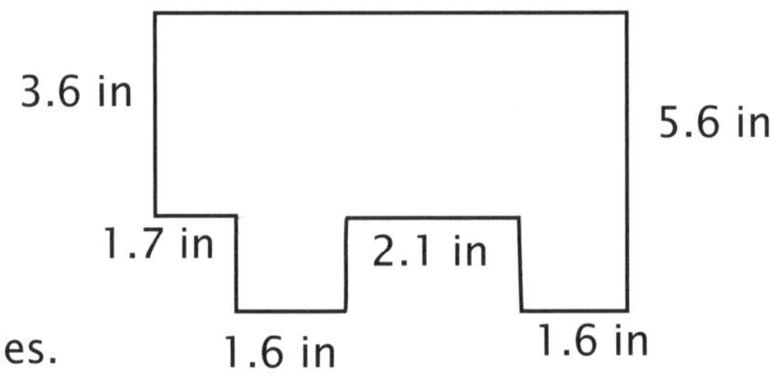

Given: All angles are right angles.

Follow the directions.

1. Describe the triangle according to the sides.

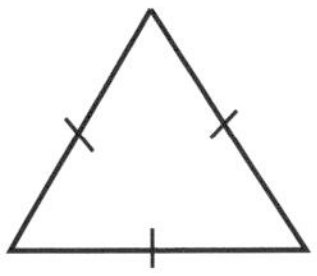

2. Describe the triangle according to the angles.

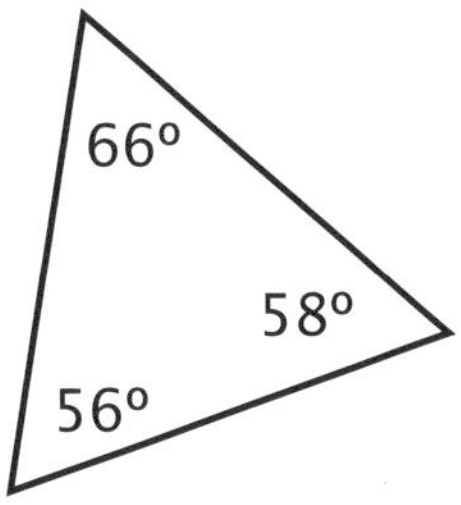

3. Describe the triangle according to the sides and the angles.

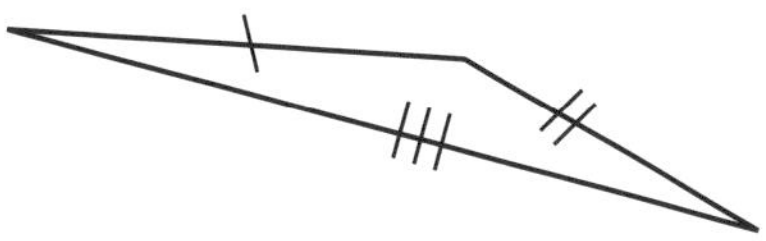

4. Construct an isosceles obtuse triangle.

5. Can there be a scalene right triangle?

6. Give the reason for your answer to #5.

Find the area and perimeter of each figure.

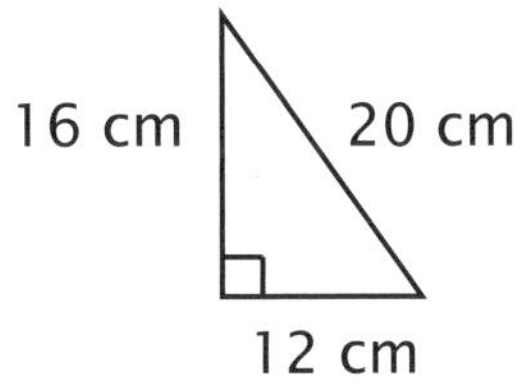

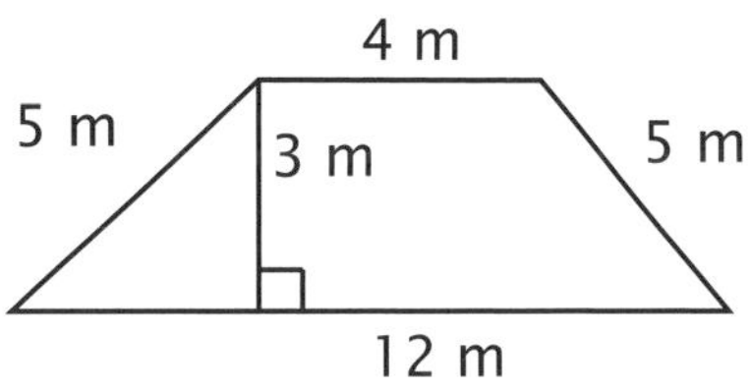

7. A = ________________ 8. A = ________________

9. P = ________________ 10. P = ________________

Use the drawing as needed to answer the questions.

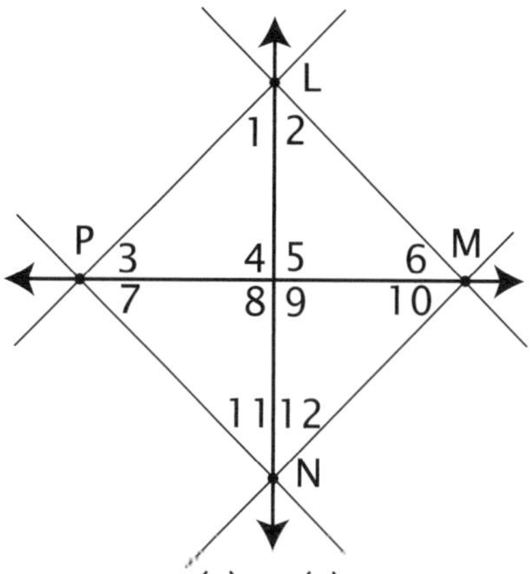

Given: $\overleftrightarrow{MP} \perp \overleftrightarrow{LN}$

PLMN is a parallelogram.

11. Is $\angle 7 \cong \angle 6$? Why or why not?

12. Is $\angle 3 \cong \angle 10$? Why or why not?

13. If m $\angle 11 = 35°$, then m$\angle 7$ = _____°.

14. $\angle 4$ and $\angle 9$ are ____________ angles and ____________ angles.

15. What is the sum of the measures of the interior angles of a triangle?

16. α is the Greek letter ____________.

17. Would it be possible for the triangles in the drawing to have short sides of 3 and 4 and long sides of 5?

18. Two of the angles in a triangle are 90° and 60°. What is the measure of the third angle?

19. Draw a 41° angle and bisect it.

Find the perimeter.

20. P = ______________

All angles are right angles.

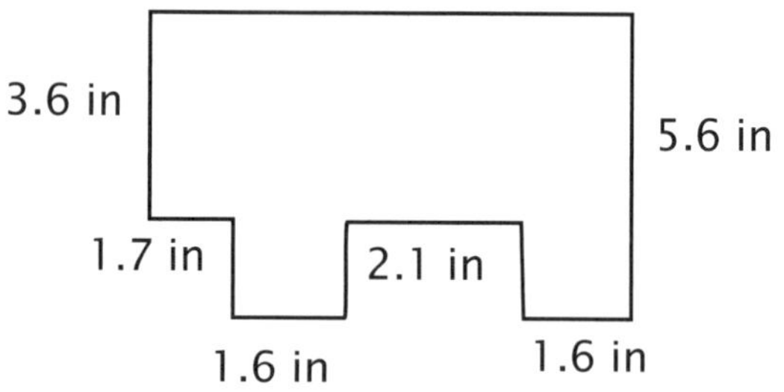

Follow the directions.

1. Describe the triangle according to the sides.

2. Describe the triangle according to the angles.

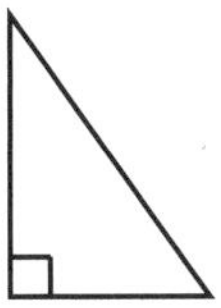

3. Describe the triangle according to the sides and the angles.

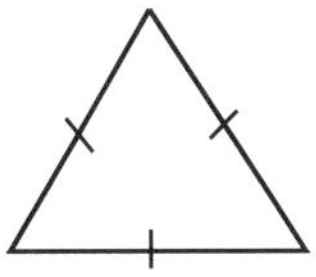

4. Construct an acute scalene triangle.

5. Can there be an acute right triangle?

6. Give the reason for your answer to #5.

Find the area and perimeter of each figure.

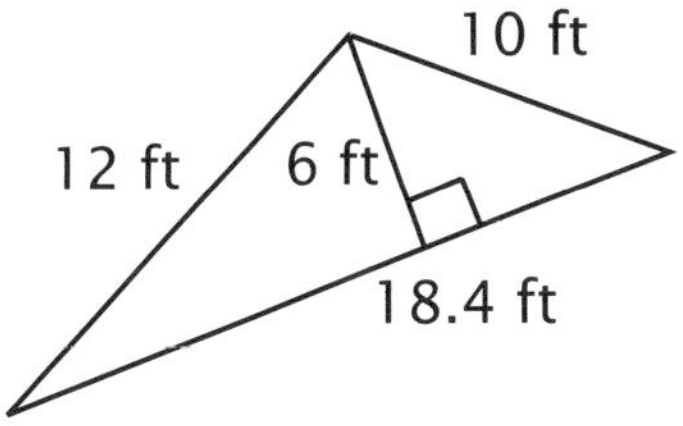

Given: Opposite sides are congruent.

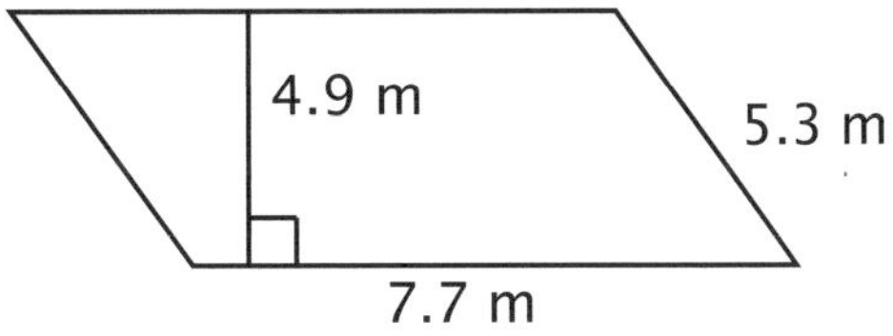

7. A = ________________ 8. A = ________________

9. P = ________________ 10. P = ________________

Use the drawings to answer the questions.

11. $\overline{AC}$ ◯ $\overline{BD}$. Why?

12. $\overline{AC}$ ______________ ∠BAD. Why?

13. $\overline{AC}$ is the common side for ∠ ______ and ∠ ______.

14. BC = CD. How do you know?

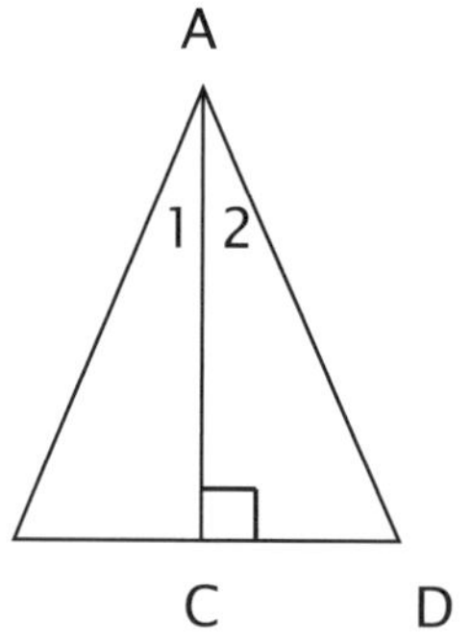

Given:
C is the midpoint of $\overline{BD}$.
∠1 ≅ ∠2

Given: All angles are right angles.

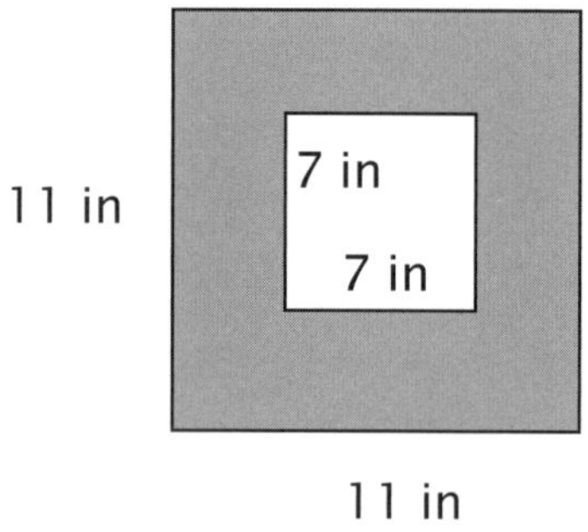

15. Find the area of the shaded part of the figure.

16. Find the outside perimeter.

Sharpen your algebra skills!
Two parallel lines have the same slope but different intercepts. Perpendicular lines have slopes that are negative reciprocals of each other.

EXAMPLE: Y = 3X + 1 is parallel to Y = 3X - 4
and perpendicular to Y = - 1/3 X + 5.

The intercept in each case may vary; only the slope determines if lines are parallel or perpendicular.

17. Write an equation for a line perpendicular to Y = 2X -1.

18. Write an equation for a line parallel to Y = 3X + 2.

19. Write an equation for a line perpendicular to Y = 1/2 X.

20. Write an equation for a line parallel to Y = 4X - 6.

A "golden rectangle" is a rectangle with a particular relationship between its sides. Many people consider it to have the most pleasing proportions of any rectangle. Here is an introduction to the subject.

Follow the directions to construct your own golden rectangle. The first three steps are done for you.

1. Find the midpoint of $\overline{AB}$ and label it D.

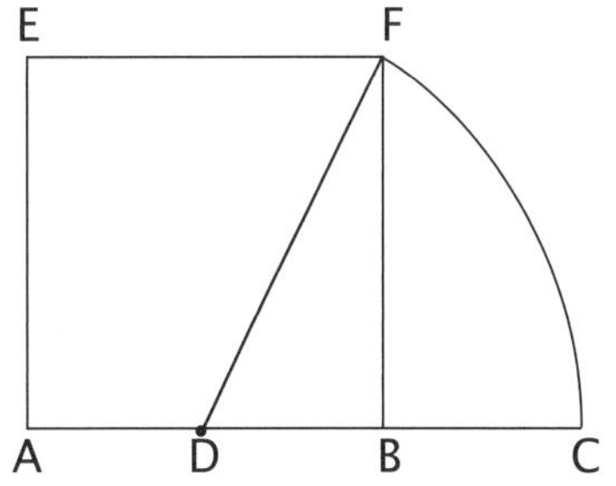

2. Extend $\overline{AB}$ to the right.

3. Place the point of your compass at D, and use it to measure the distance to F. Keeping your compass at the same setting, draw an arc from F that crosses the extension of $\overline{AB}$. Label the point where the arc crosses the line as C.

4. AC is the base of your golden rectangle. Draw a perpendicular line from C to form the right side of the rectangle and extend $\overline{EF}$ to finish the rectangle. Label the point where the extension crosses the perpendicular line as G. The rectangle defined by the points A, C, G, and E is a golden rectangle.

5. Use a ruler to measure the base and height of the golden rectangle as accurately as possible. You may want to use the metric side of your ruler. Make a ratio by putting the height over the base. Use a calculator to find the value in decimal terms, and record your answer to three or four decimal places.

6. Follow the above procedure with the larger square at right, and record the ratio between the two sides as a decimal.

You may repeat with squares of other sizes if you wish.

The relationship between the sides of a golden rectangle is a constant. It is also an irrational number. (π is another example of a constant value that is an irrational number.) This "golden ratio" is also referred to by a Greek letter, in this case **phi** or ϕ. The value of ϕ is given to five places in the answer key.

It is interesting to measure rectangular objects and see how close their proportions are to a golden rectangle.

Follow the directions to discover more about the golden rectangle.

7. The rectangle at the right is an approximation of a golden rectangle. Using your compass to measure lengths, mark off a square from one end of the rectangle. You should have a vertical rectangle left.

8. Continue to mark off squares from each rectangle as it is formed, until the rectangles are too small. If you have done this accurately, each smaller rectangle should also be a golden rectangle.

Match each polygon with its number of sides.

1. hexagon a. 10

2. pentagon b. 4

3. square c. 6

4. dodecagon d. 5

5. octagon e. 12

6. decagon f. 8

For #7–12, assume the given polygon is regular.

7. How many diagonals can be drawn from one vertex?

8. How many triangles are formed?

9. How many total degrees in the polygon?

10. How many degrees in each interior angle?

11. What is the measure of each exterior angle?

12. What is the total measure of the exterior angles?

Answer the questions.

13. Give the formula for finding the sum of the interior degrees in a regular polygon.

14. If the measure of an exterior angle of a regular polygon is 30°, what is the name of the polygon? How did you determine this?

15. If you can draw eight triangles in a polygon, what kind of polygon do you have?

16. Using the formula from #13, find the total degrees of the interior angles of a 15-sided polygon.

17. Find the measure of each interior angle in #16.

18. Check your answer to #17 using exterior angles.

Match each polygon with its number of angles.

1.	octagon	a.	12
2.	decagon	b.	8
3.	dodecagon	c.	5
4.	square	d.	10
5.	hexagon	e.	6
6.	pentagon	f.	4

For #7–12, assume the given polygon is regular.

7. How many diagonals can be drawn from one vertex?

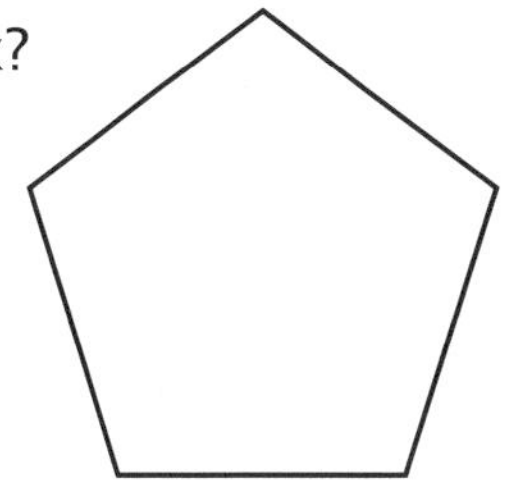

8. How many triangles are formed?

9. How many total degrees in the polygon?

10. How many degrees in each interior angle?

11. What is the measure of each exterior angle?

12. What is the total measure of the exterior angles?

Answer the questions.

13. Give the formula for finding the sum of the interior degrees in a regular polygon.

14. If the measure of an exterior angle of a regular polygon is 36°, what is the name of the polygon? How did you determine this?

15. If you can draw six triangles in a polygon, what kind of polygon do you have?

16. Using the formula, find the total degrees of the interior angles of a three-sided polygon.

17. Find the measure of each interior angle in #16.

18. Check your answer to #17 using exterior angles.

For #1–6, assume the hexagon is a regular polygon.

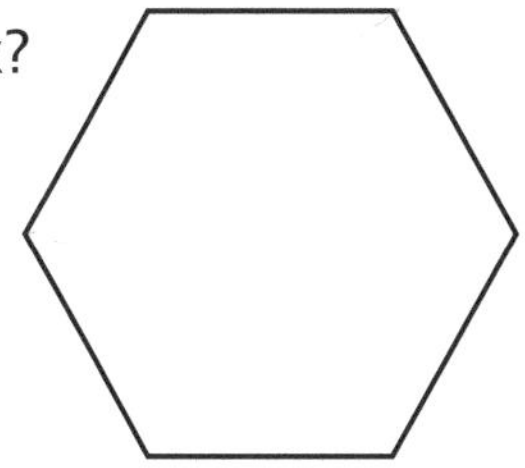

1. How many diagonals can you draw from one vertex?

2. How many triangles are there now?

3. How many total degrees in the polygon?

4. How many degrees in each interior angle?

5. What is the measure of each exterior angle?

6. What is the total measure of the exterior angles?

7. If the measure of an exterior angle of a regular polygon is 90°, what is the name of the polygon? How did you determine this?

8. If you can draw three triangles in a polygon, what kind of polygon is it?

9. Using the formula (based on the number of triangles), find the total interior degrees if a polygon has 12 sides.

10. Find the measure of each interior angle in #9. Check your answer using exterior angles.

Use the drawing as needed to answer the questions.

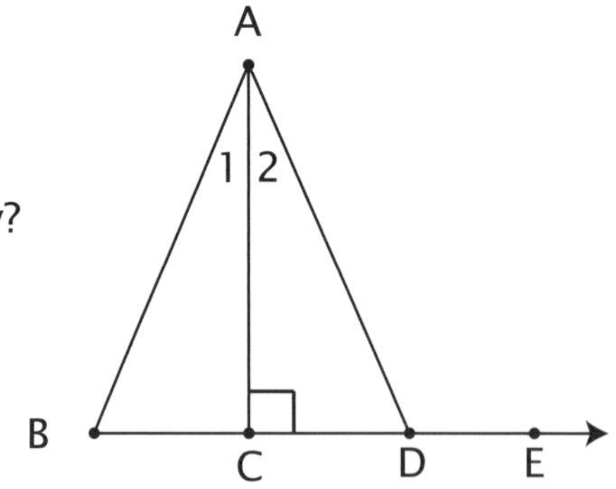

Given:
C is the midpoint of $\overline{BD}$.
$\angle 1 \cong \angle 2$

11. If $m\angle 1 = 30°$, $m\angle ABC =$ ______°.

12. $\angle 1$ and $\angle$_____ are complementary angles. Why?

13. If $m\angle CAD = 30°$, then $m\angle ADE =$ ______°.

14. $\angle ADC$ and $\angle ADE$ are adjacent and ____________ .

15. What kind of triangle has three congruent sides?

16. What kind of triangle has one 90° angle?

17. Can there be an acute isosceles triangle?

18. Could you construct a triangle with sides 15, 9 and 8?

Find the area and perimeter.

19. A = __________________

20. P = ____________

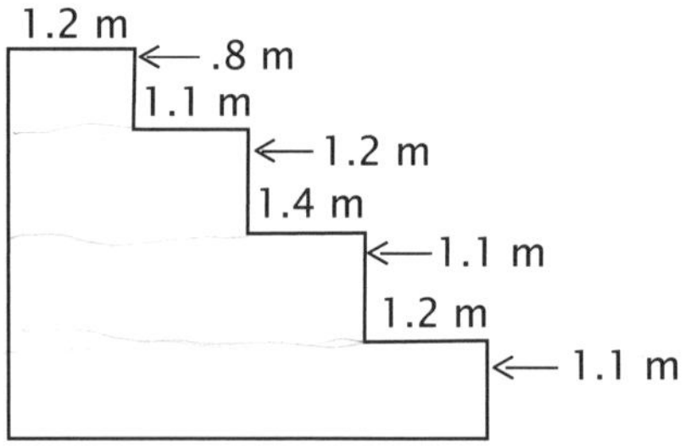

Given: All angles are right angles.

11D

For #1–6, assume the figure is a regular polygon.

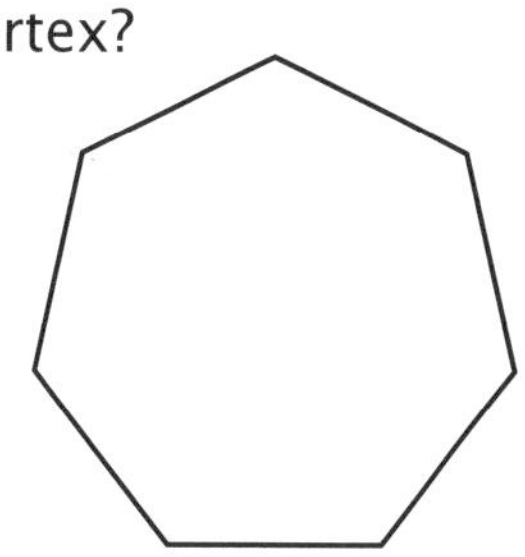

1. How many diagonals can you draw from one vertex?

2. How many triangles are there now?

3. How many total degrees in the polygon?

4. How many degrees in each interior angle?

5. What is the measure of each exterior angle?

6. What is the total measure of the exterior angles?

7. If the measure of an exterior angle of a regular polygon is 60°, what is the name of the polygon? How did you determine this?

8. If you can draw four triangles in a polygon, what kind of polygon is it?

9. Using the formula (based on the number of triangles), find the total interior degrees if a polygon has nine sides.

10. Find the measure of each interior angle in #9. Check your answer using exterior angles.

Use the drawing as needed to answer the questions.

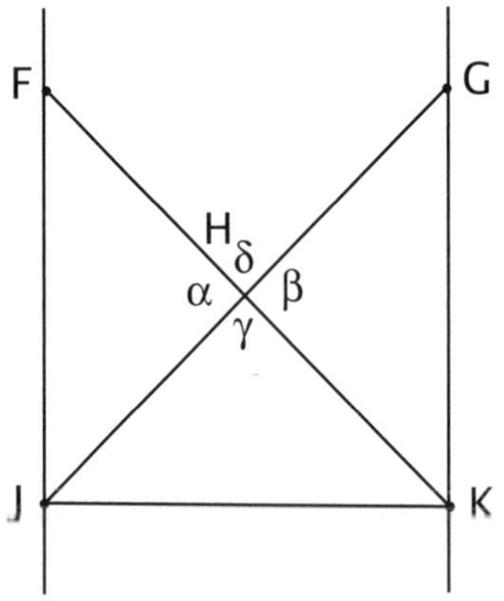

Given: $\overline{FJ} \perp \overline{JK}$

$\overline{GK} \perp \overline{JK}$

$\overline{FJ} \parallel \overline{GK}$

11. ∠FHG and ∠_____ are supplementary.

12. ∠FHG and ∠_____ are vertical angles.

13. Is ∠FJG ≅ ∠KGJ? Why or why not?

14. Is ∠JFK ≅ ∠GKF? Why or why not?

15. What kind of triangle has only two congruent sides?

16. What kind of triangle has no congruent sides?

17. Could you construct a triangle with sides 1, 1, and 2?

18. Give the basic formula for finding the area of a quadrilateral.

Follow the directions.

19. Draw a 125° angle and label it ABC.

20. Using your compass, draw a ray through point B that bisects angle ABC. Check your work with your protractor.

For #1–6, assume the decagon is a regular polygon.

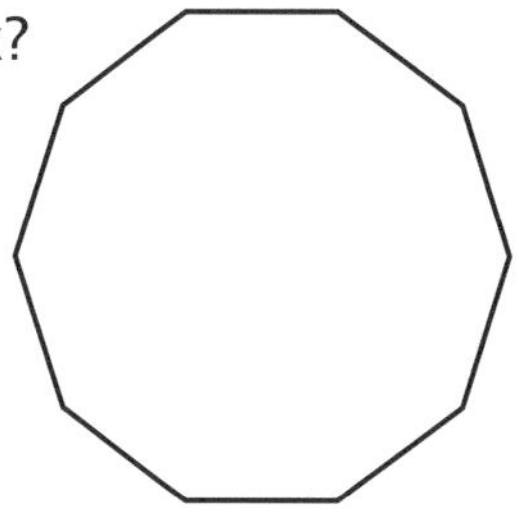

1. How many diagonals can you draw from one vertex?

2. How many triangles are there now?

3. How many total degrees in the polygon?

4. How many degrees in each interior angle?

5. What is the measure of each exterior angle?

6. What is the total measure of the exterior angles?

7. If the measure of an exterior angle of a regular polygon is 120°, what is the name of the polygon? How did you determine this?

8. If you can draw six triangles in a polygon, what kind of polygon is it?

9. Using the formula (based on the number of triangles), find the total interior degrees if a polygon has 20 sides.

10. Find the measure of each interior angle in #9. Check your answer using exterior angles.

Use the drawing as needed to answer the questions.

11. If $m\angle\alpha = 85°$, what is $m\angle\delta$? Why?

12. If $m\angle FHJ = 85°$, what is $m\angle\delta$?

13. If $m\angle\alpha = 85°$, and $m\angle FJG = 45°$, what is $m\angle JFK$?

14. If $m\angle\alpha = 85°$, and $m\angle FJG = 45°$, what is $m\angle GJK$?

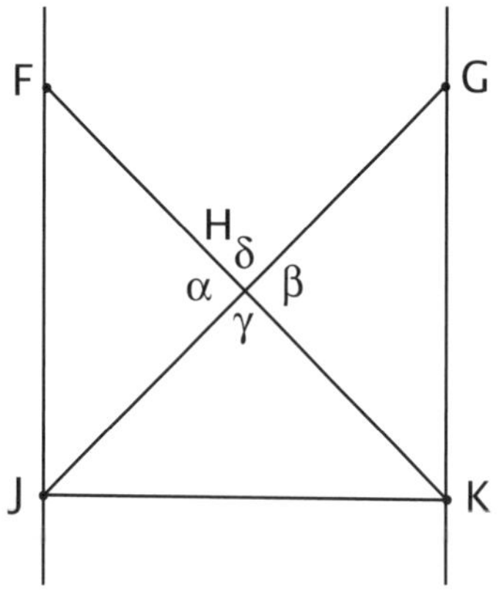

Given: $\overline{FJ} \perp \overline{JK}$
$\overline{GK} \perp \overline{JK}$
$\overline{FJ} \parallel \overline{GK}$

Find the area and perimeter.

15. A = ______________

16. P = ______________

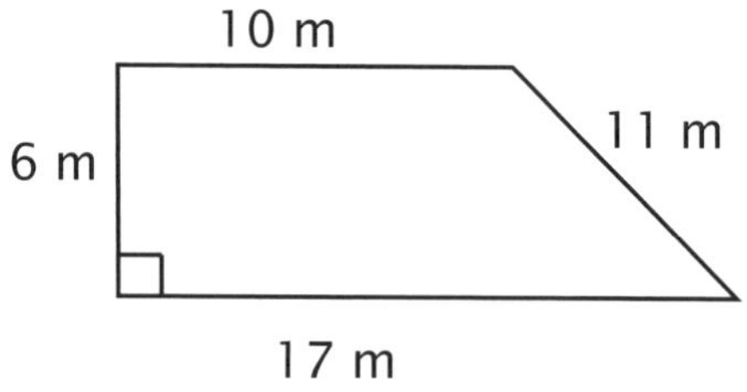

Sharpen your algebra skills!
A line can be described in slope-intercept form or in the standard form of the equation of a line.

EXAMPLE 1 Y = 3X + 1 (slope-intercept) may be written as 3X – Y = –1 (standard form).

EXAMPLE 2 2X + 3Y = 6 (standard form) may be written as Y = – 2/3 X + 2 (slope-intercept form).

17. Write Y = X – 1 in standard form.

18. Write 2X + Y + 4 = 0 in slope-intercept form.

19. Write Y = 4X + 2 in standard form.

20. Write X + 2Y – 8 = 0 in slope-intercept form.

Here are some more logic problems to try. For each problem on this page, there is only one correct choice for each person. Check off obvious wrong choices first. Remember to check off other impossible choices as you work.

Solve the logic problems using the charts.

1. Mom bought a different style of jacket for each of her four children. Both Ashley and Naomi think they look terrible in green. Chris and Ashley dislike zippers. Which jacket did each person get?

	green, buttons	green, zipper	red, zipper	blue, buttons
Chris				
Douglas				
Ashley				
Naomi				

2. Three students decide to throw a birthday party for a friend. The birthday guest's name does not start with "s." The person making refreshments lives close to the person in whose home the party will be held. Jason and Shane each live far away from all the others. Troy's home is too small to host the party. What is each person's role?

	planning games	refreshments	place for party	birthday guest
Sam				
Jason				
Shane				
Troy				

3. Four people are looking forward to their vacations. Janelle and Walter will travel on vehicles that have wheels. Janelle and Julie are terrified of flying. Walter wants to take the back roads. How will each person travel?

	train	boat	airplane	car
Janelle				
Walter				
Julie				
Jared				

4. Four friends each ordered a different lunch. Tina will not eat her lunch with a spoon. Logan's lunch was definitely not served with mustard or salad dressing. Molly and Sam can eat their food with their fingers. Tina is allergic to tomato sauce and Sam does not eat meat. What did each person have for lunch?

	hot dog	pizza	chicken soup	tossed salad
Molly				
Tina				
Logan				
Sam				

5. Write your own logic problem, and give it to a friend to solve.

12A

Fill in the blanks. Use the drawing as needed.

1. A three-dimensional circle is a ________________ .

2. The perimeter of a circle is called the ________________ .

3. $\overline{BF}$ is a ________________ .

4. Half the length of $\overline{CE}$ is the ________________ .

5. A chord that goes through the center of the circle is the ________________ .

6. _____ is a radius of this circle.

7. A piece of the area of a circle is called a(n) ________________ .

8. A piece of the circumference of a circle is called a(n) ________________ .

9. The line intersecting the circle at point D is the ________________ .

10. A(n) ________________ is a stretched circle.

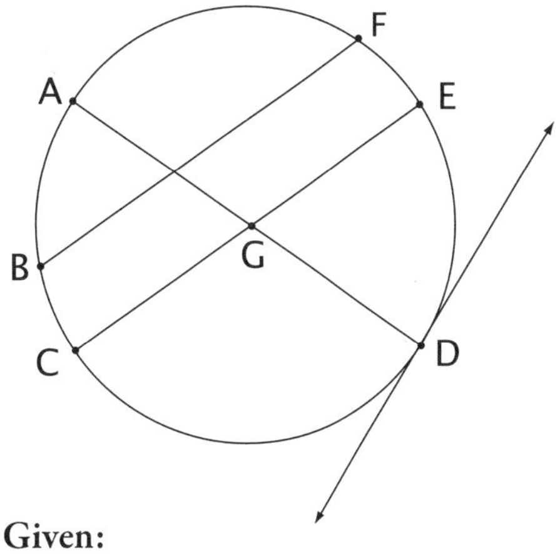

Given:
G is the center of the circle.

Fill in the blanks.

11. At its intersection, a tangent is ________________ to the radius.

12. A line that intersects the circumference of the circle at two points is a ________________ .

13. The minor arc formed by a central angle measures 60°. The measure of the major arc is __________ .

14. An inscribed square would touch the circle in _________ points.

Answer the question.

15. C is the center of the circle at right. If $m\angle ACB = 86°$, what is the measure of the minor arc?

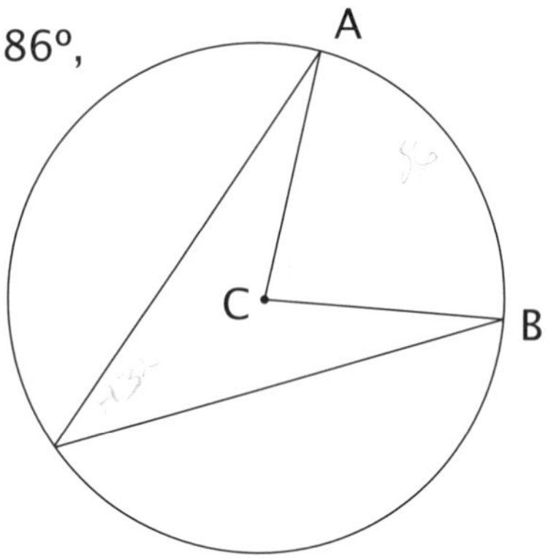

16. Since the measure of the central angle is 86°, what is the measure of the inscribed angle?

17. Using a protractor, find the measure of ∠ABC, which defines a sector of a circle in the drawing below. Use a pencil and straightedge to extend the lines if necessary.

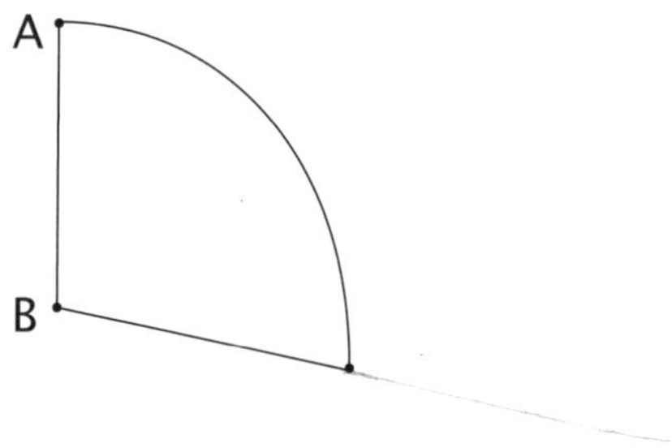

18. What is the measure of the arc between points A and C in the drawing of the sector?

Fill in the blanks. Use the drawing as needed.

1. The perimeter of a circle is called the ________________ .

2. $\overline{CG}$ is a ________________ .

3. A three-dimensional circle is a ________________ .

4. Half the length of $\overline{BG}$ is the ________________ .

5. $\overline{BD}$ is a ________________ .

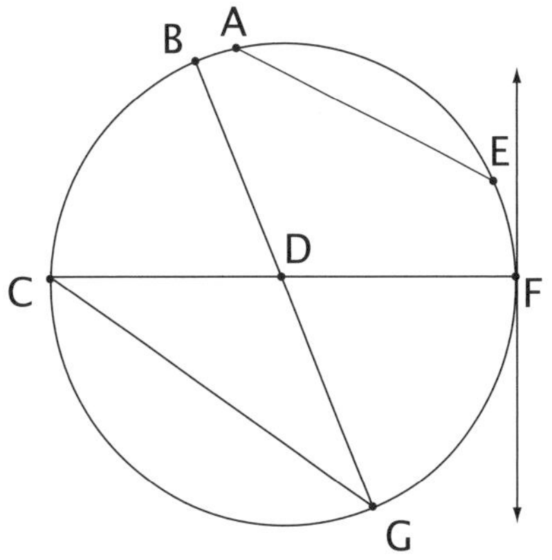

Given:
D is the center of the circle.

6. A chord that goes through the center of the circle is the ________________ .

7. The line intersecting the circle at point F is the ________________ .

8. A piece of the circumference of a circle is called a(n) ________________ .

9. A piece of the area of a circle is called a(n) ________________.

10. A line that intersects the circumference of the circle at ________________ points is a secant.

Fill in the blanks.

11. A tangent intersects the circle at exactly _______________ point.

12. A(n) _______________ is a stretched circle.

13. The major arc formed by a central angle measures 270°.
The measure of the minor arc is ________.

14. An inscribed triangle would touch the circle in ________ points.

Answer the question.

15. C is the center of the circle at right. If m∠ACB = 44°, what is the measure of the minor arc?

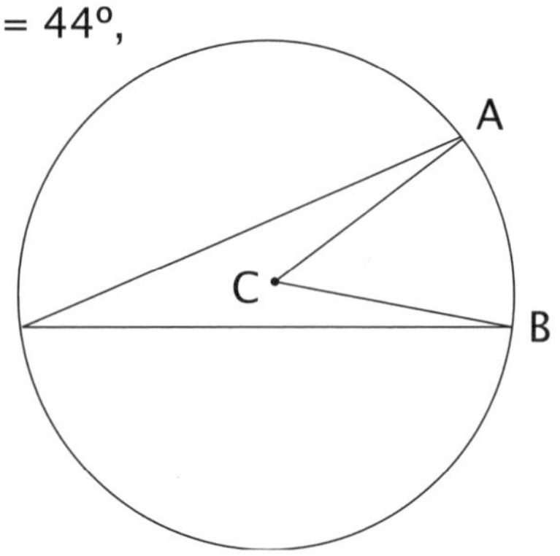

16. Since the measure of the central angle is 44°, what is the measure of the inscribed angle?

17. Using a protractor, find the measure of ∠EFG, which defines a sector of a circle in the drawing below. Use a pencil and straightedge to extend the lines if necessary.

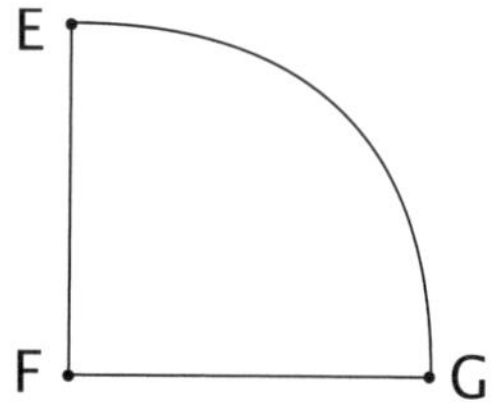

18. What is the measure of the arc between points E and G in the drawing of the sector?

Use the drawing as needed to answer the questions.

1. Name a radius of the circle shown.

2. If $\overleftrightarrow{AG}$ touches the circle at point A only, what is the line called?

3. Name a chord of the circle that is not the diameter.

4. What do we call a line that intersects the circle in exactly two points?

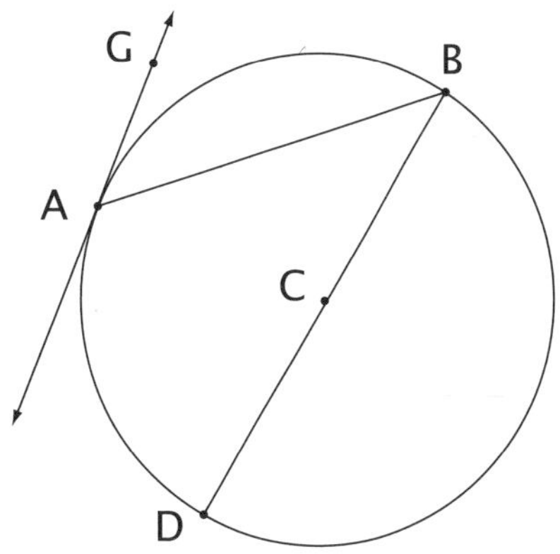

Given:
C is the center of the circle.

5. What do we call a three-dimensional circle?

6. What do we call a stretched circle?

7. What is another name for the perimeter of the circle?

8. A pentagon is inscribed in a circle. At how many points does it touch the circle?

9. An inscribed angle has a measure of 10°. What is the measure of the minor arc that it intercepts?

Follow the directions.

10. Draw an arc with a radius of 1½ inches and a measure of 60°.

11. Estimate to within 10° the measure of the arc shown by the central angle.

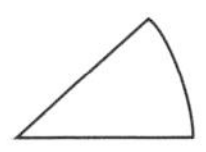

Use the drawing as needed to answer the questions.

12. What kind of angle is ∠NLM?
Tell why.

13. Is $\overleftrightarrow{LN} \parallel \overleftrightarrow{MP}$?
Tell why.

14. If m∠5 = 68°, what is m∠7?
Why?

15. If m∠5 = 68°, what is m∠RMN?
Why?

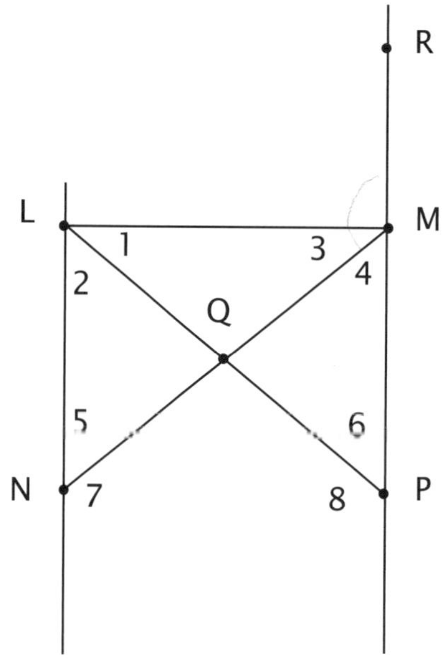

Given: ∠NLP ≅ ∠MPL
∠1 and ∠2 are complementary.

Answer the questions.

16. If the measure of an exterior angle of a regular polygon is 45°, what is the name of the polygon? How did you determine this?

17. If you can draw two triangles in a polygon, what kind of polygon is it?

18. Using the formula (based on the number of triangles), find the total interior degrees if the polygon has seven sides.

19. Find the measure of each interior angle in #18.

20. Check your answer to #19 using exterior angles.

12D

Use the drawing as needed to answer the questions.

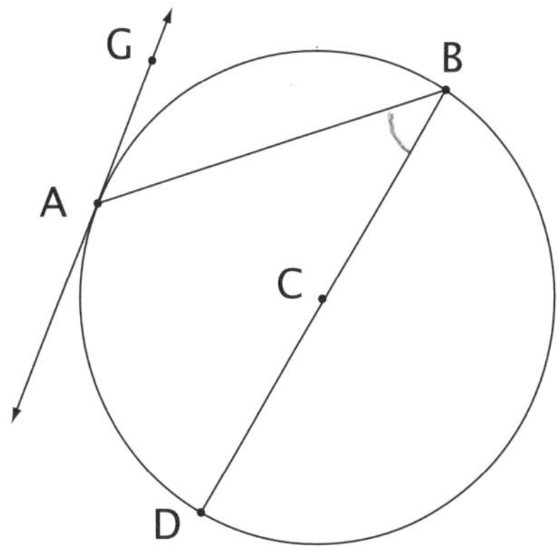

Given: C is the center of the circle.

1. Twice the length of the radius is a(n) ______________ .

2. A chord that goes through the center of a circle is the ______________ .

3. $\overline{CD}$ is a(n) ______________ .

4. If segment AB was extended into a line, it would be called a ______________ .

5. A sphere has ______________ dimensions.

6. Most race tracks are examples of ______________ .

7. Name the quadrilaterals that have two pairs of parallel sides.

8. Points A, B, and D are on the ______________ of the circle shown.

9. A polygon ______________ in a circle touches the circle with each of its vertices.

10. If m∠ABD = 35°, what is the measure of the minor arc formed by the angle?

11. What is the measure of the major arc formed by ∠ABD?

Use the drawing as needed to answer the questions.

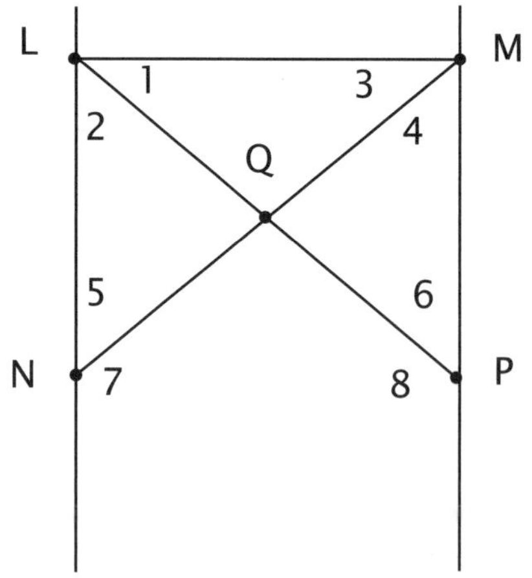

Given: $\angle NLP \cong \angle MPL$

$m\angle 1 + m\angle 2 = 90°$

12. $\angle NLP$ and $\angle$________ are complementary.

13. $\angle LQM$ and $\angle NQP$ are ______________ .

14. If $m\angle 5 = 68°$ and $m\angle 2 = 58°$, what is $m\angle 1$?

15. If $m\angle 5 = 68°$ and $m\angle 2 = 58°$, what is $m\angle 3$?

Name the figures described.

16. It has length but no width.

17. An angle with a measure greater than 90° and less than 180°.

18. It has four congruent sides, but its angles may not be congruent.

19. A triangle with no congruent sides.

20. An eight-sided convex polygon.

12E

Use the drawing as needed to answer the questions.

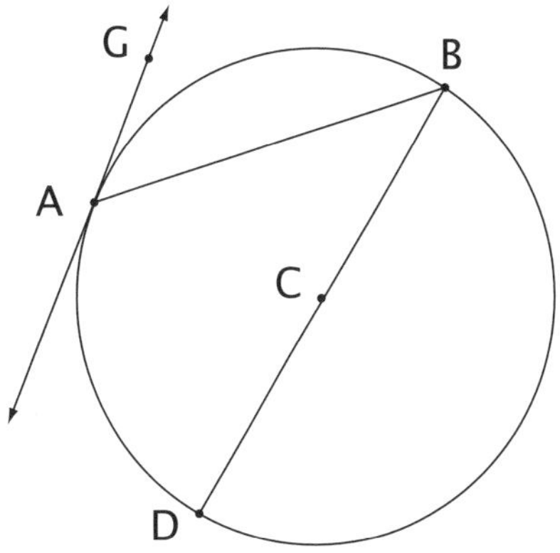

Given: C is the center of the circle.

1. An orbit of a planet, or oval, is a(n) ______________ .

2. A line segment with endpoints on the circle is a ______________ .

3. One-half of the diameter of a circle is the ______________ .

4. $\overline{BD}$ is a ______________ .

5. The tangent intersects the line at point ______________ .

6. A piece of the circumference is a(n) ______________ .

7. A piece of the area is a(n) ______________ .

8. The measure of an inscribed angle is ______________ of the measure of the intercepted arc.

9. At its intersection, a tangent is ______________ to the radius.

Follow the directions.

10. Draw an arc with a radius of $2\frac{1}{8}$ inches and a measure of 84°.

11. Estimate to within 10° the measure of the arc shown:

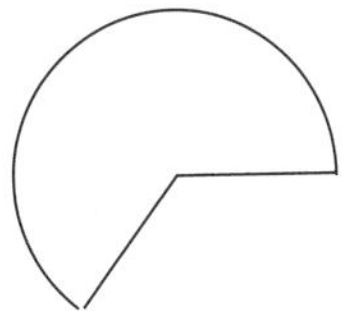

Assume the octagon is a regular polygon.

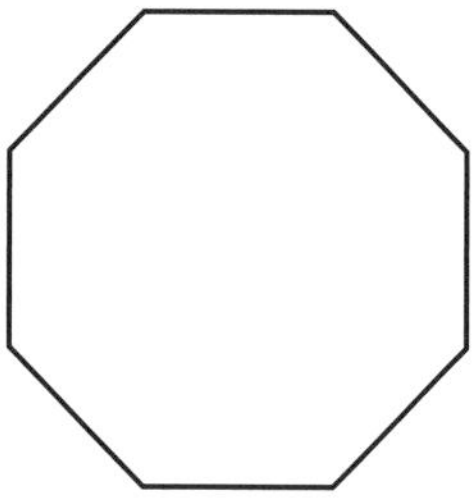

12. How many diagonals can you draw from one vertex?

13. How many triangles are there now?

14. How many total degrees in the polygon?

15. How many degrees are there in each interior angle?

16. What is the measure of each exterior angle?

17. What is the total measure of the exterior angles?

Sharpen your algebra skills!

Equations with two unknowns can be solved simultaneously by substituting one equation into the other.

EXAMPLE Solve Y - X = 4 and Y + 2X = 1.

The first equation may be written as Y = X + 4.

Substitute the new value of Y for Y in the second equation.

(X + 4) + 2X = 1, so X = -1.

Substitute -1 for X in either equation and solve for Y.

Y - (-1) = 4, so Y = 3. Solution (-1, 3).

Solve by substitution.

18. Y + X = -5
Y - 2X = 4

19. Y - 4X = 4
Y + 2X = -2

20. Y - X = 0
Y - 3X = -6

SYSTEMATIC REVIEW 12H

Follow the directions.

1. It is possible to construct an equilateral triangle using only a compass and straightedge. (Use your ruler as a straightedge, but do not measure with it.) Start with line segment AB at right. Put the point of your compass at A and the other side at B. Using that distance as a radius, draw an arc from B up past where you think the point of the triangle should fall. Now put the point of your compass at B and draw another arc upward from A. The point where the arcs cross is the upper vertex of an equilateral triangle.

   Label that point C, and use your straightedge to connect it to A and to B.

2. What is the measure of each angle in the triangle you constructed in #1?

3. The regular octagon at right is divided by straight lines into eight equal sections. What do you think the measure of each of the small center angles is?

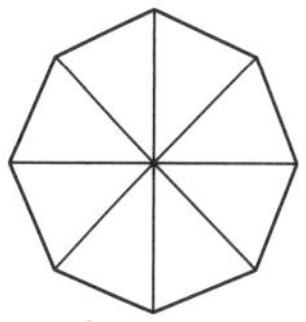

It is possible to construct a regular octagon inside a circle using only a compass and straightedge.

4. Make a dot for the center, and then use your compass to draw a circle around the center. You don't need to measure, but a diameter of about two inches will work.

5. Use your straightedge to draw a diameter through the center.

6. Construct the perpendicular bisector of the diameter.

7. Bisect each of the four angles you have produced.

8. Your lines should touch the circle in eight points. Use your straightedge to connect each point to its neighbor. You should have a regular octagon inscribed in a circle.

9. Can you construct a regular hexagon inside a circle? Think about your answers to #1, 2, and 3 on the previous page.

It is possible to inscribe a circle inside any triangle, so that the circle just touches each side of the triangle.

10. Bisect each angle of the first triangle shown.

11. Use the point where the three bisectors cross as the center, and draw a circle that is circumscribed by the triangle.

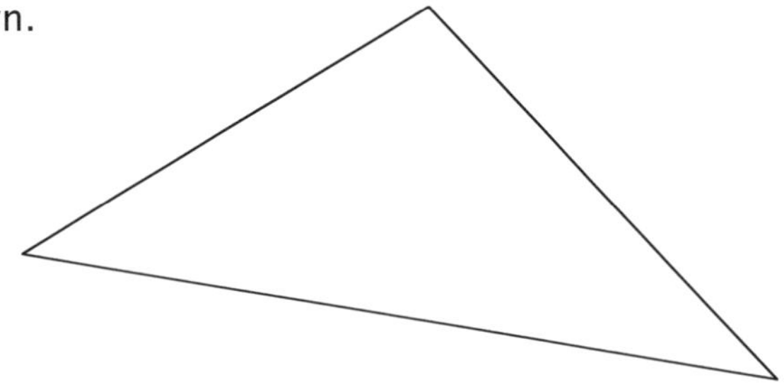

12. Inscribe a circle inside the second triangle shown.

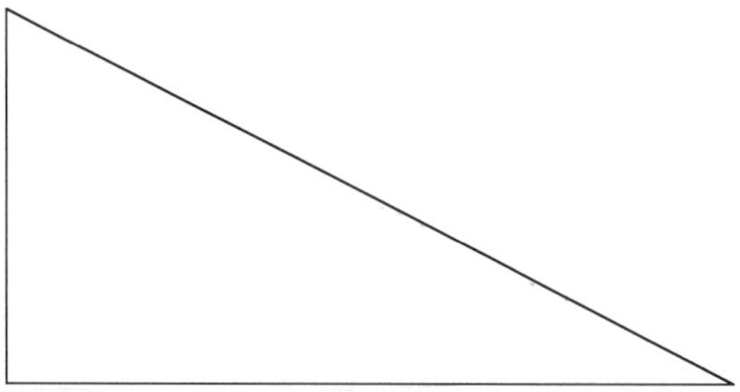

13A

Fill in the blanks.

1. Half the diameter of a circle is the ______________ .

2. The perimeter, or distance around, a circle is the ______________ .

3. The formula for the circumference of a circle is _______.

4. The formula for the area of a circle is ________ .

5. To find the area of an ellipse, multiply one-half the ________ axis times one-half the ________ axis times ________ .

6. Area is always labeled with ______________ units.

7. The equator is a line of ______________ .

8. Lines of ______________ go through the North and South Poles.

9. There are 60 ______________ in a degree.

10. The longitudinal line going through Greenwich, England, is called the _________________________ .

Use the given information to find the circumference and/or area of the figures shown.

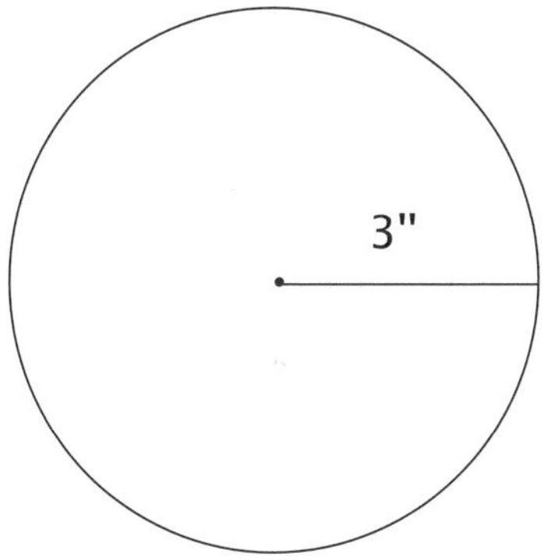

11. circumference = _________

12. area = ________________

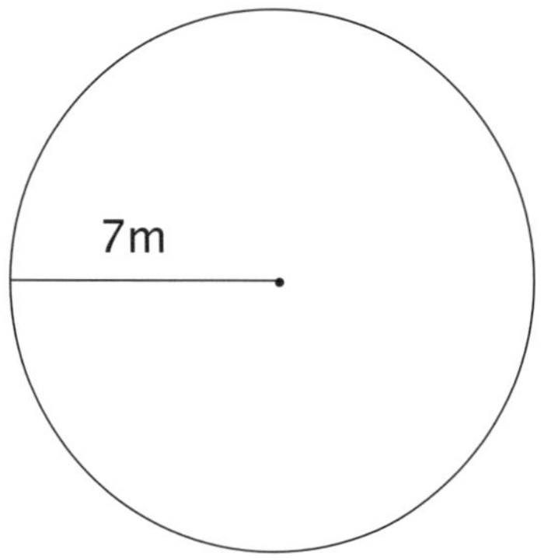

(Use the fractional value of π.)

13. area = ______________

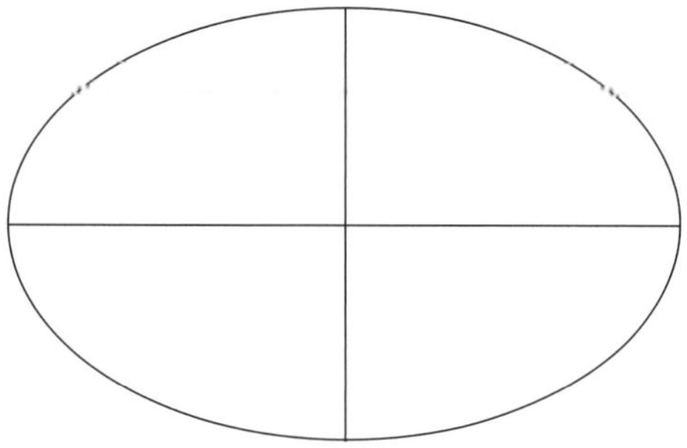

14. area = ______________

long axis = 12 ft
short axis = 8 ft

Problems 15–18 are optional. You will need a map and a mileage chart. Be as accurate as possible given the size of your map.

15. What are the latitude and longitude of Frankfurt, Germany?

16. What are the latitude and longitude of Bombay, India?

17. What is the distance in miles between these two cities?

18. A mile is approximately 1.6 kilometers. What is the distance in kilometers between the two cities?

13B

Fill in the blanks.

1. Twice the radius of a circle is the _______________ .

2. $2\pi r$ is the formula for the _______________ of a circle.

3. πr^2 is the formula for the _______________ of a circle.

4. To find the area of an ellipse, you must first find _______________ of the long and short axes.

5. Lines of latitude and longitude measure distance in _______________ .

6. The prime peridian has a measure of ______° and is a line of _______________ .

7. The horizontal lines on most maps are lines of _______________ .

8. Any location on earth may be pinpointed by giving its degrees of _______________ and _______________.

9. There are 60 _______________ in a minute.

10. Area is always measured in _______________ units.

Use the given information to find the circumference and/or area of the figures shown.

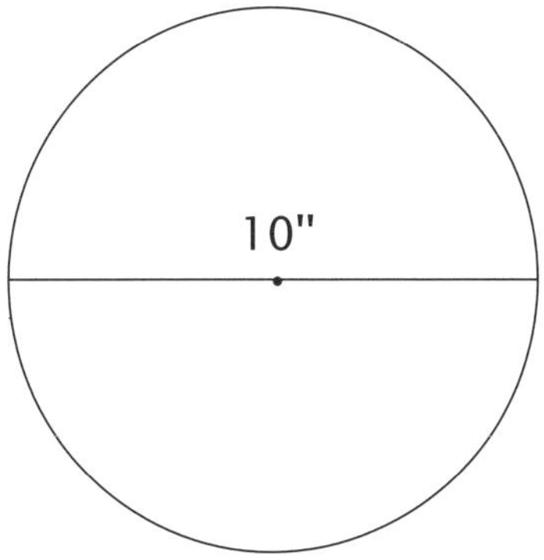

11. C = __________

12. A = __________________

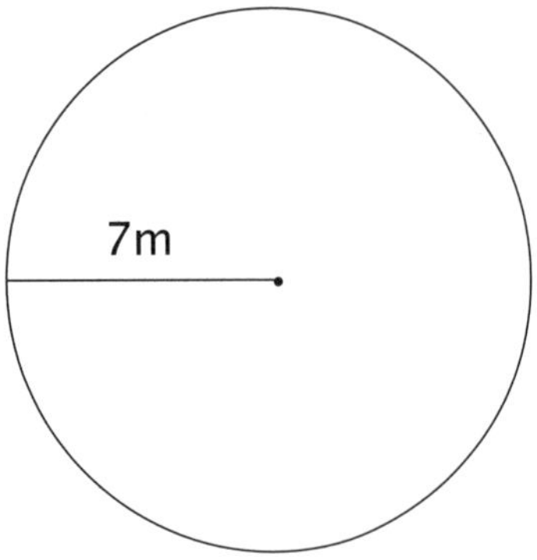

(Use the fractional value of π.)

13. circumference = ______________

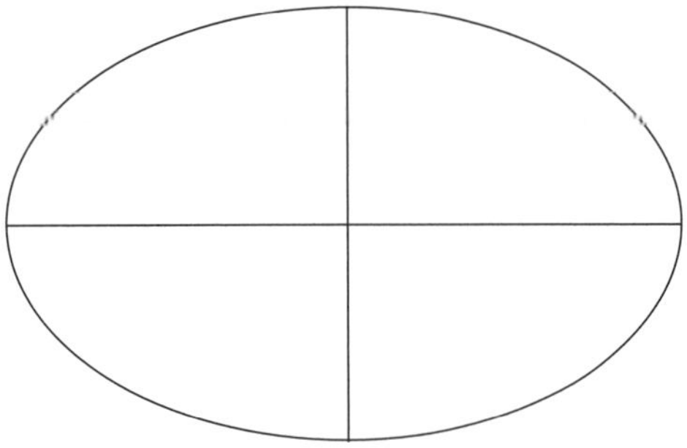

long axis = 10 ft
short axis = 6 ft

14. area = ______________

Problems 15–18 are optional. You will need a map and a mileage chart. Be as accurate as possible given the size of your map.

15. What are the latitude and longitude of New York City, USA?

16. What are the latitude and longitude of Cape Town, South Africa?

17. What is the distance in miles between these two cities?

18. A mile is approximately 1.6 kilometers. What is the distance in kilometers between the two cities?

Answer the questions.

1. Find the area of a circle with a radius of 3½ inches. Use $\pi = 22/7$.

2. Name a quadrilateral that has only one pair of parallel sides.

3. On another piece of paper, draw a circle with a radius of 3.75", and find the circumference. Use the decimal value of π rounded to hundredths.

4. What is the term for a line segment from the center of a circle to the edge?

5. What are the lines drawn around the earth parallel to the equator?

6. What are the lines drawn through the North and South Poles of the earth?

7. What is the area of an ellipse whose long axis is 14" and whose short axis is 4"?

8. If a regular parallelogram is inscribed in a circle, in how many points will it touch the circumference of the circle?

Follow the directions.

9. Draw an arc with a radius of 4.4 cm and a measure of 260°.

10. Estimate within 10° the measure of the arc shown at right.

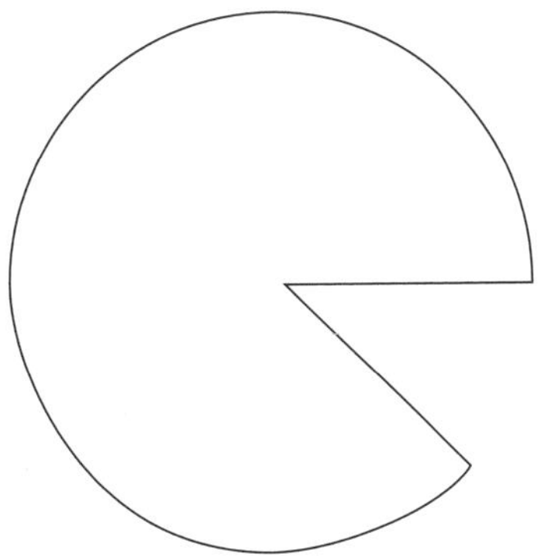

Problems 11–14 are optional. You will need a map and a mileage chart. Be as accurate as possible given the size of your map.

11. What are the latitude and longitude of Reykjavik, Iceland?

12. What are the latitude and longitude of Peking, China?

13. What is the distance in miles between these two cities?

14. A mile is approximately 1.6 kilometers. What is the distance in kilometers between the two cities? (optional)

Use the drawings to answer the questions.

15. $\angle AGB \cong \angle$ ______ .
Why?

16. $\angle AGB$ and $\angle BGC$ are ____________ .
Why?

17. $\angle BGD$ is a(n) ____________ angle.

18. $\angle CGF$ is a(n) ____________ angle.

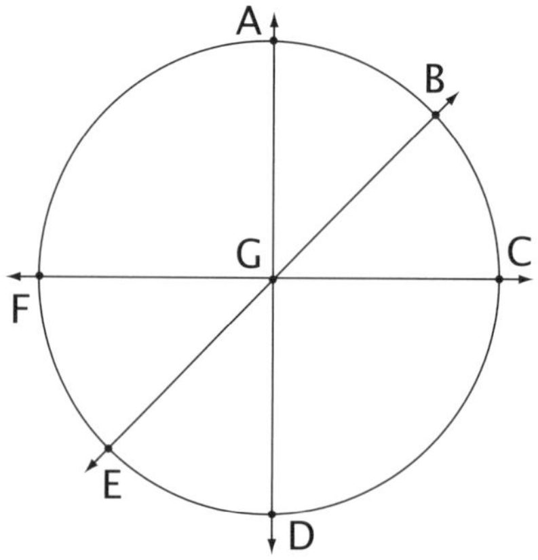

Given: G is the center of the circle.
$\overleftrightarrow{FC} \perp \overleftrightarrow{AD}$

19. If the distance from F to G is eight units, what is the circumference of the circle?

20. A = ____________________

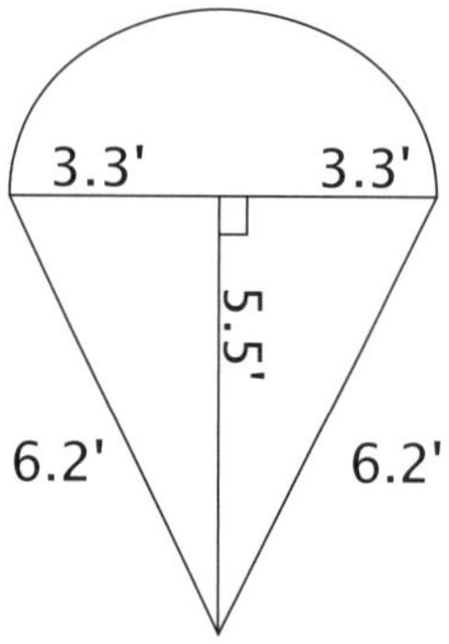

Given: The curved section is a semicircle (exactly half a circle).

13D

Answer the questions.

1. Find the circumference of a circle with a radius of 3.5". Use $\pi = 22/7$.

2. Name a quadrilateral that has four right angles.

3. Twice the length of the radius is a(n) __________________ .

4. A line that touches a circle at only one point is a(n) __________________ .

5. Lines of __________________ measure distances north and south of the equator.

6. Lines of __________________ measure distances east and west from Greenwich, England.

7. What is the area of an ellipse whose long axis is six inches and whose short axis is two inches?

8. A line that touches a circle at two points is called a _____________ .

9. How many degrees are there per interior angle of a 20-sided regular polygon?

10. What is the measure of each exterior angle?

Use the drawing at right to answer the questions.

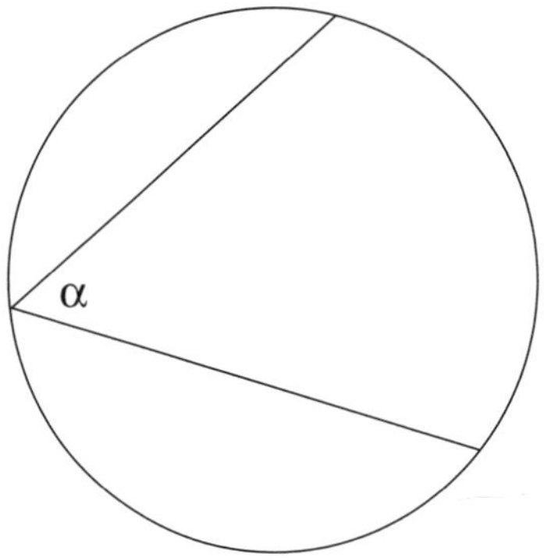

11. If m∠α is 50°, what is the measure of the minor arc formed by the angle?

12. What is the measure of the major arc formed by the angle?

13. What would be the measure of a central angle inscribed in the minor arc?

Use an atlas or wall map to answer the questions. Be as accurate as possible given the size of your map.

14. What are the latitude and longitude of Buenos Aires, Argentina?

15. What are the latitude and longitude of Melbourne, Australia?

Use the drawings to answer the questions.

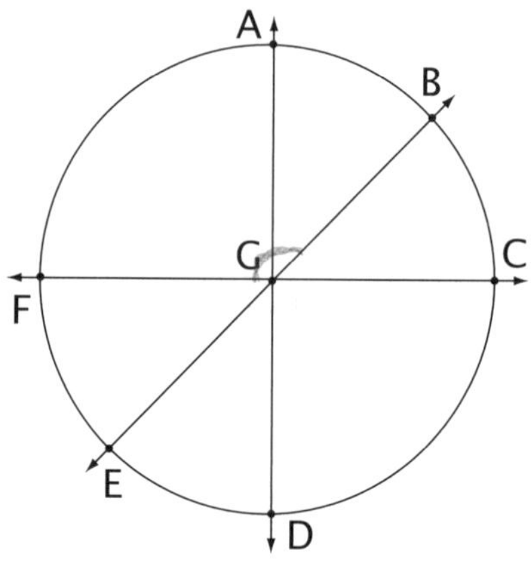

Given: G is the center of the circle. $\overleftrightarrow{FC} \perp \overleftrightarrow{AD}$

16. If m∠FGE = 43°, then m∠AGB = ______°.

17. If m∠FGE = 43°, then m∠EGC = ______°.

18. If m∠FGB = 135°, then m∠BGC = ______°.

19. If m∠FGB = 135°, then m∠EGD = ______°.

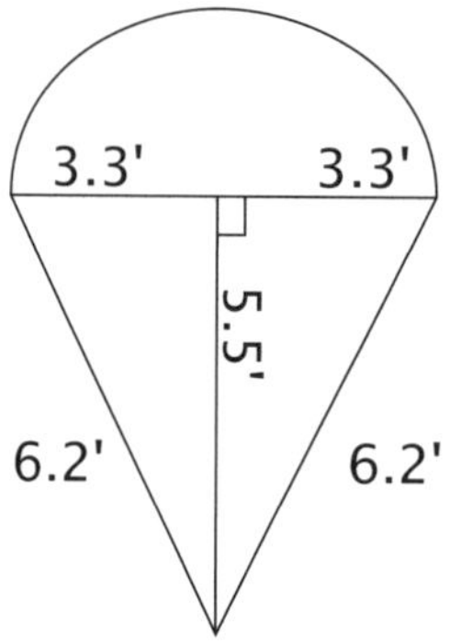

Given: The curved section is a semicircle.

20. P = __________

13E

Answer the questions.

1. To find the circumference of a circle, multiply the ________________ by π.

2. Give the formula for the area of a circle.

3. What is the fractional value of π?

4. What is the decimal value of π to the nearest hundredth?

5. What are the lines drawn around the earth parallel to the equator?

6. What are the lines drawn through the North and South Poles of the earth?

7. What is the area of an ellipse whose long axis is 9" and whose short axis is 3"?

8. How many minutes are there in a degree?

9. What is a three-dimensional circle called?

10. What is the name of a chord that goes through the center of a circle?

11. What is the area of a circle with a diameter of 7 m?

12. What is the circumference of a circle with a diameter of 1.25 cm?

13. If the measure of an exterior angle of a regular polygon is 40°, how many sides does the polygon have?

14. How many points are there in a line?

Use the drawings to answer the questions.

15. $\angle ACB$ and $\angle KLH$ are alternate ________________ angles.

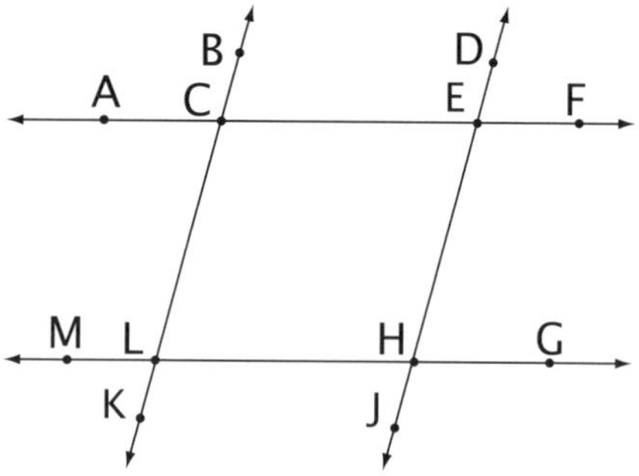

16. $\angle ACB$ and $\angle HEF$ are ____________ ____________ angles.

17. Which angles correspond to $\angle ACL$?

Given: Quadrilateral CEHL is a parallelogram.

18. If $\angle BCE \cong \angle CLH$, and $\angle CLH \cong \angle GHE$, then $\angle BCE \cong \angle$ _____.

Sharpen your algebra skills!

Simultaneous equations with two unknowns can also be solved using elimination.

EXAMPLE Solve 2Y + 3X = -2 and 2Y - X = 6.

$$\begin{array}{rcr} 2Y + 3X = -2 & \Rightarrow & 2Y + 3X = -2 \\ -(2Y - X = 6) & \Rightarrow & -2Y + X = -6 \\ \hline & & 4X = -8 \\ & & X = -2 \end{array}$$

Substituting -2 for X:

$$\begin{aligned} 2Y + 3(-2) &= -2 \\ 2Y &= 4 \\ Y &= 2 \end{aligned}$$

Solve by elimination. (Hint for #19: Multiply each term in the second equation by 2 before starting elimination.)

19. 3Y + 2X = 12 and 4Y - X = 5

20. Y - X = -3 and Y - 2X = -4

We have found the area of irregular polygons by dividing them into regular polygons whose individual areas we could compute. Below is another way to find the area of an irregular polygon. We will use rows of dots, with each row one unit from the next row.

Follow the directions.

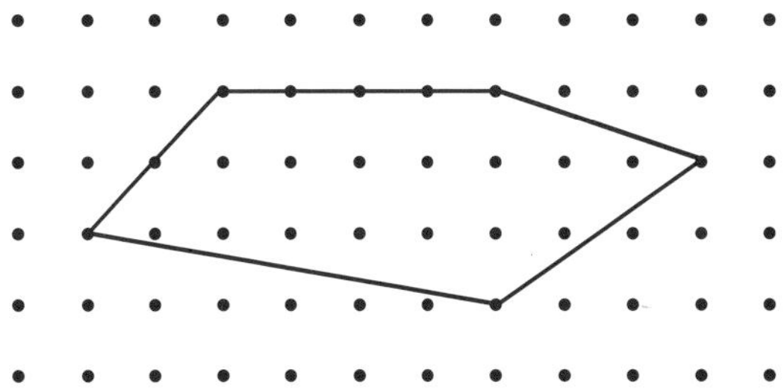

1. At right is a five-sided irregular polygon. Carefully circumscribe a rectangle around the polygon, so that each vertex of the polygon touches the rectangle. You should have formed four small triangles.

2. Count to find the number of units on each side of the rectangle, and find the area in terms of square units.

3. Find the area of each of the small triangles.

4. What is the area of the irregular polygon?

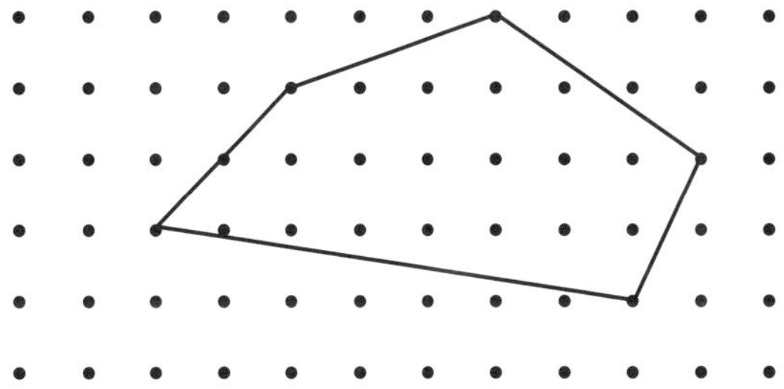

5. Try to circumscribe a rectangle around the polygon at right. You will find that one vertex does not touch the rectangle.

6. Draw a small rectangle touching the vertex inside the leftover irregular space, so that you have divided the space into a rectangle and two right triangles.

7. Find the area of the large rectangle.

8. Find the area of each of the small regular polygons.

9. What is the area of the irregular polygon?

Find the areas of the irregular polygons shown below.

10.

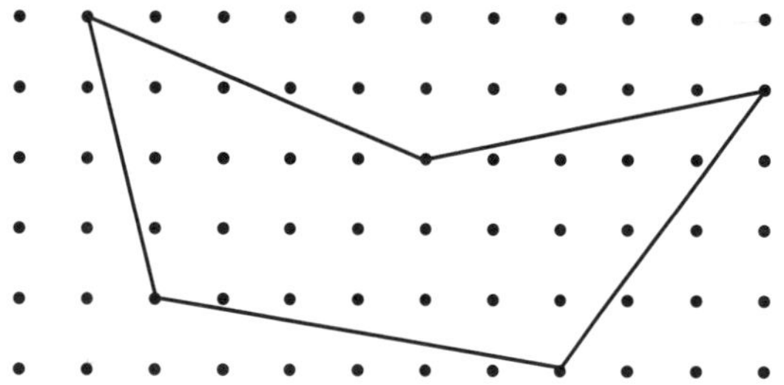

11.

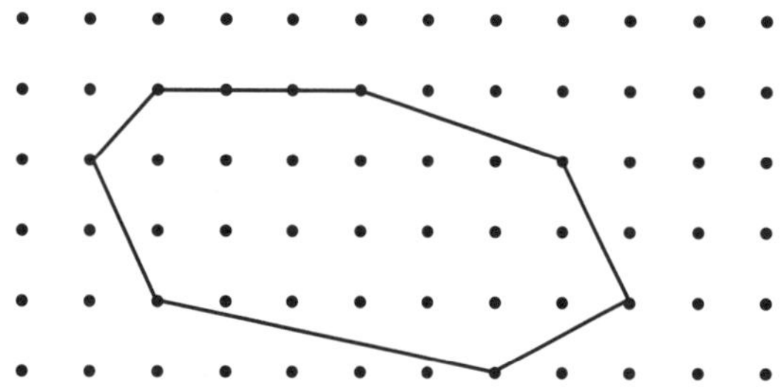

Draw your own irregular polygons. Find the area of each one.

Fill in the blanks.

1. The basic formula for volume is area of the _______________ times the _______________ .

2. The flat surfaces that make up a rectangular solid are called _______________ .

3. All the faces of a cube are _______________ .

4. The lines where the faces of a rectangular solid meet are called _______________ .

5. The base of a cylinder is a _______________ .

6. The volume of a geometric solid is given in _______________ units.

7. The edges of a rectangular solid meet in points called _______________ .

8. The volume of a cube with edges 4" long is _______________ .

Find the volume of the solids.

9. 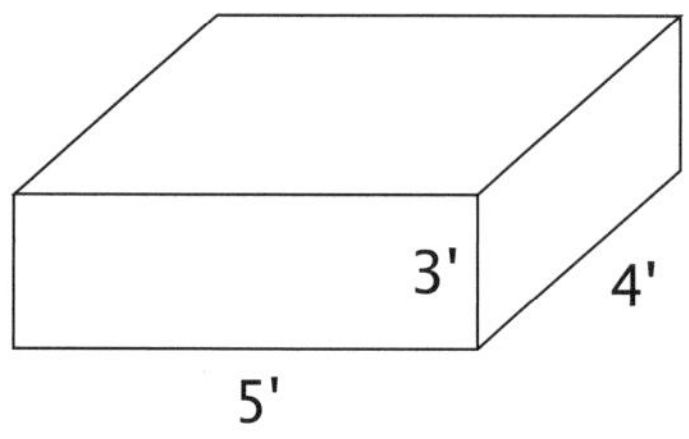

V = ____________

10. 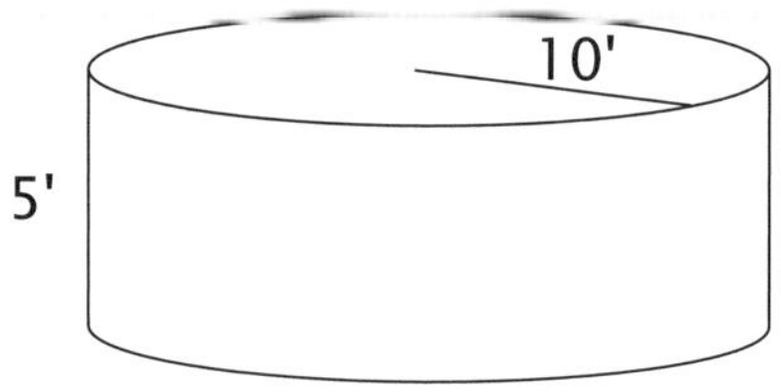

V = ____________

11. 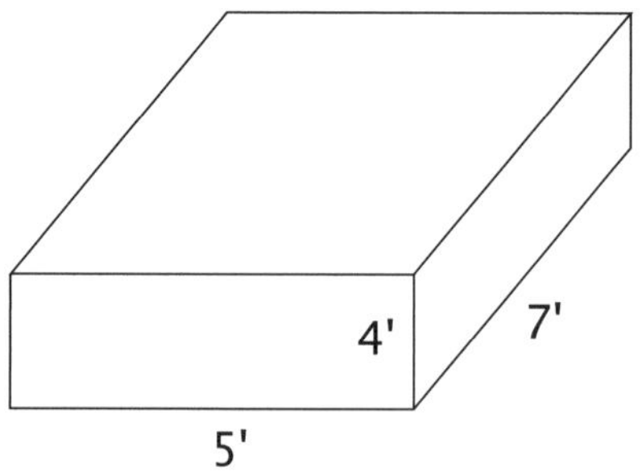

V = ____________

12. 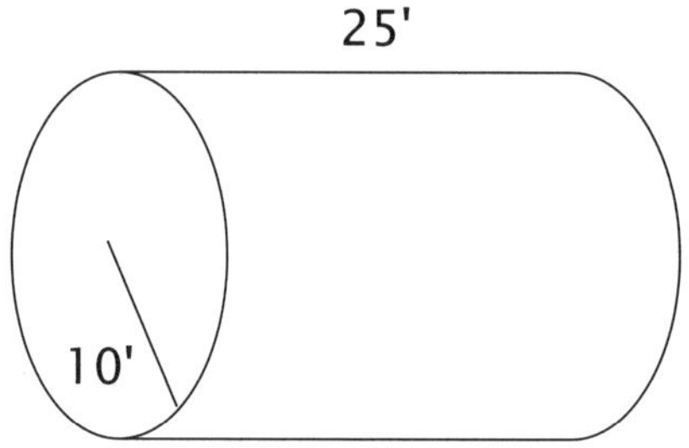

V = ____________

14B

Matching. Write the letter of the answer by each description.

1. the flat surface of a rectangular solid	a. twelve
2. number of edges on a cube	b. square
3. number of vertices on a cube	c. eight
4. kind of units with which area is measured	d. cubic
5. kind of units with which volume is measured	e. six
6. geometric solid with a circular base and sides perpendicular to the base	f. cube
7. a geometric solid whose faces are all squares	g. face
8. number of faces on a rectangular solid	h. cylinder

Find the volume of each solid.

9. 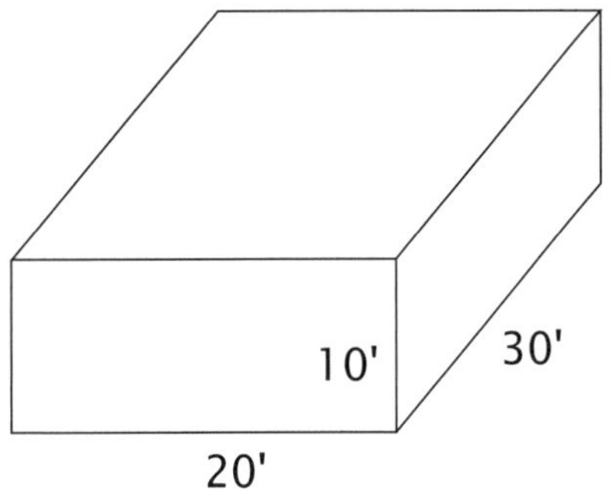

V = ____________

10. 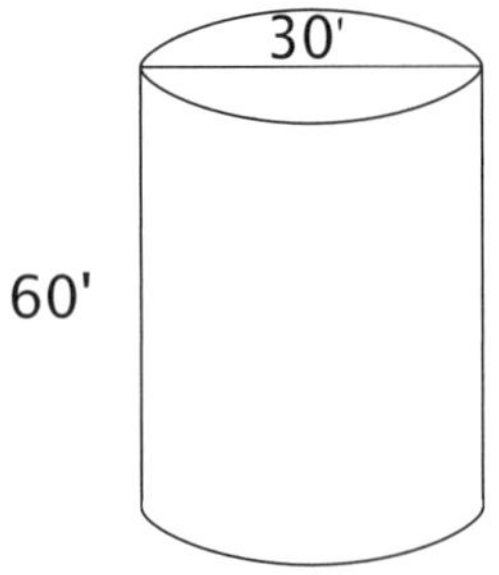

V = ____________

11. 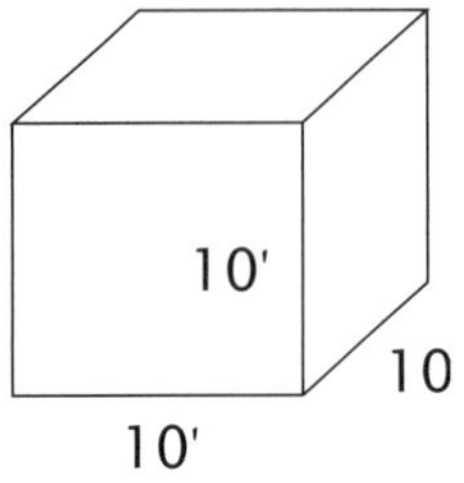

V = ____________

12. 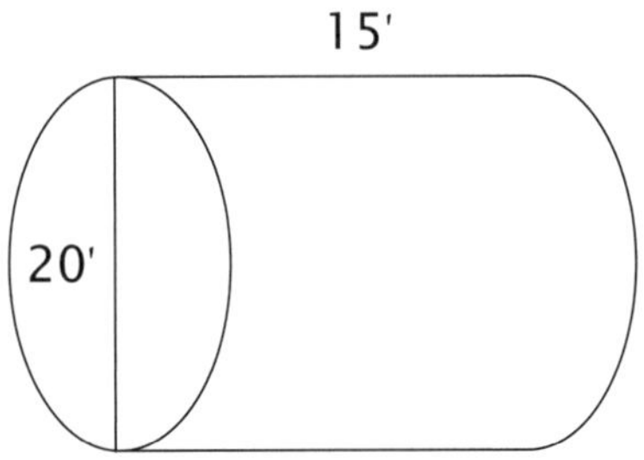

V = ____________

Find the volume or area.

1.

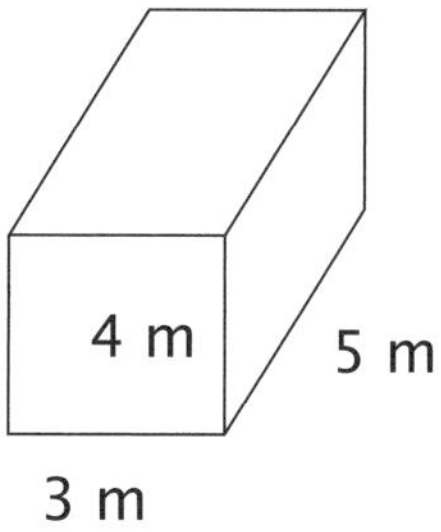

V = ______________

2.

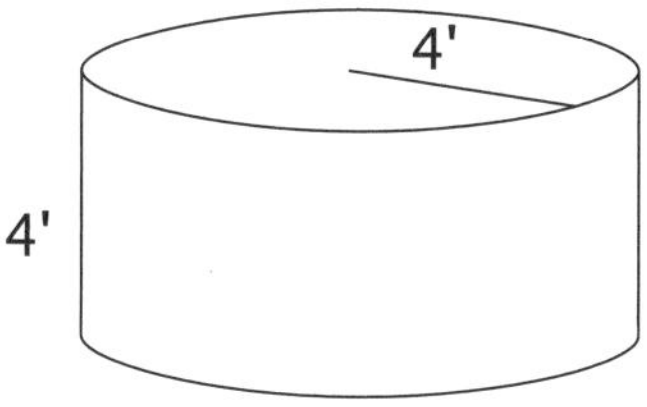

V = ______________

3.

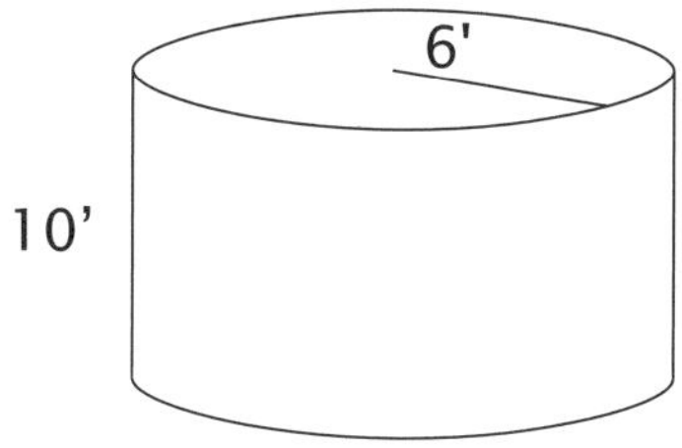

V = ______________

4.

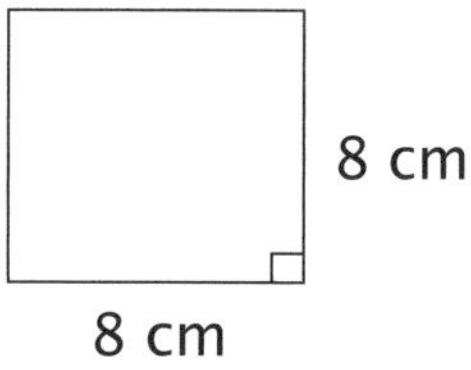

A = ______________

5.

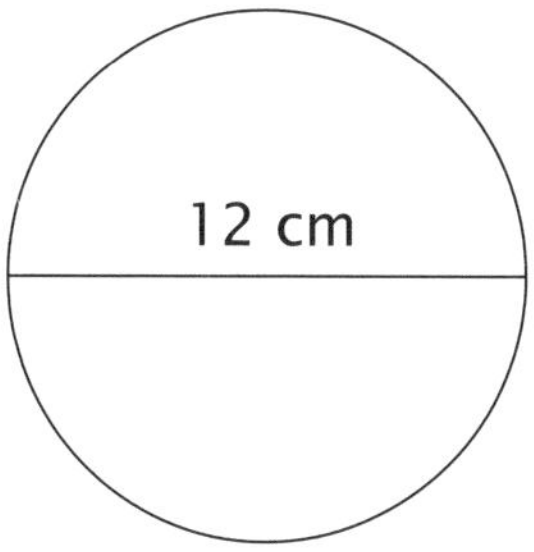

A = ______________

6.

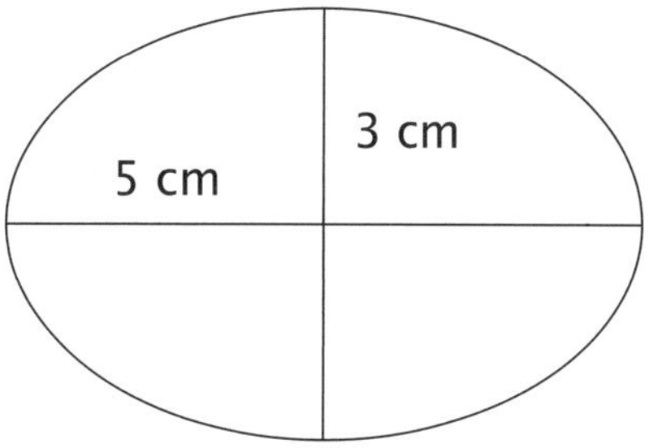

(Measurements are ½ the axes.)

A = ______________

Answer the questions.

7. How many degrees per interior angle are there in an eight-sided regular polygon?

8. What is the measure of each exterior angle in #7? What is the total measure of the exterior angles?

9. If the measure of an exterior angle of a regular polygon is 10°, how many sides does the polygon have?

Answer the questions.

10. What is a three-dimensional circle called?

11. What is the circumference of a circle with a radius of 6"?

12. What is the latitude of the equator?

13. What geometric figure has no length or width?

14. A trapezoid has a height of 13" and bases of 5" and 7".
What is its area?

15. A triangle has angles measuring 65° and 15°.
What is the measure of the third angle?

16. Name the triangle in #15 according to its angles.

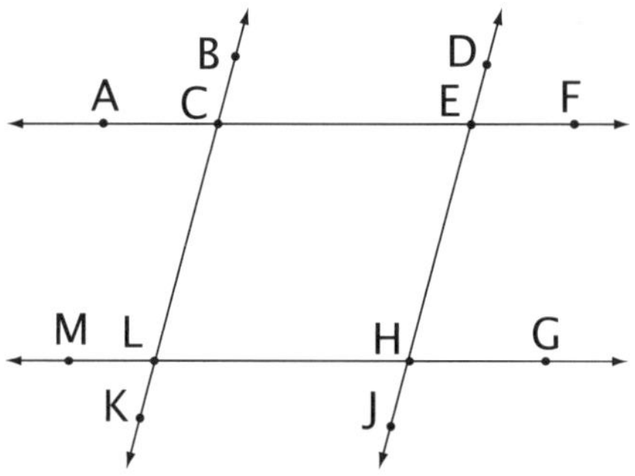

Given: Quadrilateral CEHL is a parallelogram.

Use the drawing to answer the questions.

17. If m∠EHL = 115°, then m∠MLK = _____°.

18. If m∠EHL = 115°, then m∠ACL = _____°.

19. If m∠EHL = 115°, then m∠CED = _____°.

20. If m∠EHL = 115°, then m∠EHG = _____°.

SYSTEMATIC REVIEW 14D

Find the volume or area.

1.

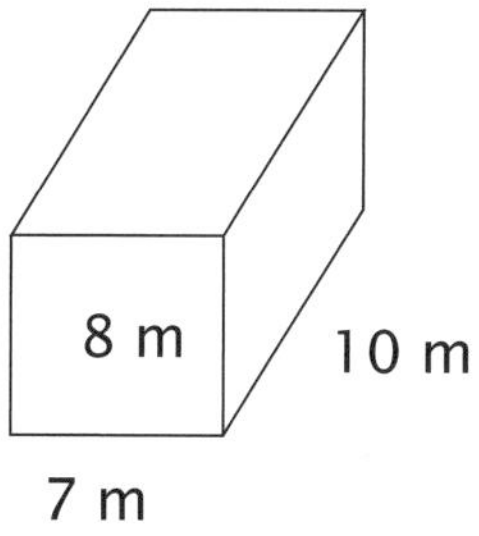

V = ______________

2.

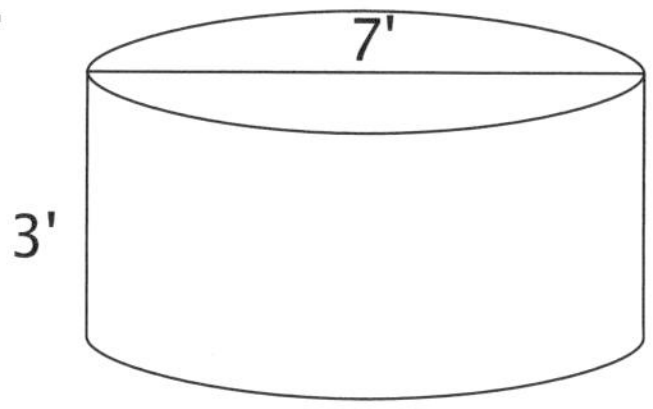

V = ______________

3.

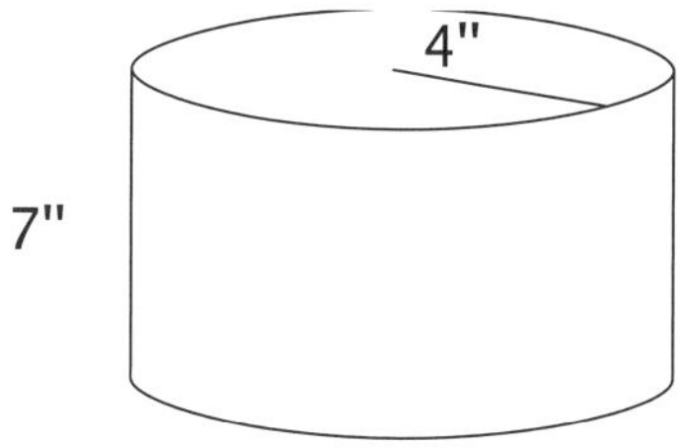

V = ______________

4.

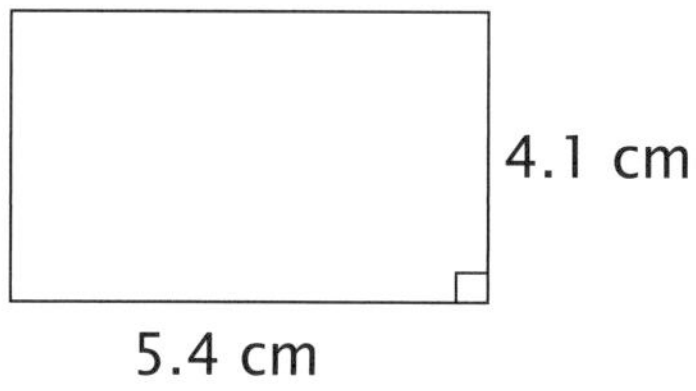

A = ______________

5.

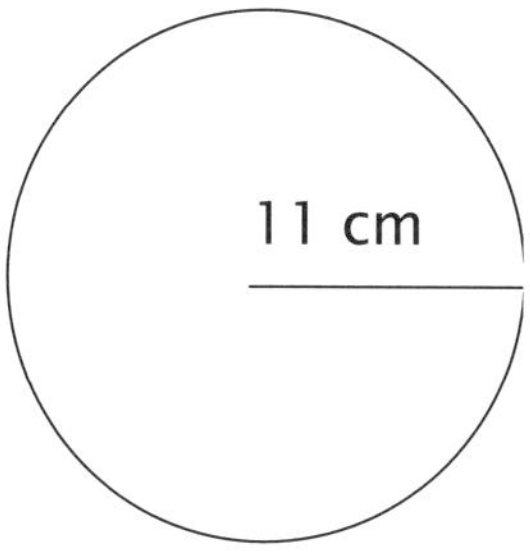

A = ______________

6.

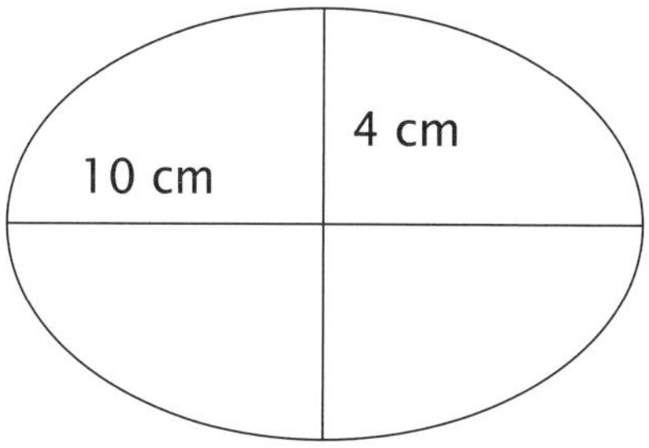

(Measurements are ½ the axes.)

A = ______________

Answer the questions.

7. How many degrees per interior angle are there in a 10-sided regular polygon?

8. What is the measure of each exterior angle in #7?

   What is the total measure of the exterior angles?

9. If the measure of an exterior angle of a regular polygon is 45°, how many sides does the polygon have?

Answer the questions.

10. A chord that goes through the center of a circle is the _______________ .

11. If the measure of the central angle of a circle is 23°, what is the measure of the intercepted minor arc?

12. What is the longitude of Greenwich, England?

13. What geometric figure has two dimensions and extends infinitely in all directions?

14. Is it possible to have a triangle with sides measuring 3, 4, and 5 units?

Use the drawing to answer the questions.

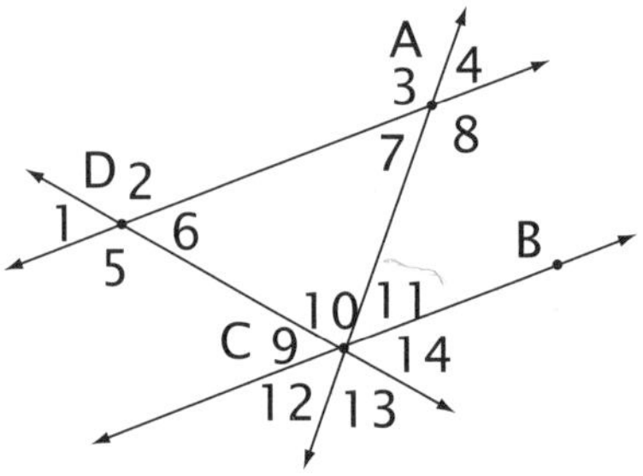

Given: $\overleftrightarrow{AD} \parallel \overleftrightarrow{BC}$ and $\overleftrightarrow{AC}$ bisects $\angle BCD$.

15. If $m\angle BCA = 62°$, then $m\angle 10 =$ _____°. Why?

16. If $m\angle BCA = 62°$, then $m\angle 10 + m\angle 11 =$ _____°.

17. Given your answer to #16, $m\angle 9 =$ _____°.

18. If $m\angle BCA = 62°$, then $m\angle 1 =$ _____°. Why?

19. If $m\angle BCA = 62°$, then $m\angle 7 =$ _____°. Why?

20. If $m\angle 12 = 58°$, then $m\angle 7 =$ _____°. Why?

Find the volume or area.

1.

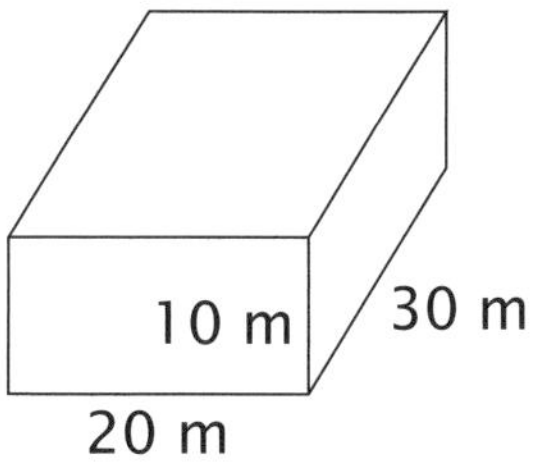

V = ______________

2.

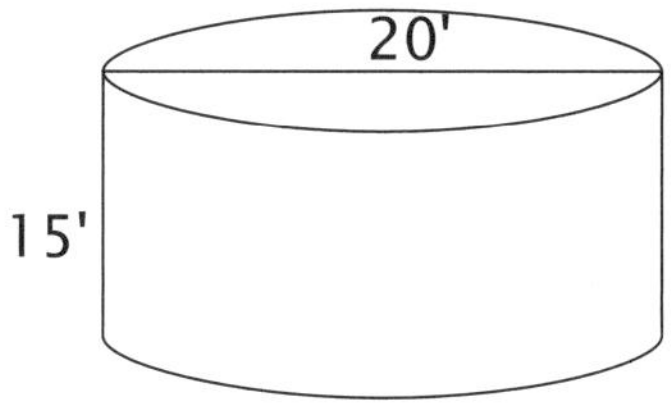

V = ______________

3.

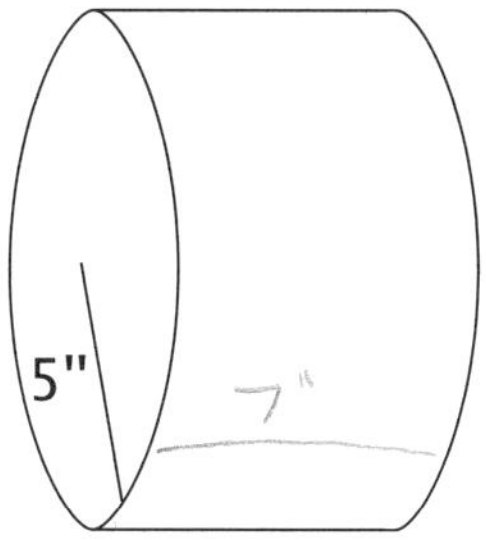

V = ______________

4.

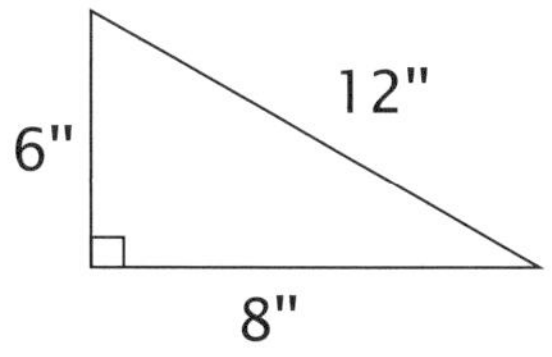

A = ______________

5.

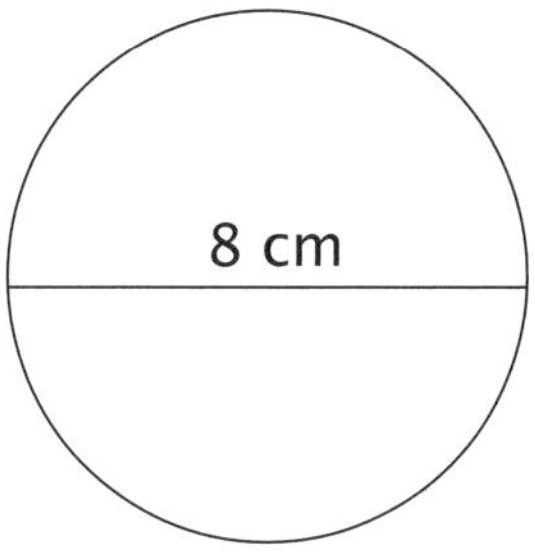

A = ______________

6.

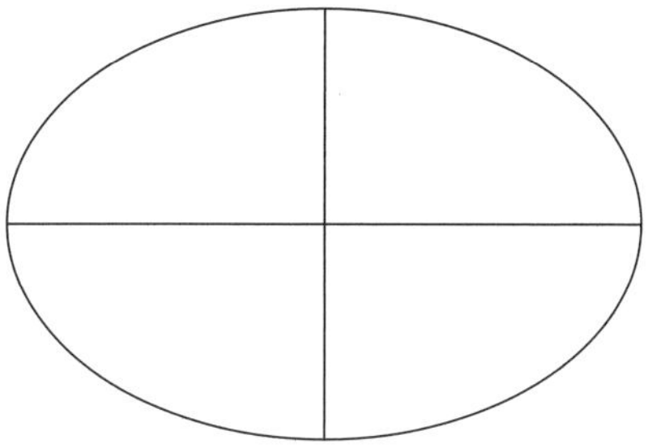

long axis = 20 units
short axis = 15 units

A = ______________

Answer the questions.

7. How many degrees per interior angle are there in a six-sided regular polygon?

8. What is the measure of each exterior angle in #7?

   What is the total measure of the exterior angles?

9. If the measure of an exterior angle of a regular polygon is 60°, how many sides does the polygon have?

10. What is the line that touches a circle in only one point?

11. What is the circumference of a circle with a radius of 15"?

12. How many minutes are there in a degree?

13. Name a geometric figure that has length but no width.

14. One side of a rhombus measures 25 feet. What is its perimeter?

15. A triangle has angles measuring 23° and 35°. What is the measure of the third angle?

16. If the measure of the central angle of a circle is 23°, what is the measure of the intercepted major arc?

Sharpen your algebra skills!

The radical sign is used to indicate the square root of a number, or the factor that must be multiplied by itself to get the original number.

EXAMPLE 1 $\sqrt{9} = 3$ and $3 \times 3 = 9$.

EXAMPLE 2 Many numbers do not have a simple whole number square root. $\sqrt{2} = 1.414213562\ldots$

Solve.

17. $\sqrt{16}$

18. $\sqrt{100}$

19. $\sqrt{25}$

20. $\sqrt{144}$

HONORS LESSON 14H

You know how to find the area of a right triangle or any triangle for which the height is given. There is a formula for finding the area of any triangle if the lengths of all three sides are known.

The formula is Area = $\sqrt{s(s-a)(s-b)(s-c)}$, where a, b, and c are the lengths of the three sides and s equals one-half of the sum of a, b, and c.

Follow the directions.

1. Find the area of the right triangle shown using 1/2 bh.

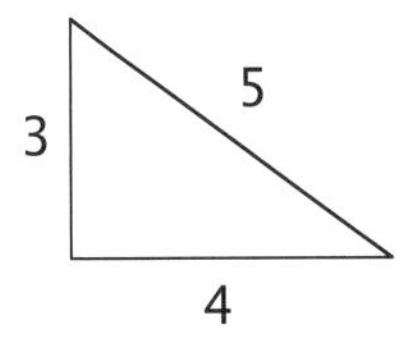

2. Use the formula above to find the area of the triangle. Is your answer the same as #1?

Use the new formula to find the area of each of the triangles shown. Use a calculator to find the square roots, and give your answers to the nearest hundredth.

3.

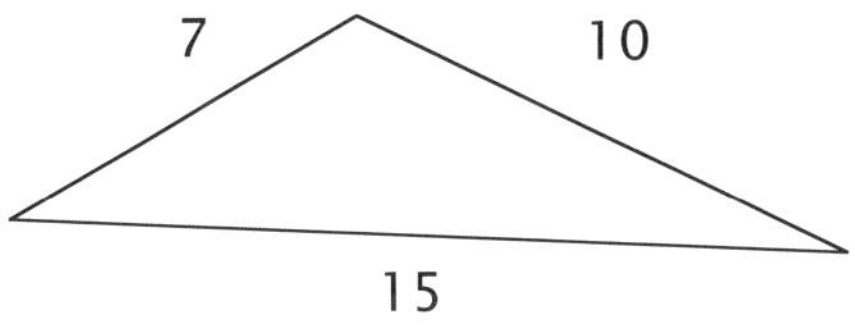

4.

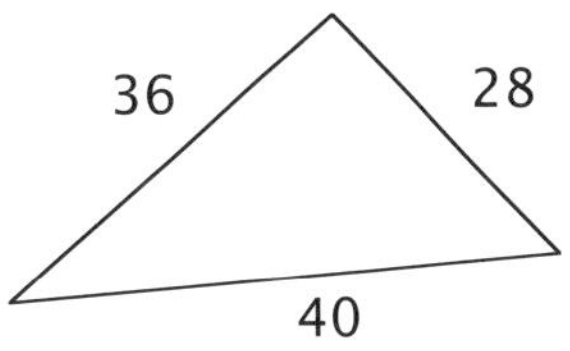

It is interesting to explore how changing one dimension of a solid changes the volume.

Follow the directions.

5. Consider a cylinder with a radius of 2" and a height of 10". What is its volume?

Follow the directions.

6. Find the volume of a cylinder with half the radius of #5 and the same height. What is the relationship between the two volumes?

7. Find the volume of a cylinder with half the height of #5 and the same radius. What is the relationship between the two volumes?

8. Double only the radius of the cylinder in #5, and describe what happens to the volume.

9. Double only the height of the cylinder in #5, and describe what happens to the volume.

10. Use words to write a general rule describing what happens to the volume of a cylinder when the dimensions are halved or doubled.

11. Try your rule using dimensions of your own choosing. Please understand that you have not proven your rule, only observed that it is true for a couple of examples.

12. The formula for the volume of a cylinder may be written as $V = \pi r^2 h$. Use algebra to show why doubling the value of h always has the result you found by experiment. Then do the same to prove your rule for doubling the value of r.

Fill in the blanks.

1. The height of the face of a pyramid is the ______________ .

2. The length of a line perpendicular to the base of the pyramid is the ______________ .

3. The point where the faces of a pyramid meet is the ______________ .

4. When finding the volume of a pyramid or cone, multiply the area of the base by the height, and then multiply the answer by ______________ .

5. The base of a cone is a ______________ .

6. A prism has two bases that are ____________ and ____________ .

7. The lateral, or side, surfaces of a prism are always ______________ .

8. The formula for the volume of a sphere is ______________ .

Find the volume of each solid.

9. 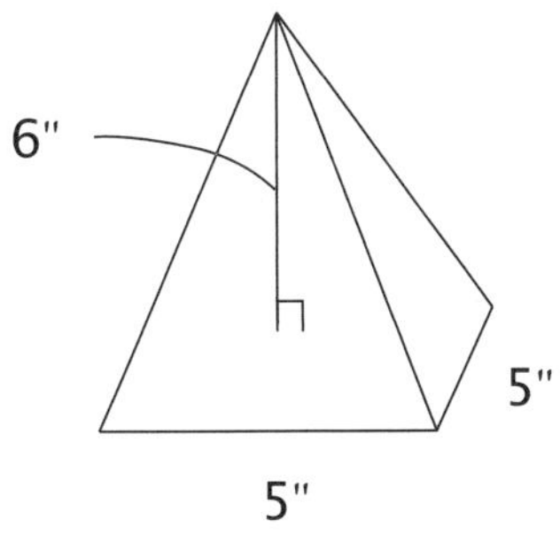

V = ____________________

10. 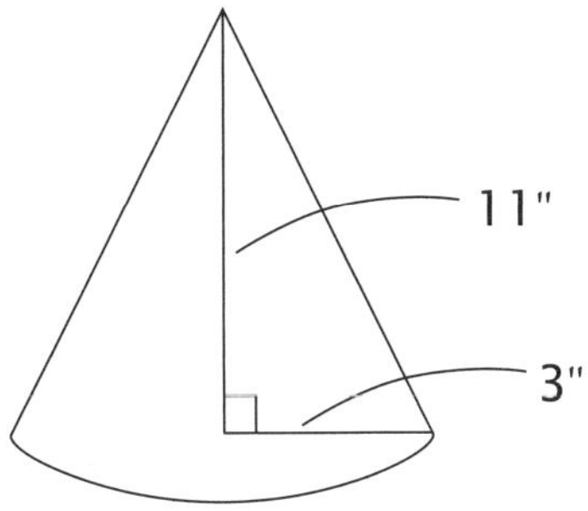

V = ____________________

11. 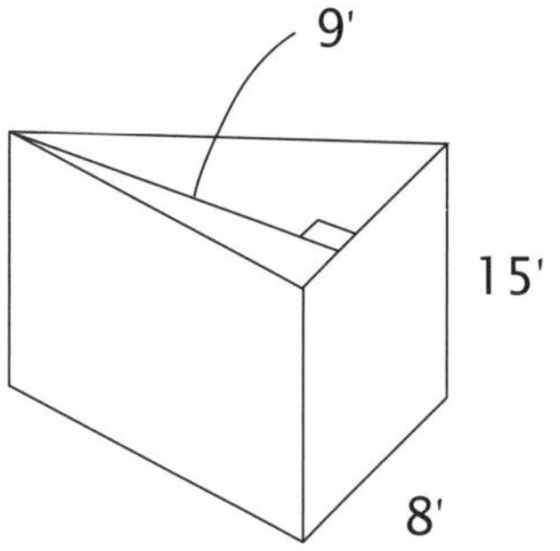

V = ____________

12. 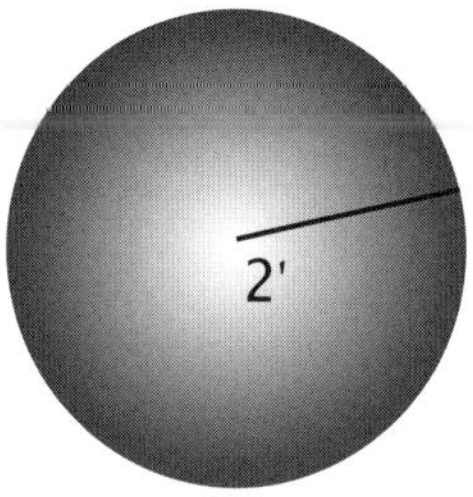

V = ____________

Round your answer to the nearest hundredth when answering volume of a sphere questions in this lesson.

13. 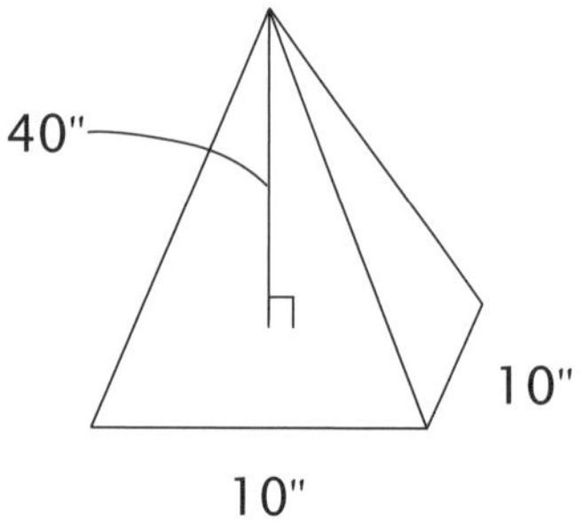

V = ____________

14. 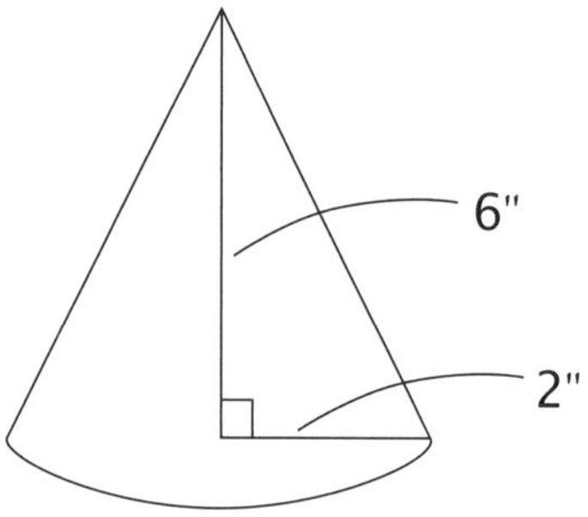

V = ____________

15B

Fill in the blanks.

1. A ______________ has lateral surfaces that are parallelograms and two parallel bases.

2. $\frac{4}{3}\pi r^3$ is the formula for the ______________ of a ______________.

3. To find the volume of a prism, multiply the area of the ______________ by the ______________ .

4. The volume of a cone is ______________ the volume of a cylinder with the same base and height.

5. The base of a pyramid can be a triangle or a ______________ .

6. The perpendicular height of a pyramid is the ______________ .

7. The volume of a pyramid is ______________ the volume of a rectangular solid with the same base and height.

8. Slant height is the height of a ______________ of a pyramid.

Find the volume of each solid.

9. 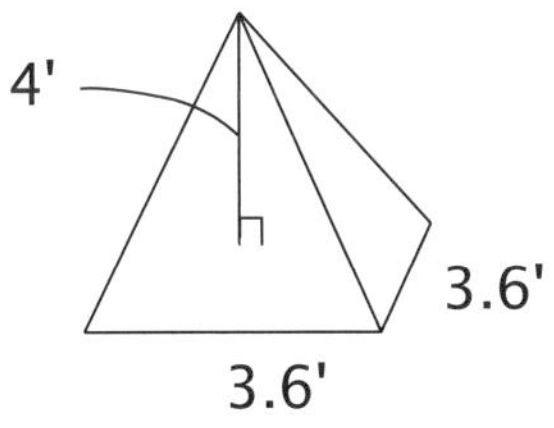

V = ____________________

10. 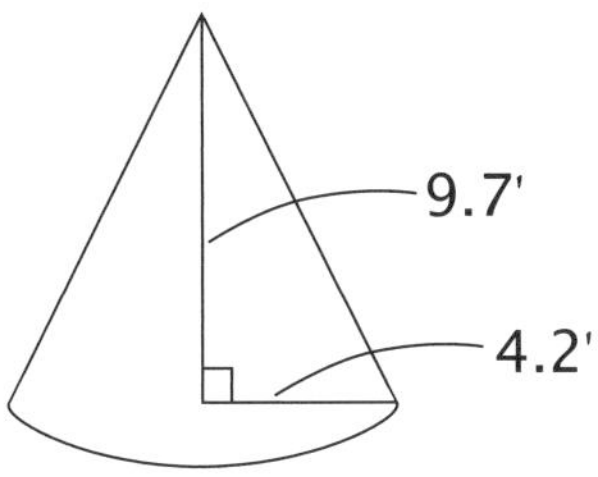

V = ____________________

Find the volume of each solid.

11. 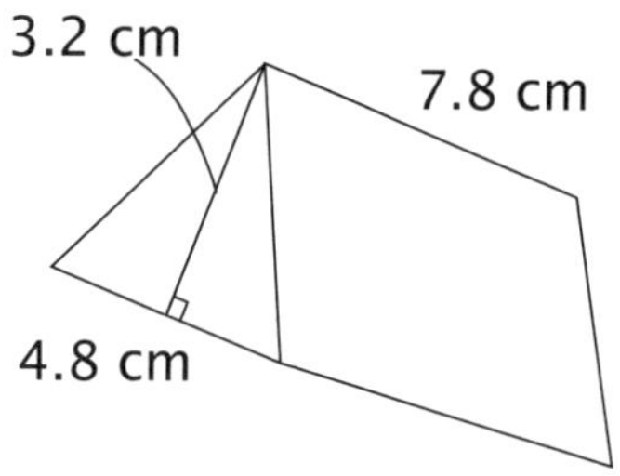

V = ____________________

12. 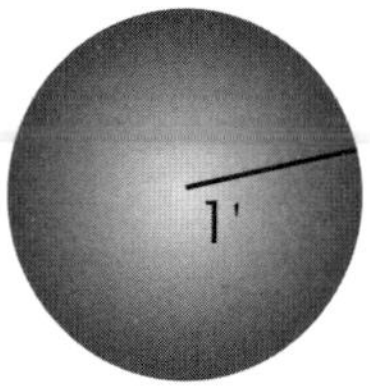

V = ____________________

Find the volume of each part of the figure. Then add to find the total volume.

13. 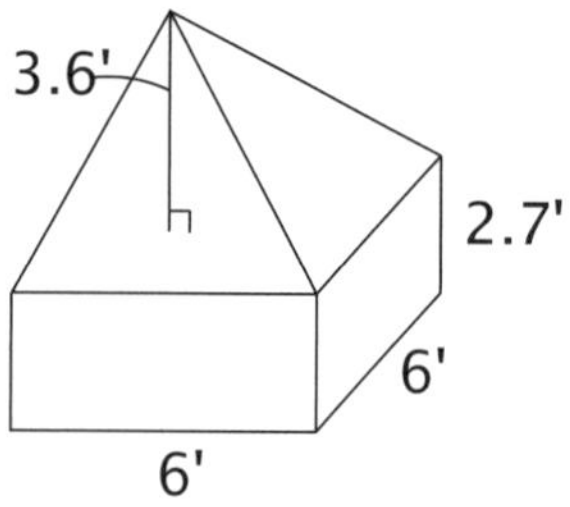

V = ____________________

14. 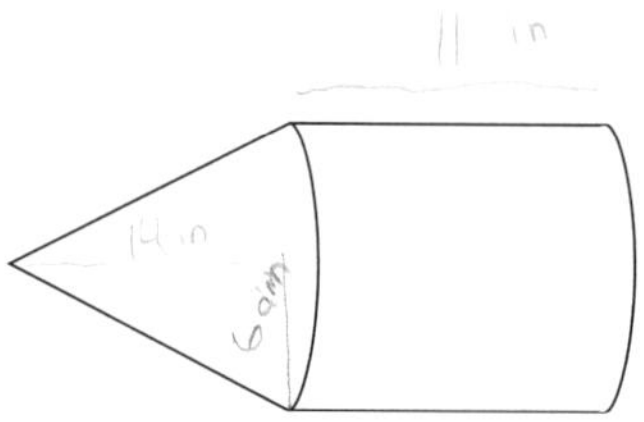

V = ____________________

radius = 6 in
height of the cylinder = 11 in
height of the cone = 14 in

Find the volume of each solid.

1.

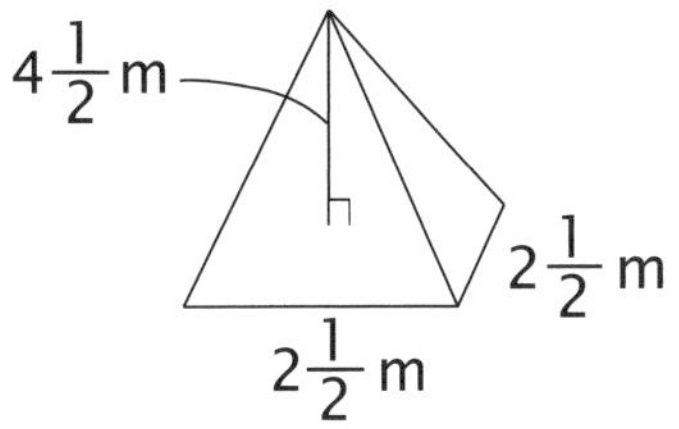

2.

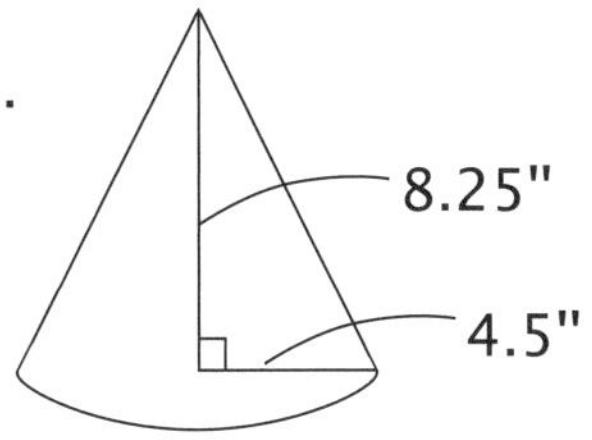

3.

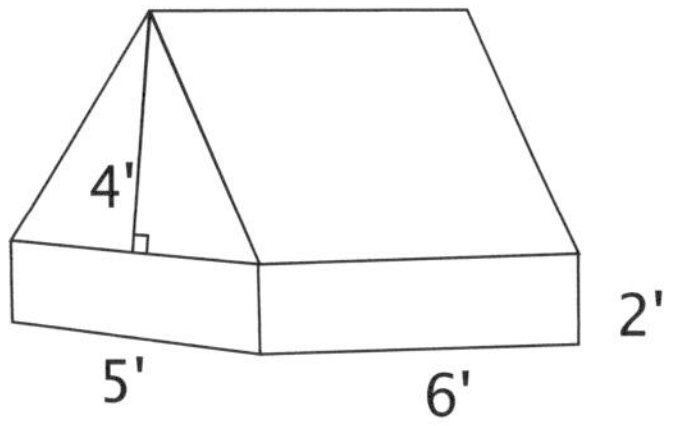

V = ______________ V = ______________ V = ______________

Answer the questions.

4. What is the volume of a sphere with a radius of four inches?

5. Which measurement is used in finding the volume of a pyramid: altitude or slant height?

6. What is the relationship between the bases of a prism?

7. One edge of a cube is 20 inches. What is its volume?

8. What is the area of a circle with a diameter of 10 feet?

9. What is the area of an ellipse with a short axis of two feet and a long axis of 10 feet?

10. What is the perimeter of a circle called?

11. How many degrees per interior angle are there in a 10-sided regular polygon?

12. Find the number of sides of a regular polygon if the measure of each interior angle is 120º.

Draw, using another piece of paper if necessary.

13. Draw a 125º angle and label it ∠ABC.

14. Use a compass to draw a ray through point B that bisects ∠ABC in #13. Check with a protractor.

15. Draw a circle with the radius perpendicular to the tangent.

Use the drawing as needed to answer the questions.

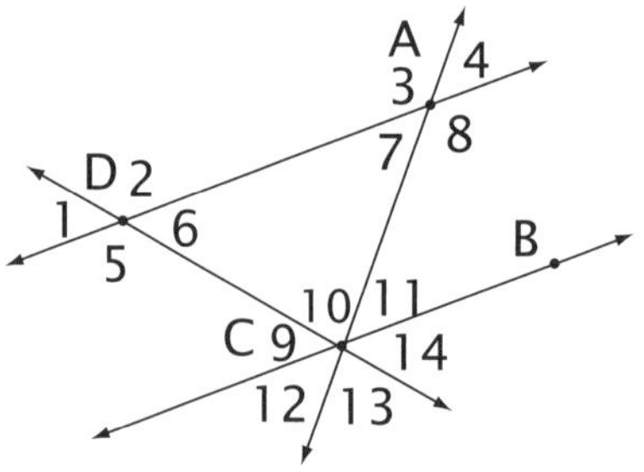

Given: $\overleftrightarrow{AD} \parallel \overleftrightarrow{BC}$ and $\overleftrightarrow{AC}$ bisects ∠BCD

16. If m∠14 = 50º, then m∠5 = ______º. Why?

17. If m∠14 = 50º, then m∠10 = ______º. Why?

18. If m∠14 = 50º, then m∠8 = ______º. Why?

19. If m∠14 = 50º, then m∠12 = ______º. Why?

Complete and state the converse.

20. If two angles add up to 90º, they are...

Find the volume of each solid.

1. 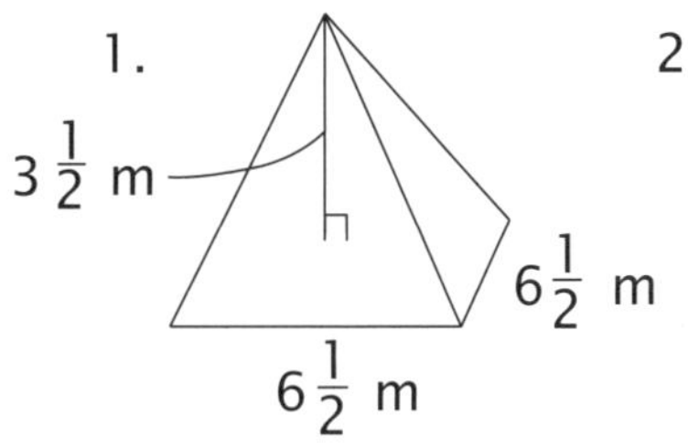

2. 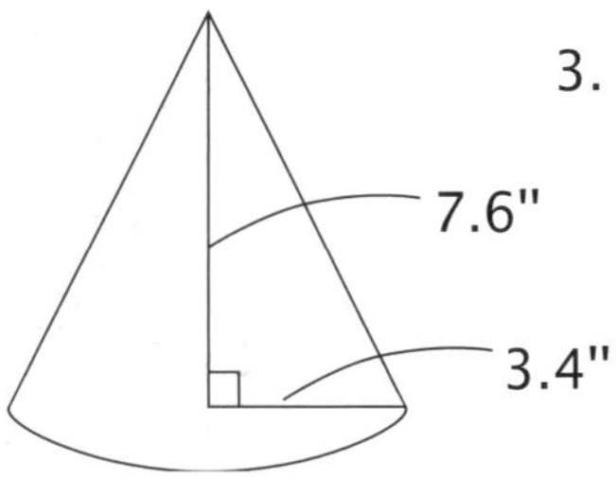

3. r = 4 in
height of the cylinder = 10 in
height of the cone = 12 in

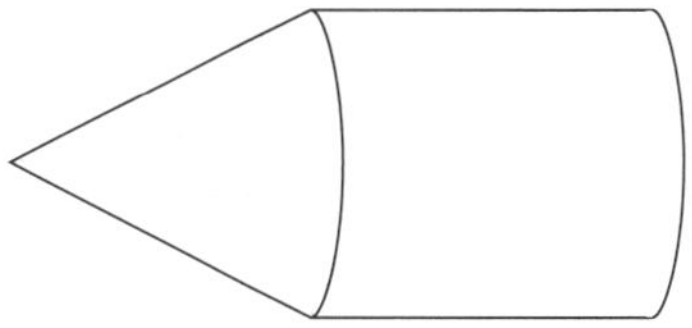

V = ______________ V = ______________ V = ______________

Answer the questions.

4. What is the volume of a sphere with a diameter of four inches?

5. What geometric shape are the lateral surfaces of a prism?

6. What line segment touches the circumference of a circle in exactly two places?

7. One side of a rhombus is 20 inches and the height is 15 inches. What is the area of the rhombus?

8. What is the perimeter of the rhombus in #7?

9. What is the area of an ellipse with a short axis of three feet and a long axis of six feet?

10. Identify a triangle with no equal sides.

11. How many degrees per interior angle in an eight-sided regular polygon?

12. Find the number of sides of a regular polygon, if the measure of each interior angle is 150°.

Draw, using another piece of paper if necessary.

13. Draw a line segment with a measure of 4¾ inches and label it AB.

14. Use a compass and straightedge to draw the perpendicular bisector of AB in #13. Label the midpoint of AB "C."

15. Draw an arc with a measure of 120°.

Use the drawing as needed to answer the questions.

16. If $\overline{AF} \cong \overline{FD}$, then F is the __________________ of $\overline{AD}$.

17. Given #16, if $\overline{AD}$ = 2 7/8", then $\overline{AF}$ = ________ .

18. If m∠AFE = 88.5°, then m∠BFC = ________°.
Why?

19. If m∠AFE = 88.5°, then m∠EFD = ________°.
Why?

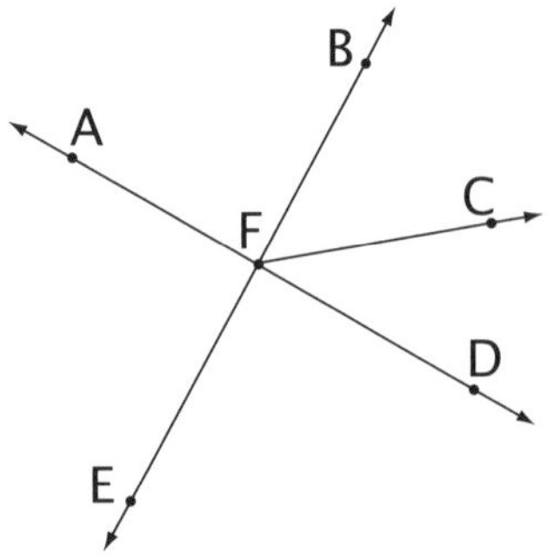

Given: $\overleftrightarrow{AD}$, $\overleftrightarrow{BE}$ and $\overrightarrow{FC}$ are coplanar.
$\overrightarrow{FC}$ bisects ∠BFD.

Complete and state the converse.

20. If two angles are ________________, then their measures add up to 180°.

Find the volume of each solid.

1.

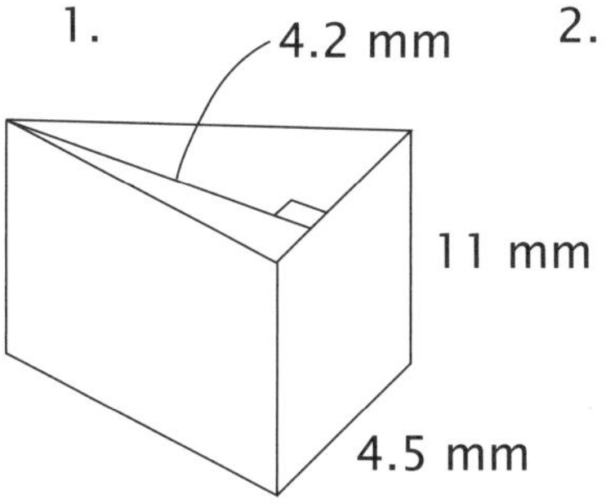

V = ______________

2.

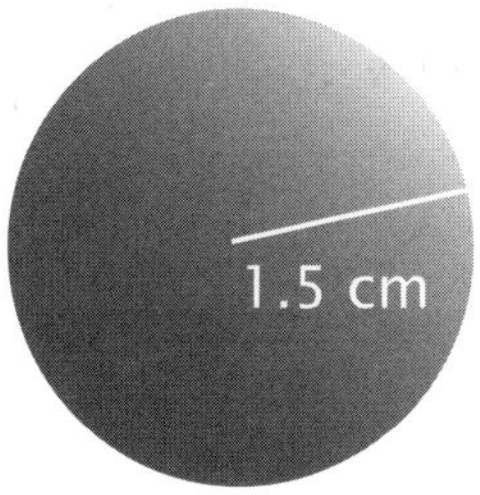

V = ______________

3.

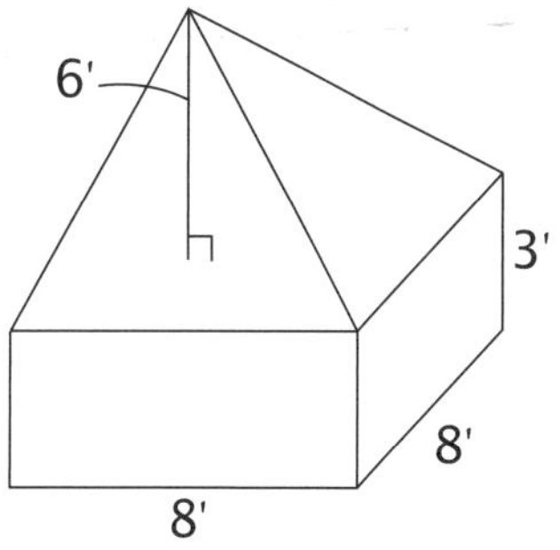

V = ______________

Answer the questions.

4. The height of a pyramid used in finding its volume is the ______________ .

5. A figure with lateral surfaces that are parallelograms and two parallel bases is a ______________ .

6. The volume of a cone is ______________ of the volume of a cylinder with the same radius and height.

7. The base of a parallelogram is 8 inches, one side is 4 inches, and its height is 3.5 inches. What is its area?

8. What is the perimeter of the figure in #7?

9. What is the area of an ellipse with a short axis of 8 feet and a long axis of 10 feet?

10. Identify a triangle with all sides equal.

11. How many degrees are there per interior angle in a five-sided regular polygon?

Answer the questions.

12. An octagon is inscribed in a circle. In how many points will it touch the circle?

13. Find the number of sides of a regular polygon if the measure of each interior angle is 135°.

Draw, using another piece of paper if necessary.

14. Draw perpendicular line segments with the base 4.3 cm long and the height 2.8 cm.

15. Draw a 110° angle, and then bisect it.

16. Draw a triangle with angle measures of 40°, 60°, and 80°.

Sharpen your algebra skills!

Remember the following rules when using numbers involving exponents:

RULE 1 $X^A \cdot X^B = X^{A+B}$ RULE 2 $X^A \div X^B = X^{A-B}$ RULE 3 $\frac{1}{X^A} = X^{-A}$

EXAMPLE $5^2\,5^3 = 5^5$

Simplify. Write your answers with exponents.

17. $8^3 \cdot 8^4 =$

18. $2^8 \div 2^3 =$

19. $X^2X^3Y^5Y^{-1} =$

20. $\frac{1}{10^3} =$

SYSTEMATIC REVIEW

15H

These word problems all involve volume. Read and follow the directions.

1. Sometimes a problem uses more than one unit of measure. You know there are three feet in a yard. How many cubic feet are there in a cubic yard?

2. How many cubic inches are there in a cubic foot?

3. Steel weighs 0.3 pounds per cubic inch. What is the weight of a block of steel that measures eight inches by four inches by two inches?

4. Could you lift a gold brick that measures eight by four by two inches? Gold weighs 1,200 pounds per cubic foot. Find the weight of the gold brick.

64 cu. in

5. A piece of metal pipe has an inside diameter of 0.5 inches and an outside diameter of one inch. What is the volume of iron in a piece of this pipe that is one foot long?

6. If the metal used for the pipe in #5 weighs 0.26 pounds a cubic inch, what is the weight of the piece described?

7. The steel ball bearings in a box weigh a total of 25 pounds. Each bearing is 0.5 inches in diameter. If the steel weighs 0.3 pounds a cubic inch, how many bearings are in the box? (Round your answers to the nearest hundredth.)

8. A swimming pool is 40 ft long by 20 ft wide. It is 3 ft deep at one end and slopes uniformly to a depth of 10 ft at the other end. If the pool is full to the brim, what is the volume of the water? (Sketching a side view of the pool may help with this one.)

9. A solid sphere with a diameter of two units just fits inside a cube with a side of two units. What is the volume of the leftover space inside the cube? (Round volumes to the nearest hundredth.)

10. A solid sphere with a diameter of two units just fits inside a cylinder with a diameter of two units and a height of two units. What is the volume of the leftover space inside the cylinder? (Round volumes to the nearest hundredth.)

Answer the questions or fill in the blanks.

1. How many faces, or flat surfaces, does a cube or rectangular solid have?

2. How many faces does a pyramid with a square base have?

3. How many faces does a pyramid with a triangular base have?

4. In order to find the surface area of a cylinder, you must add the area of two _______________ and one _______________ .

5. Surface area is measured in _______________ units.

6. In order to find the area of the lateral side of a cylinder, multiply the _______________ by the _______________ of the base.

Find the surface area of each solid. Sketch the flattened figure if you find it helpful.

7. 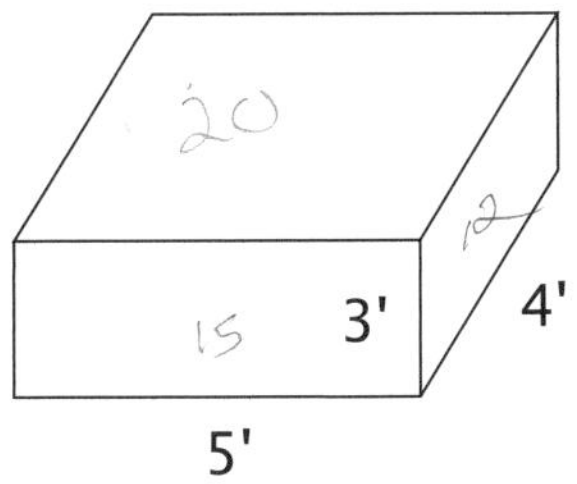

SA = _____________________

8. 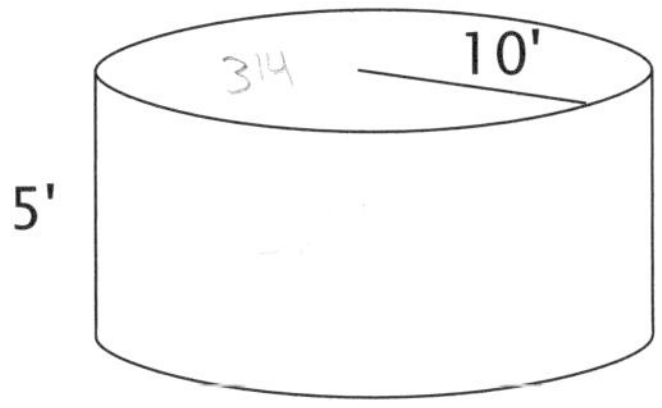

SA = _____________________

9. 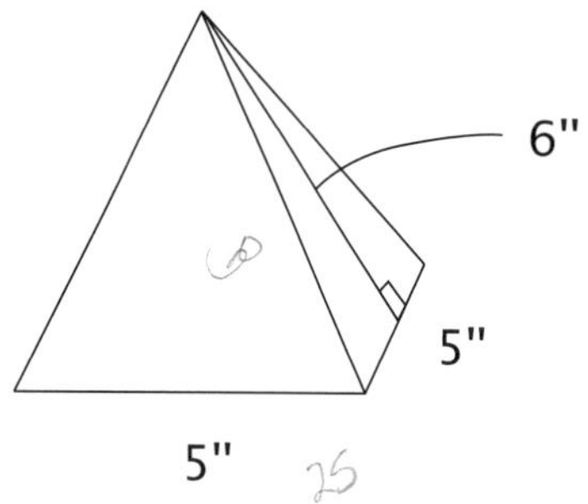

SA = ____________________

10. 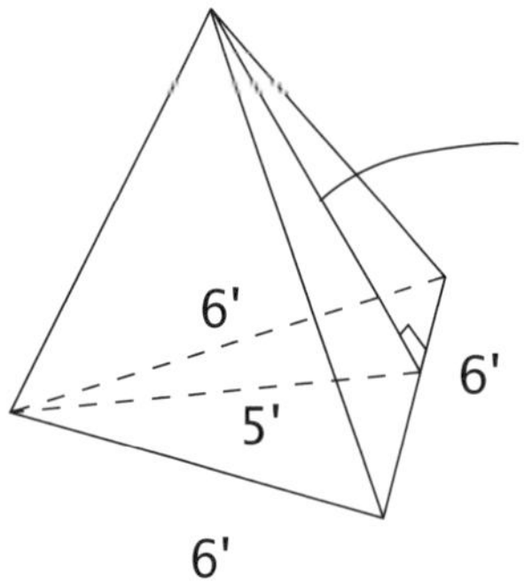

height is 7 ft

SA = ____________________

11. 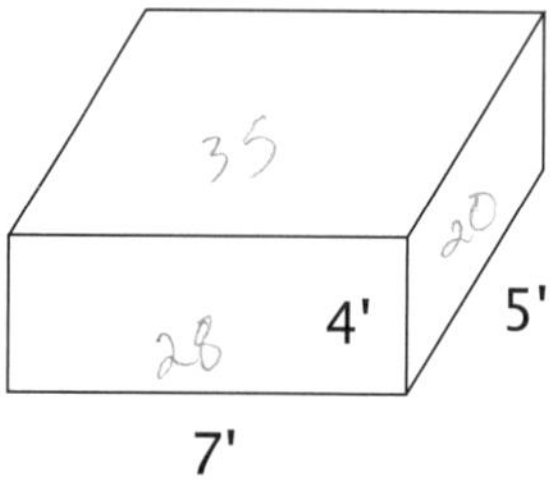

SA = ____________________

12. 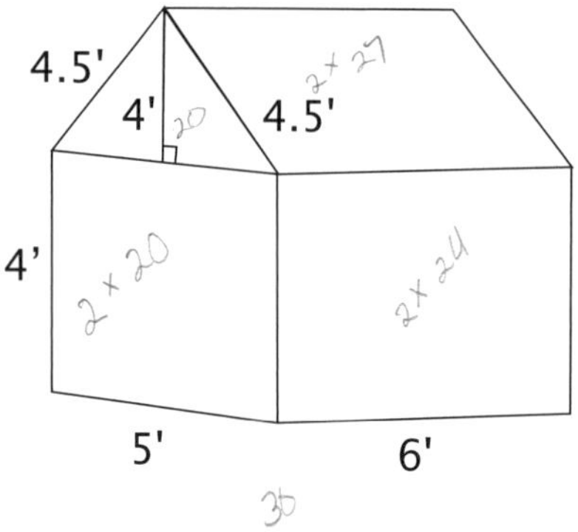

SA = ____________________

Hint for #12: You will need to find the area of seven rectangles and two triangles.

Fill in the blanks.

1. _______________ units are used to measure surface area.

2. A figure with a square base and four triangular faces is a _______________ .

3. A figure with six square faces is a _______________ .

4. A figure with a _______________ base and three triangular faces is a pyramid.

5. Add the areas of two circles and a rectangle to find the surface area of a _______________ .

6. Add the area of six rectangles to find the area of a _______________ solid.

Find the surface area of each solid. Sketch the flattened figure if you find it helpful.

7.

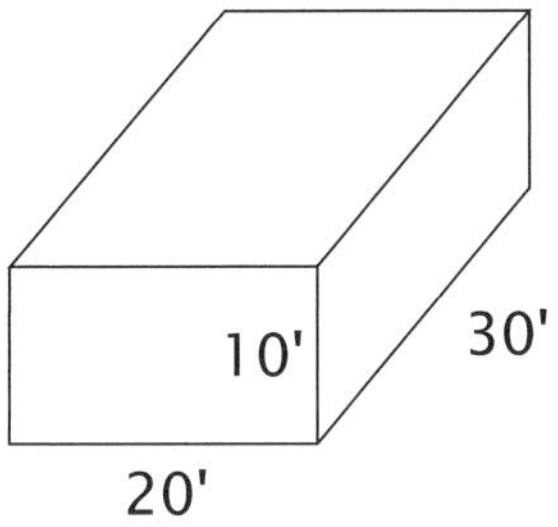

SA = ____________________

8.

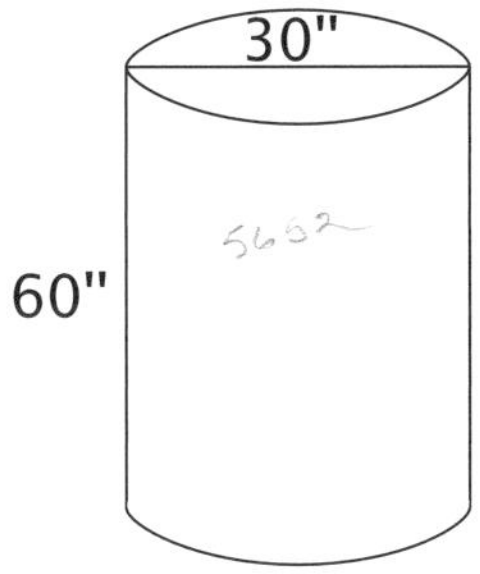

SA = ____________________

9. 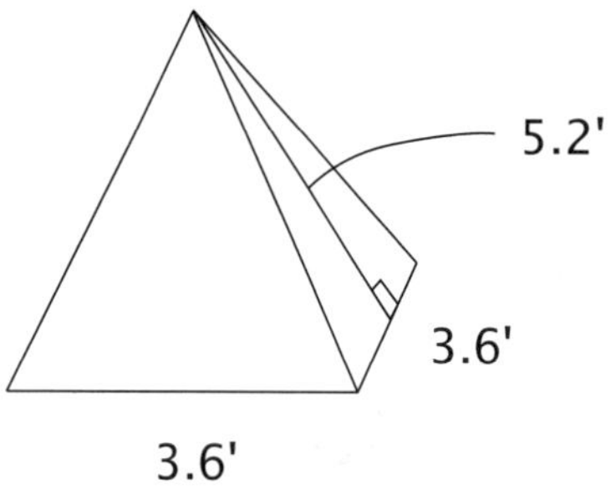

SA = ______________

10. 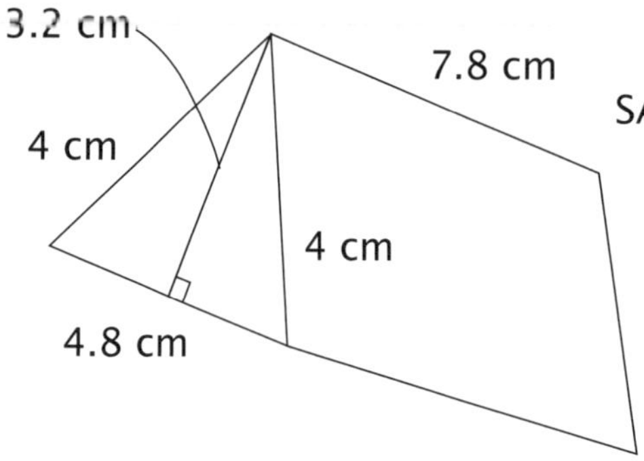

SA = ______________

11. 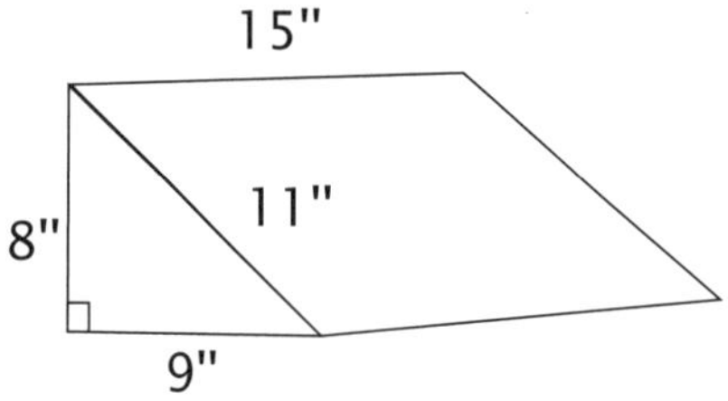

SA = ______________

12. 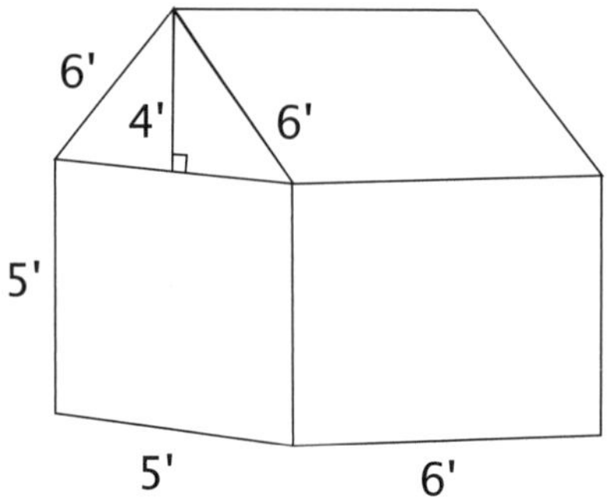

SA = ______________

Find the surface area of each solid. Sketch the flattened figure if you find it helpful.

1.

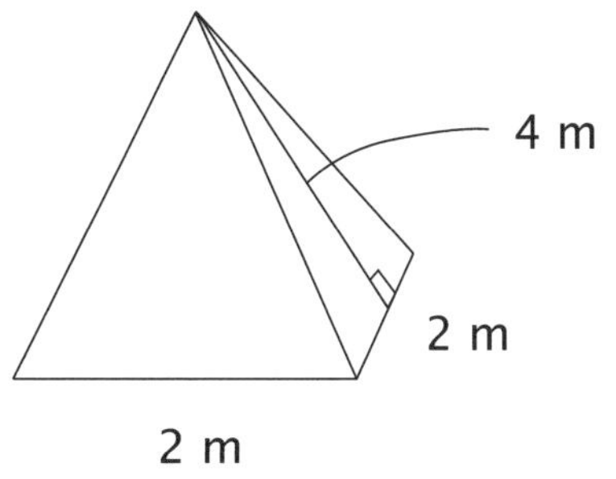

SA = ______________

2.

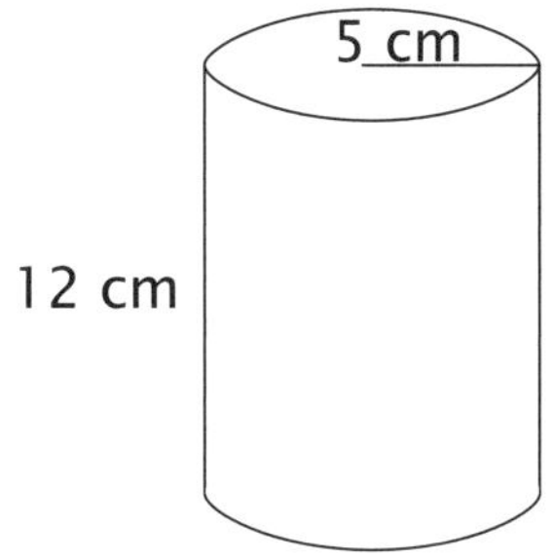

SA = ______________

3.

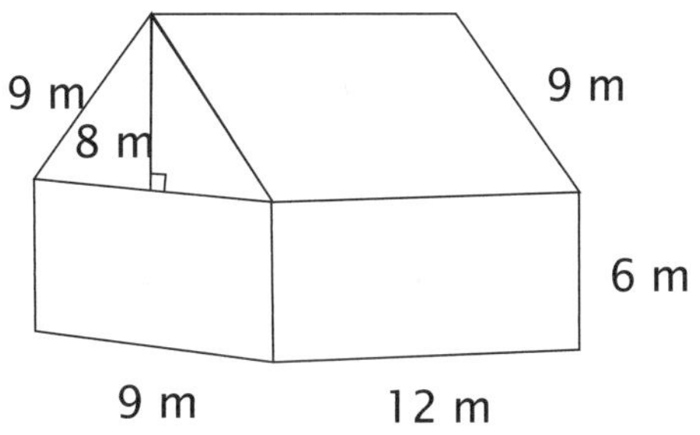

SA = ______________

Answer the questions.

4. What is the height of the face of a pyramid called?

5. Find the volume of a sphere with a radius of 1.66 inches.

6. What are the lines that measure the distance north and south of the equator?

7. Give the name for a 180° angle.

8. What is the circumference of a circle with a radius of seven feet?

Answer the questions.

9. Find the volume of a cylinder with a radius of 5 centimeters and a height of 12 centimeters.

10. What is a line that intersects a circle in exactly two places called?

11. How many degrees per interior angle in a 12-sided regular polygon?

12. Find the number of sides of a regular polygon, if the measure of each interior angle is 108°.

Draw, using another piece of paper if necessary.

13. Draw a trapezoid with interior angle measures of 64°, 116°, 113°, and 67°.

14. Draw a parallelogram with interior angle measures of 70° and 110°.

15. Draw a rectangle with sides measuring 2" and 3".

Use the drawing as needed to answer the questions.

16. Name three rays contained in the line $\overleftrightarrow{BE}$.

17. Name three line segments contained in $\overleftrightarrow{AD}$.

18. If $\overline{AF} \perp \overline{BE}$, what is m∠AFC?
Why?

19. If m∠DFE = 90°, then $\overleftrightarrow{AD}$ ____________ $\overleftrightarrow{BE}$.

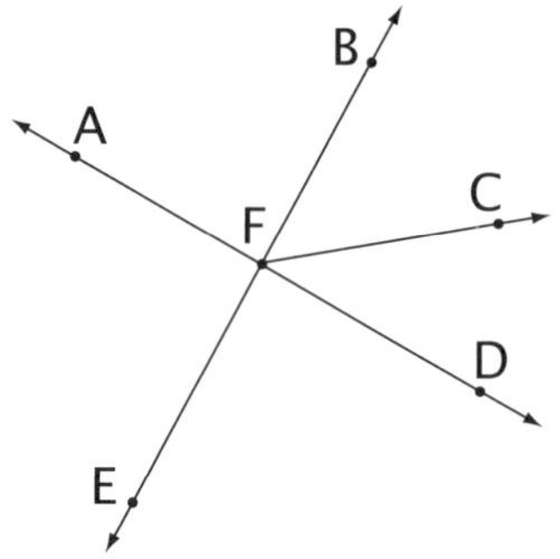

Given: $\overleftrightarrow{AD}$, $\overleftrightarrow{BE}$ and $\overrightarrow{FC}$ are coplanar.

$\overrightarrow{FC}$ bisects ∠BFD.

Complete and state the converse.

20. If two parallel lines are cut by a transversal, then alternate interior angles are ________________ .

Find the surface area of each solid. Sketch the flattened figure if you find it helpful.

1.

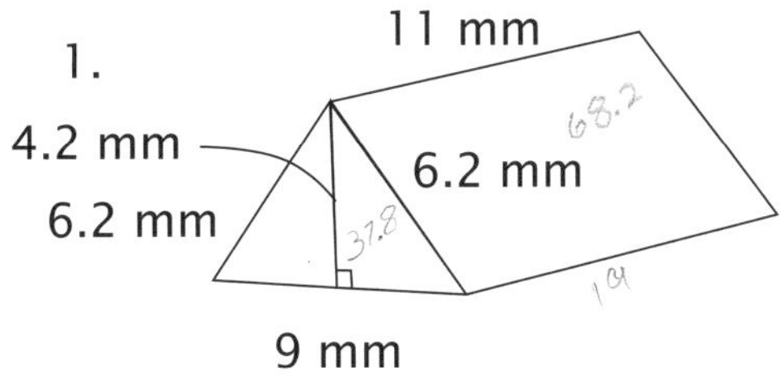

SA = _______________

2.

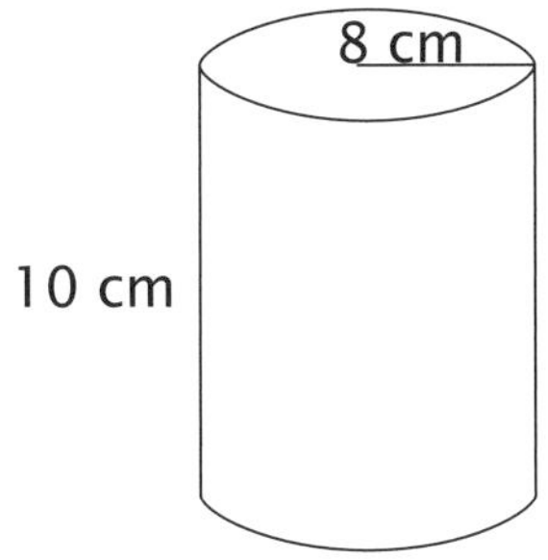

SA = _______________

3.

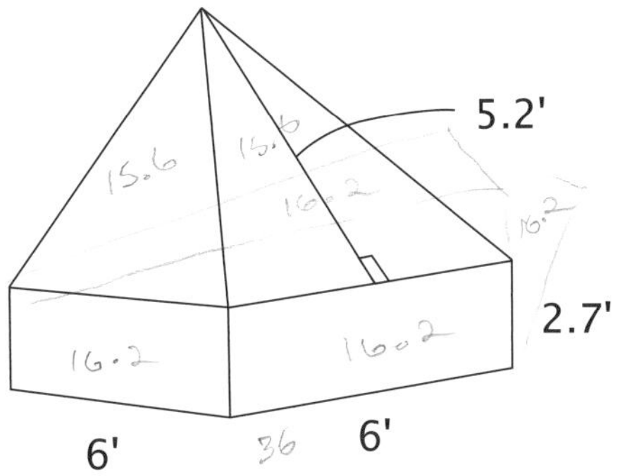

SA = _______________

Answer the questions.

4. What is the term for the height of a pyramid that rises perpendicularly from the base to the vertex?

5. Find the volume of a sphere with a radius of 1.5".

6. What is the volume of a cone with a radius of 2.8 cm and a height of 4.7 cm?

7. Give the name for a 269º angle.

8. How many flat surfaces does a pyramid with a triangular base have?

9. Find the area of an ellipse with axes of 10 inches and 20 inches.

Answer the questions.

10. What is the term for a pie-shaped piece of a circle?

11. What is the total number of interior degrees in a pentagon?

12. Find the number of sides of a regular polygon, if the measures of the interior angles add up to 360°.

Draw, using another piece of paper if necessary.

13. Draw a square with each side measuring $2\frac{7}{16}$ inches.

14. Draw a trapezoid with three of its angles measuring 65°, 115°, and 120°.

15. What is the measure of the fourth angle in #14?

Use the drawing as needed to answer the questions.

16. m∠1 + m∠2 = ______°.
Why?

17. ∠1 and ∠2 are ______________ angles.
Why?

18. ∠BGD and ∠AGB are ______________ angles.
Why?

19. If m∠EGF = 34°, then m∠BGC is ______°.
Why?

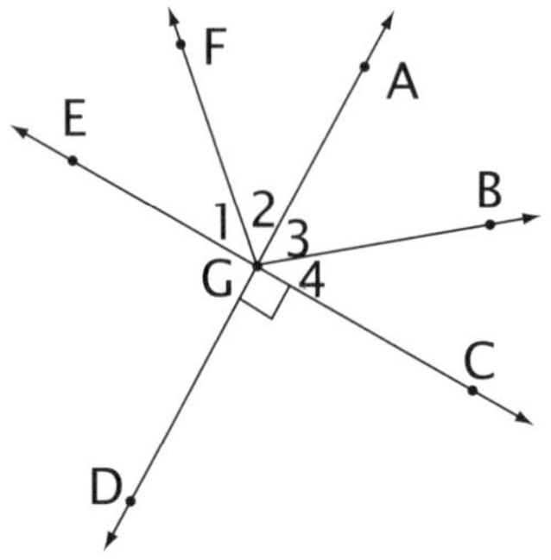

Given:
$\overleftrightarrow{AD} \perp \overleftrightarrow{EC}$, m∠2 + m∠3 = 90°

Complete and state the converse.

20. If two lines are __________________, then the angles formed where the lines intersect are 90° angles.

Find the surface area of each solid. Sketch the flattened figure if you find it helpful.

1.

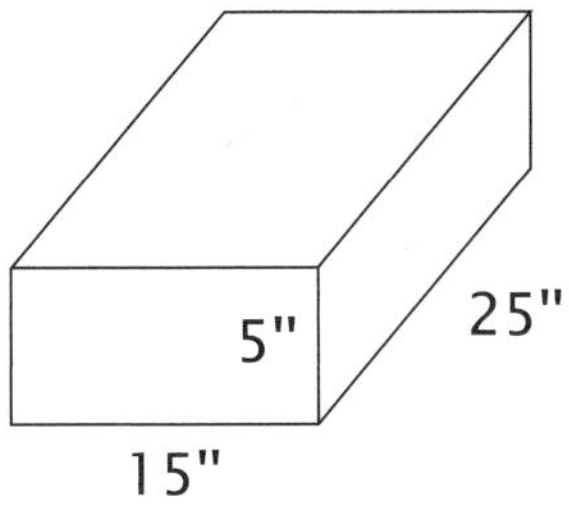

SA = _______________

2.

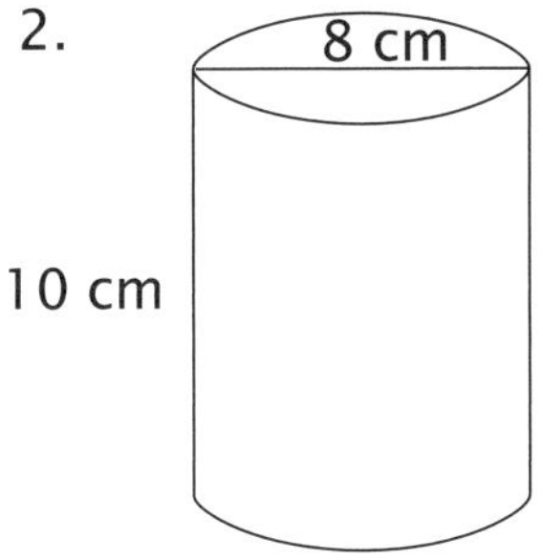

SA = _______________

3.

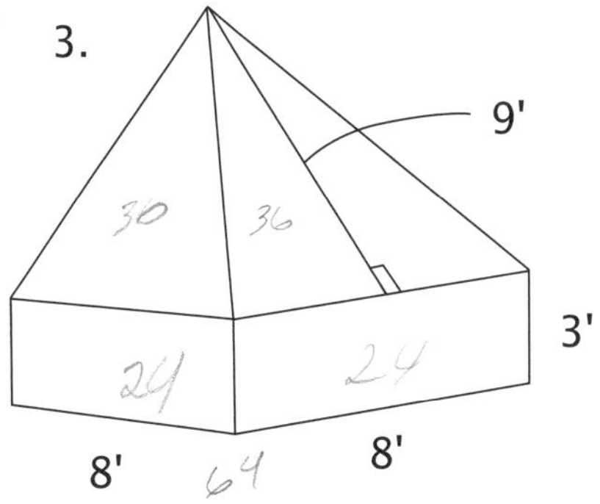

SA = _______________

Matching. Write the letter of the answer by each description.

4. a rectangular solid with six congruent faces
5. a polygon with four congruent sides
6. height of the face of a pyramid
7. perpendicular height of a pyramid
8. units used to measure area
9. units used to measure volume
10. may have a square base and four triangular faces
11. has parallel congruent bases, and lateral surfaces that are parallelograms.
12. sides are perpendicular to a circular base
13. a regular polygon with eight congruent sides

a. slant height
b. cubic
c. cube
d. rhombus
e. altitude
f. prism
g. octagon
h. square
i. cylinder
j. pyramid

Use the figure at right to find the measure of each of the following arcs.

14. What is the measure of minor arc AB?

15. What is the measure of arc ABC?

16. What is the measure of arc ABCD?

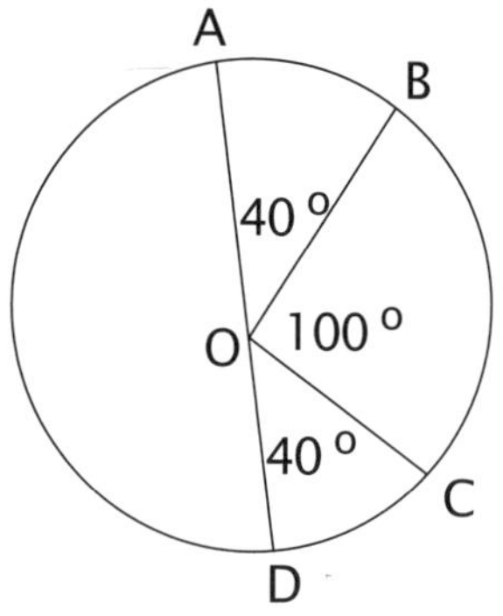

Given: O is the center of the circle.

Sharpen your algebra skills!
A binomial may be multiplied by another binomial.
See examples to multiply $(X + 3)(X + 4)$ and $(X - 3)(X + 2)$.

EXAMPLE 1

$$\begin{array}{r} X + 3 \\ X + 4 \\ \hline 4X + 12 \\ X^2 + 3X \quad \\ \hline X^2 + 7X + 12 \end{array}$$

EXAMPLE 2

$$\begin{array}{r} X - 3 \\ X + 2 \\ \hline 2X - 6 \\ X^2 - 3X \quad \\ \hline X^2 - X - 6 \end{array}$$

17. $(X + 4)(X + 8) =$

18. $(X + 5)(X + 2) =$

19. $(X + 3)(X - 1) =$

20. $(X - 4)(X + 6) =$

Here is a way to visualize where the formula for the area of a circle comes from.

Try to visualize each step as it is described. You may actually draw and cut a circle if you wish.

A. Imagine a circle with many diameters drawn through it.

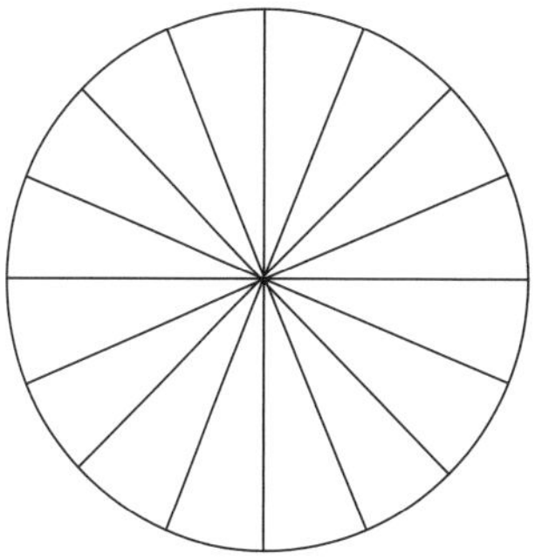

B. Divide the circle in half, and separate the sections.

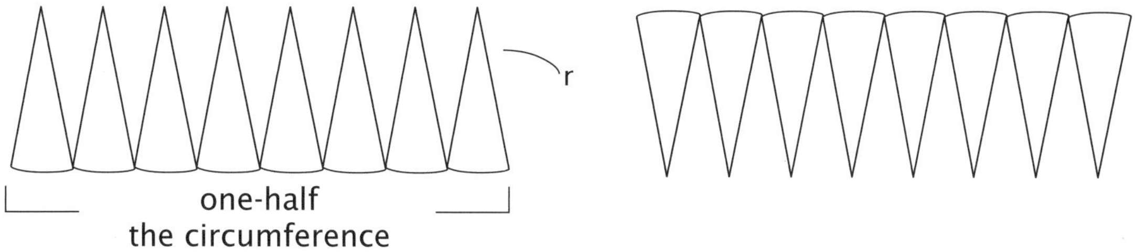

C. Fit the two sections together.
You can imagine each section to be very small, so that the figure is a rectangle.
The width of the rectangle is the same as the radius of the circle (r).
The length of the rectangle is one-half of the circumference or 1/2 C.

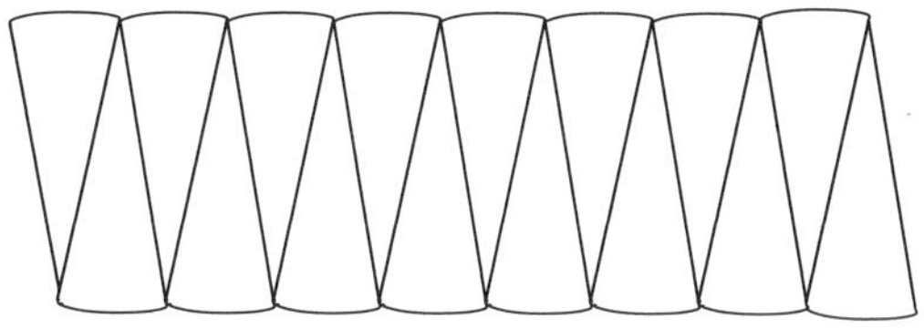

D. We know the circumference of a circle is π times twice the radius, or $2\pi r$.
So the length of the rectangle may be written as $(1/2)(2\pi r)$ or πr.

1. Multiply the length times the width of the rectangle to find its area, which is the same as the area of the circle. What is your result?

Read and solve.

2. If L = length, W = width and H = height, the formula for the volume of a rectangular solid can be written as V = LWH. Write a formula for the surface area of a rectangular solid using L, W, and H. Simplify your formula.

3. In a cube, length, width and height all have the same measure. Using S to represent that measure, adapt your formula from #2 to a formula for the surface area of a cube.

4. Greg built a rectangular, metal storage bin. Its base was 3 ft by 11 ft and its height was 3 ft. Find the volume and the surface area of the bin.

5. Greg used the same number of square feet of metal (#4) to build a cube-shaped bin. What were the dimensions of the new bin?

6. Which bin will hold the greater volume? What is the difference in their volumes?

Simplify the radical expressions. Some may require more than one step to simplify completely.

1. $5\sqrt{2}+3\sqrt{5}=$

2. $8\sqrt{7}+3\sqrt{3}=$

3. $12\sqrt{6}-10\sqrt{6}=$

4. $11\sqrt{2}+3\sqrt{2}+5\sqrt{2}=$

5. $\frac{12\sqrt{24}}{6\sqrt{3}}=$

6. $\frac{25\sqrt{10}}{5\sqrt{5}}=$

7. $\sqrt{24}=$

8. $\sqrt{300}=$

9. $\sqrt{48}=$

10. $(5\sqrt{3})(6\sqrt{5})=$

11. $(6\sqrt{6})(7\sqrt{2})=$

12. $(2\sqrt{3})(2\sqrt{3})=$

Use a calculator to find the value of the radicals to the nearest hundredth.

13. $\sqrt{5} =$

14. $\sqrt{3} =$

15. $\sqrt{14} =$

Fill in the blanks.

16. The symbol $\sqrt{}$ is known as a square root, or _______________ sign.

17. When multiplying radicals, take numbers times _______________ and radicals times _______________.

18. A number whose square root is a whole number is known as a perfect _______________.

Simplify the radical expressions. Some may require more than one step to simplify completely.

1. $6\sqrt{7}+5\sqrt{3}=$

2. $8\sqrt{3}+5\sqrt{3}=$

3. $8\sqrt{7}-7\sqrt{7}=$

4. $13\sqrt{2}+11\sqrt{2}-20\sqrt{2}=$

5. $\dfrac{36\sqrt{8}}{6\sqrt{2}}=$

6. $\dfrac{42\sqrt{10}}{7\sqrt{5}}=$

7. $\sqrt{108}=$

8. $\sqrt{250}=$

9. $\sqrt{180}=$

10. $\left(6\sqrt{7}\right)\left(-5\sqrt{7}\right)=$

11. $\left(6\sqrt{2}\right)\left(4\sqrt{3}\right)=$

12. $(8)\left(3\sqrt{20}\right)=$

Use a calculator to find the value of the radicals to the nearest hundredth.

13. $\sqrt{6} =$

14. $\sqrt{11} =$

15. $\sqrt{21} =$

Fill in the blanks.

16. You can only add or subtract things if they are the ________________ kind.

17. The square root of three times the square root of three equals ________________ .

18. The square root of a perfect square is a ________________ number.

SYSTEMATIC REVIEW

17C

Simplify the radical expressions as completely as possible.

1. $4\sqrt{3} + 5\sqrt{3}$

2. $\sqrt{7} + 3\sqrt{7}$

3. $16\sqrt{2} - 8\sqrt{2}$

4. $(\sqrt{7})(\sqrt{10})$

5. $(\sqrt{5})(2\sqrt{3})$

6. $\dfrac{\sqrt{28}}{\sqrt{7}}$

7. $\sqrt{8} =$

8. $\sqrt{28} =$

9. Use a calculator to solve #7 and #8. Round your answers to hundredths.

Use the figure at right for #10–11. Follow the directions.

10. Find the volume of the solid.

11. Find the surface area of the solid.

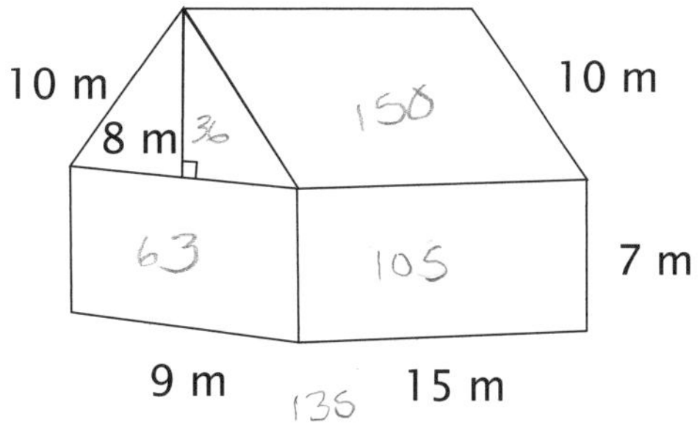

12. Find the volume of a cone with a radius of 11 feet and a height of 14.3 feet.

13. Find the volume of a sphere with a radius of 2.4 inches.

14. In the figure at right, a circle with center X is inscribed inside square ABCD. The measure of one side of the square is 6". What is the area of the square?

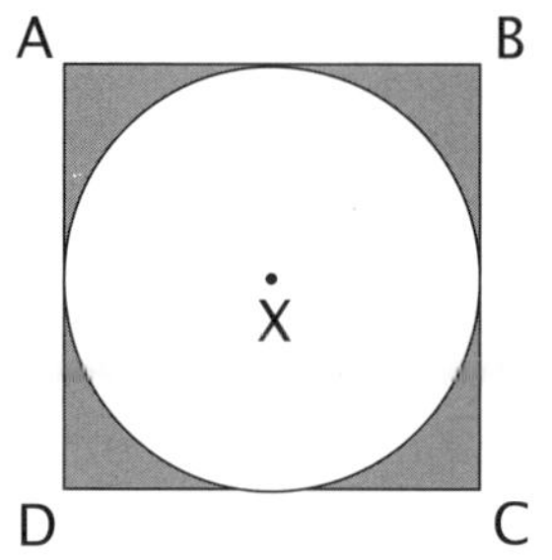

15. What is the area of the circle in #14? (Hint: the diameter has the same measure as one side of the square.)

16. What is the area of the shaded part of the figure above?

Use the drawing as needed to answer the questions.

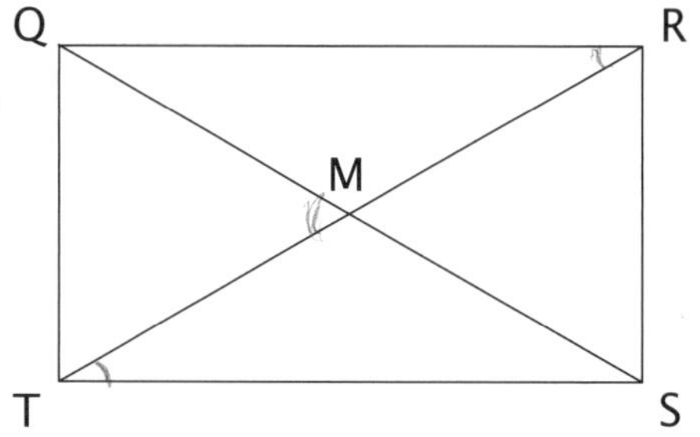

Given: QRST is a rectangle.

17. ∠QMR ≅ ∠______

18. ∠QMR and ∠TMS are ____________________ angles.

19. ∠QRM and ∠MTS are ____________________ angles.

20. If m∠QMT = 70°, then m∠RMS is ______°. Why?

SYSTEMATIC REVIEW

17D

Simplify the radical expressions as completely as possible.

1. $9\sqrt{6} + 23\sqrt{6} =$

2. $7\sqrt{2} + 8\sqrt{2} =$

3. $\sqrt{7} - 5\sqrt{7} =$

4. $(3\sqrt{6})(2\sqrt{7}) =$

5. $(\sqrt{11})(\sqrt{11}) =$

6. $\dfrac{2\sqrt{30}}{\sqrt{5}} =$

7. $\sqrt{12} =$

8. $\sqrt{200} =$

9. Use a calculator to solve #7 and #8. Round your answers to hundredths.

Follow the directions.

10. Find the volume of the solid.

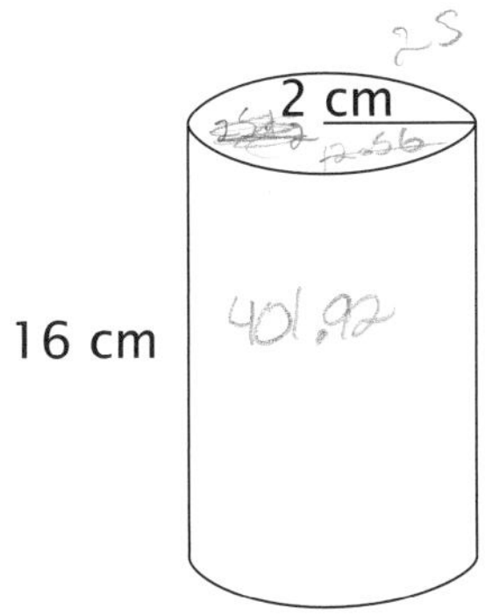

11. Find the surface area of the solid.

12. Find the area of a trapezoid
with bases of four and five and a height of six.

13. Find the area of a circle with a radius of 2.4 inches.

14. Give the name for a section of the circumference of a circle.

15. If an exterior angle of a regular polygon equals 45°, what is the measure of each interior angle?

16. Find the number of sides of a regular polygon if the measures of the interior angles add up to 540°.

Use the drawing as needed to answer the questions.

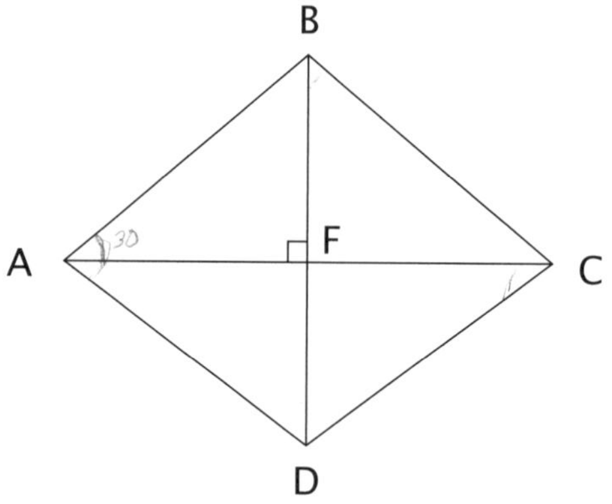

Given: ABCD is a rhombus.

17. m∠AFB ≅ ∠ ______

18. If $\overline{BD}$ is a perpendicular bisector of $\overline{AC}$, and m$\overline{AF}$ = 5 cm, then m$\overline{FC}$ = ______.

19. ∠CBF ≅ ∠ ______

20. If m∠BAF = 30°, then m∠DCF is ______°.
Why?

SYSTEMATIC REVIEW

17E

Simplify the radical expressions as completely as possible.

1. $5\sqrt{5} + 2\sqrt{2} =$

2. $3\sqrt{5} + 8\sqrt{5} =$

3. $13\sqrt{10} - 15\sqrt{10} =$

4. $(5\sqrt{10})(3\sqrt{13}) =$

5. $(3\sqrt{8})(2\sqrt{8}) =$

6. $\dfrac{8\sqrt{12}}{2\sqrt{6}} =$

7. $\sqrt{27} =$

8. $\sqrt{20} =$

9. Use a calculator to solve #7 and #8. Round your answers to hundredths.

Follow the directions.

10. Find the volume of the solid.

11. Find the surface area of the solid.

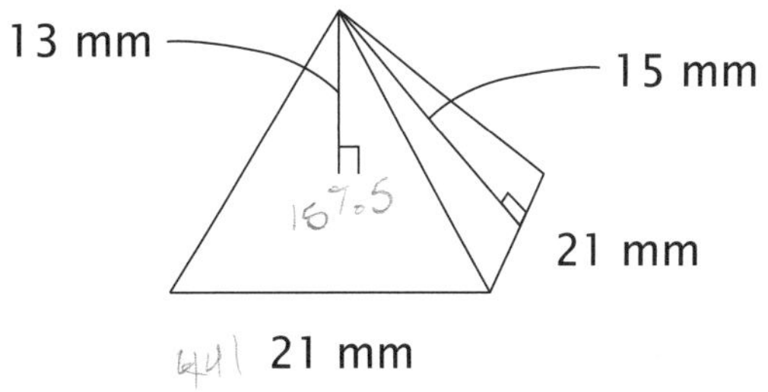

Follow the directions.

12. Find the area of a parallelogram with a base of 11 and a height of 8.

13. Find the circumference of a circle with a diameter of 6.4 inches.

14. Give the name for a triangle with only two sides congruent.

15. If an exterior angle of a regular polygon equals 72°, what is the measure of each interior angle?

16. How many sides does the polygon described in #15 have?

Sharpen your algebra skills!

A trinomial is a polynomial with three terms. When factoring a trinomial, notice that the factors of the last term are the addends of the coefficient of the middle term. In *Algebra 2*, you will learn how to factor trinomials when the factors and addends do not work out to be whole numbers.

EXAMPLE 1 $X^2 + 7X + 12 = (X + 4)(X + 3)$

EXAMPLE 2 $X^2 + (A+B)X + AB = (X + A)(X + B)$

Factor the trinomials.

17. $X^2 + 10X + 16 =$

18. $X^2 + 5X + 6 =$

19. $X^2 + 8X + 7 =$

20. $X^2 + 9X + 20 =$

Archimedes is a famous mathematician who lived around 250 BC. He worked out geometric relationships between cylinders and spheres.

Follow the directions to discover these relationships. Round your answers to the nearest hundredth.

1. Find the volume of the cylinder shown.

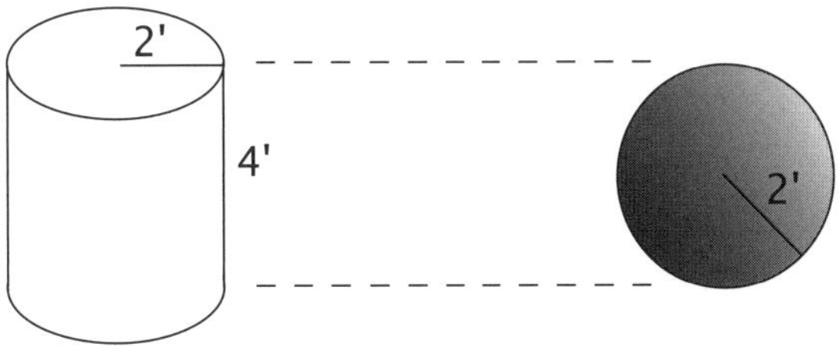

2. Find the volume of the sphere shown.

Notice that the diameters of both figures are the same, and the height of the cylinder is equal to its diameter.

3. Find the volume of a cylinder with a height and diameter of six units.

4. Find the volume of a sphere with a diameter of six units.

5. Find the volume of a cylinder with a height and diameter of two units.

6. Find the volume of a sphere with a diameter of two units.

7. Write a ratio for each set of volumes in #1-6. Put the volume of the sphere in the numerator and the volume of the cylinder in the denominator. Divide each ratio, and write each one as a decimal rounded to hundredths.

8. To what common fraction is each of the decimals in #7 close?

The surface area of a sphere is more difficult to demonstrate visually than that of the other solids you have studied so far. Imagine shining a light directly on the sphere from the top, bottom, left, and right. Add the area of the four circular shadows formed, and you have the surface area of a sphere. The formula is $SA = 4\pi r^2$.

9. Find the surface area of a cylinder with a height and diameter of six units.

10. Find the surface area of a sphere with a diameter of six units.

11. Write your answers to #9 and #10 as a ratio, and simplify to fraction form as you did above.

12. Summarize what you have observed about the relationships between the volumes and surface areas of spheres and cylinders of equal heights and diameters. Keep in mind that you have not proved this relationship; you've merely observed it in certain cases.

Fill in the blanks.

1. A triangle with one 90° angle is a ________________ triangle.

2. The two sides of the 90° angle are called the ________________ of the triangle.

3. The side opposite the 90° angle is the ________________ .

4. The ________________ theorem states the relationship between the sides of a right triangle.

Complete and state the converse.

5. If a triangle is a right triangle, leg squared plus leg squared equals...

Find the lengths of the unknown side of each triangle. Keep any radicals in your answers, but be sure the radicals are simplified.

6. 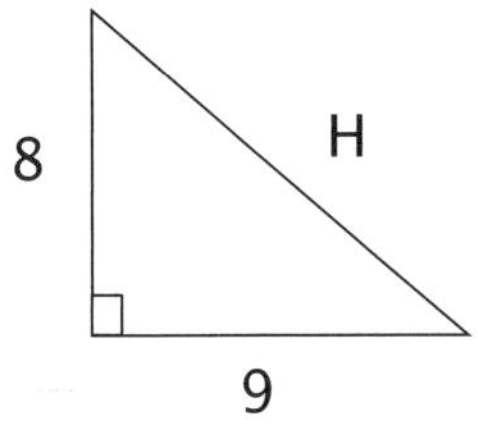

H = ______________

7. 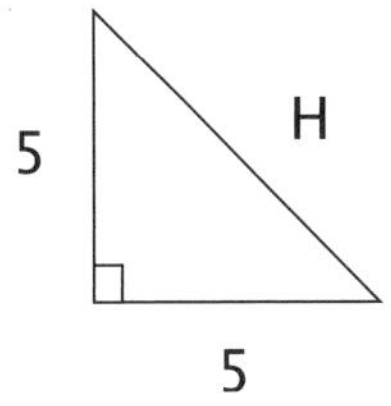

H = ______________

8. 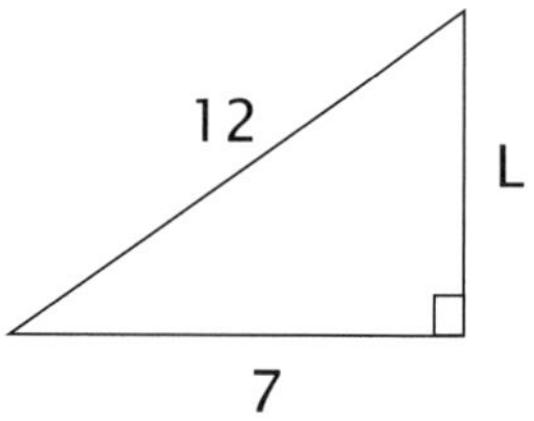

L = ______________

9. 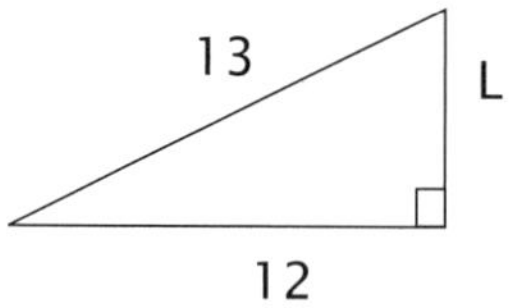

L = ______________

Given three sides of a triangle, use the Pythagorean theorem to determine if the triangle is a right triangle.

10. 5, 6, 8

11. 2, 4, 6

12. 6, 8, 10

18B

Answer the questions.

1. How many degrees are there in a right angle?

2. What are the two shortest sides of a right triangle called?

3. What is the name for the longest side of a right triangle?

4. What theorem states the relationship between the sides of a right triangle?

Complete and state the converse.

5. If one leg squared plus the other leg squared equals...

Find the lengths of the unknown side of each triangle. Keep any radicals in your answers, but be sure the radicals are simplified.

6. 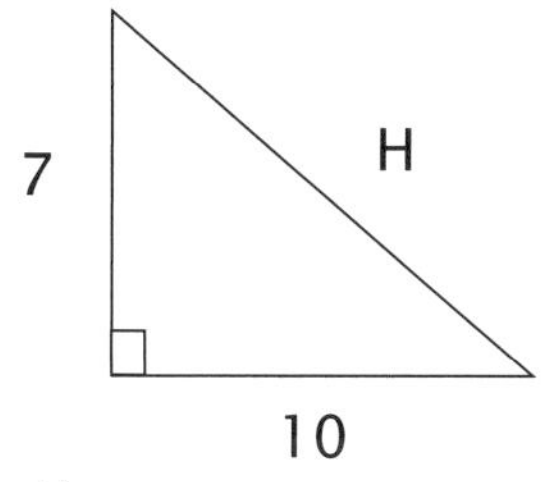

H = ______________

7. 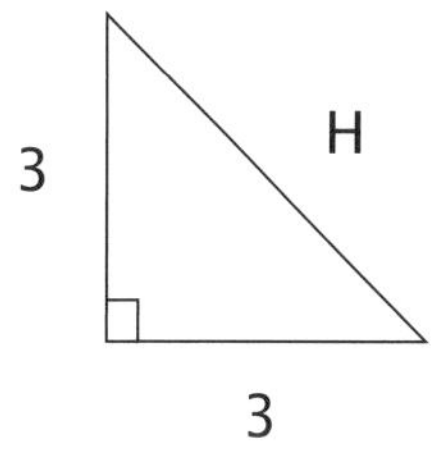

H = ______________

8.

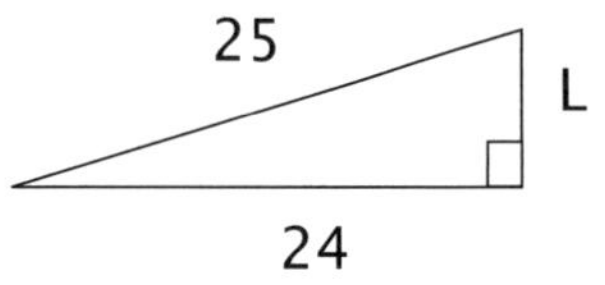

L = ______________

9.

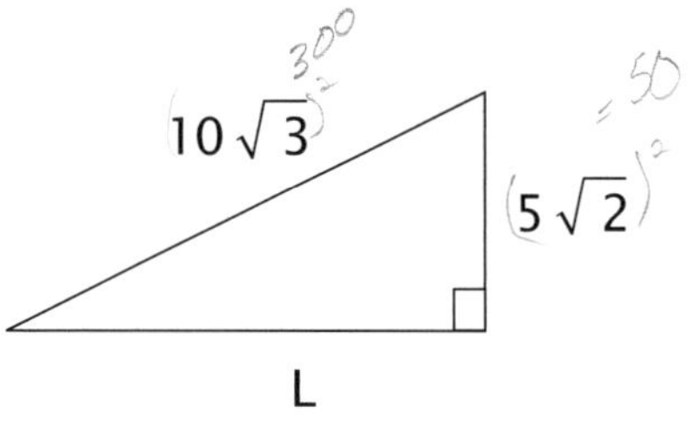

L = ______________

Given three sides of a triangle, use the Pythagorean theorem to determine if the triangle is a right triangle.

10. 4, 5, 6

11. 10, 24, 26

12. 12, 16, 20

18C

Follow the directions.

1. Estimate H.

2. Write the equation
using the Pythagorean theorem.

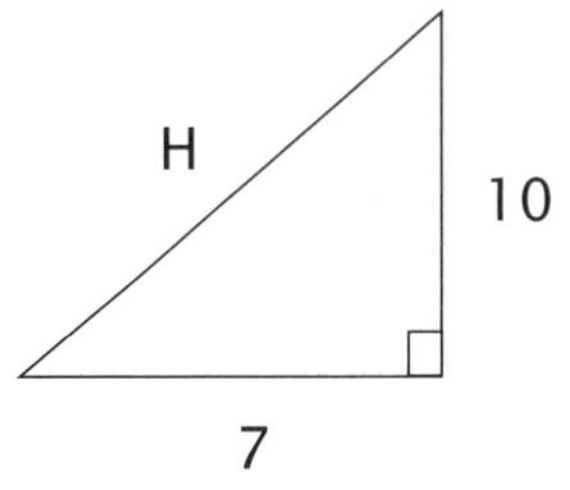

3. Solve the equation.

4. Simplify the radical if possible.

5. Estimate L.

6. Write the equation
using the Pythagorean theorem.

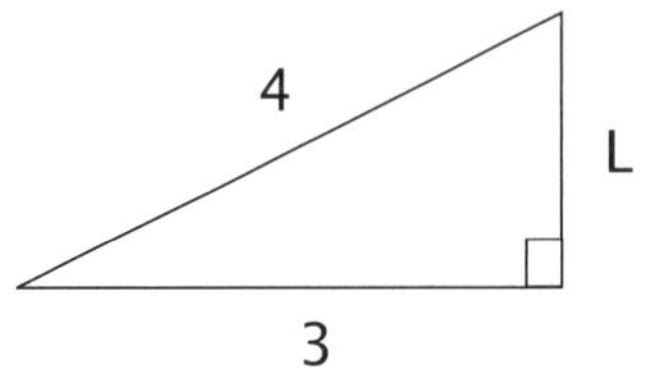

7. Solve the equation.

8. Use your calculator to get an approximate value for the radical.

Answer the questions.

9. Could there be a right triangle with sides 5", 7", and 9"?

10. Explain the reason for your answer in #9.

11. What is the term for the longest side of a right triangle?

12. Find the area of the triangle shown.

13. Find the area of the circle.

14. Subtract your answer to #13 from the answer to #12 to find the area of the shaded part of the figure.

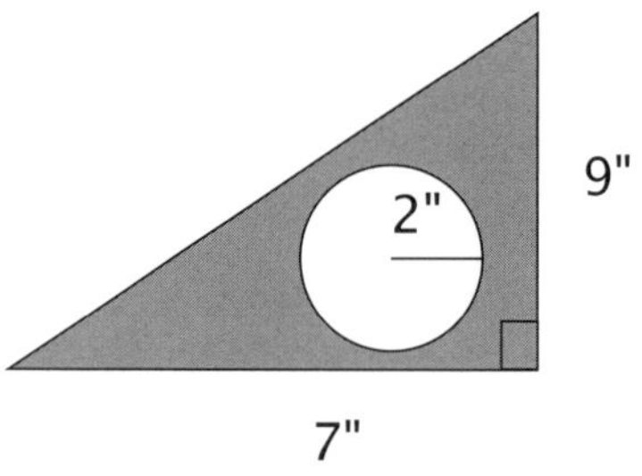

Simplify.

15. $11\sqrt{5} + 7\sqrt{5} =$

16. $(9\sqrt{2})(5\sqrt{2}) =$

17. $\dfrac{9\sqrt{200}}{12\sqrt{2}} =$

Follow the steps below to find the area of the regular polygon.

18. Find the area of one triangle with a base of 4".

19. Multiply the answer to #18 by 5 to find the area of the pentagon.

20. What is the perimeter of the pentagon?

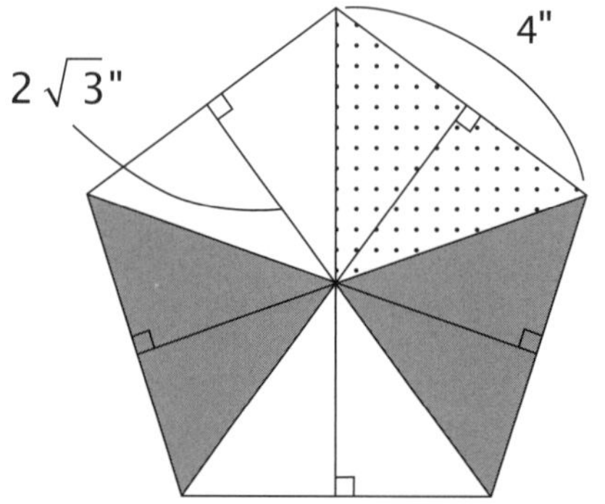

The length of each side is 4". The apothem (⊥ line from side to center) is $2\sqrt{3}$ ".

SYSTEMATIC REVIEW

18D

Follow the directions.

1. Estimate B.

2. Write the equation using the Pythagorean theorem.

3. Solve the equation.

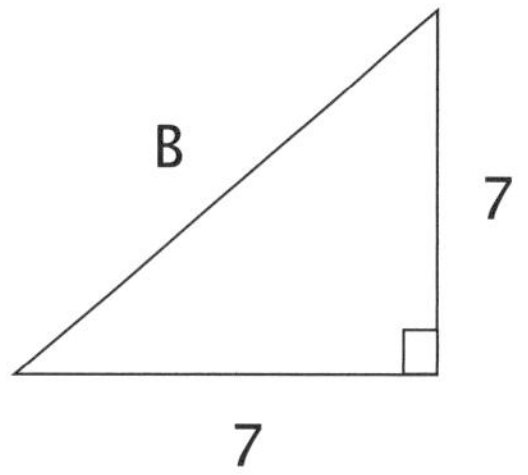

4. Simplify the radical if possible.

5. Estimate M.

6. Write the equation using the Pythagorean theorem.

7. Solve the equation.

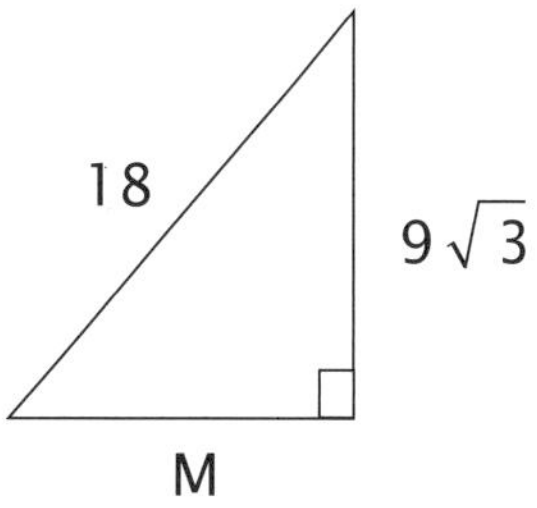

8. Use your calculator to get an approximate value for $9\sqrt{3}$.

Answer the questions.

9. Could there be a right triangle with sides 24", 10", and 26"?

10. Explain the reason for your answer in #9.

11. What kind of triangle has three equal sides?

Answer the questions.

12. In the figure at right, is length OB equal to the length OA? Why or why not?

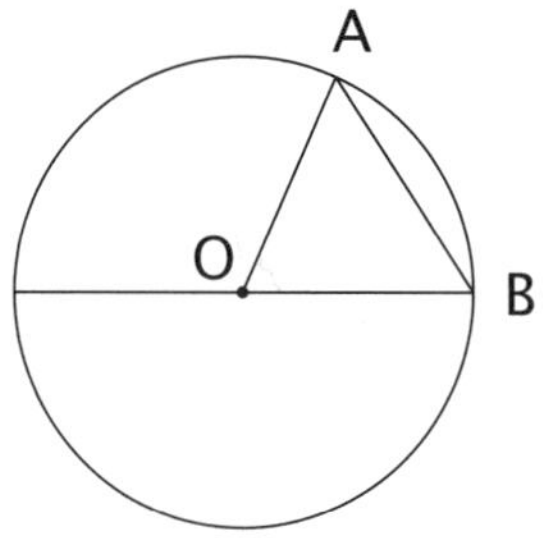

O is the center of the circle.

13. If the measure of minor arc AB is 50º, what is the measure of $\angle AOB$?

14. Given your answer to #13 and that $\angle OAB$ and $\angle OBA$ are congruent, what is the measure of $\angle OAB$?

Simplify.

15. $\sqrt{3} + \sqrt{3} =$

16. $(\sqrt{6})(-\sqrt{24}) =$

17. $\dfrac{2\sqrt{15}}{\sqrt{5}} =$

Follow the steps below to find the area of the regular polygon.

18. Find the area of one triangle with a base of 12". How many triangles of the same size will fit in the polygon?

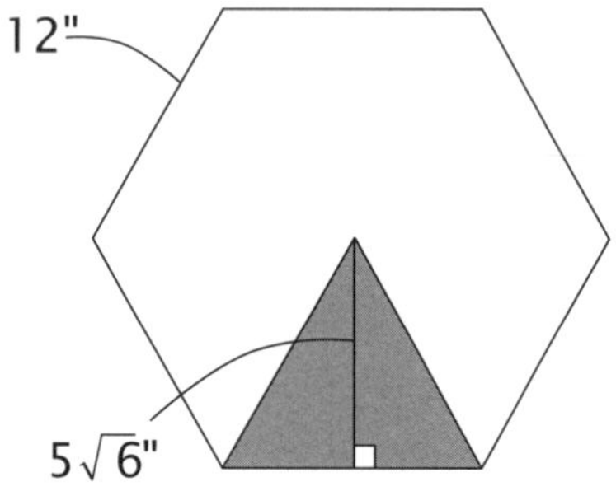

The length of each side is 12". The apothem (⊥ line from side to center) is $5\sqrt{6}$".

19. Multiply to find the area of the polygon.

20. What is the perimeter of the polygon?

Follow the directions.

1. Estimate R.

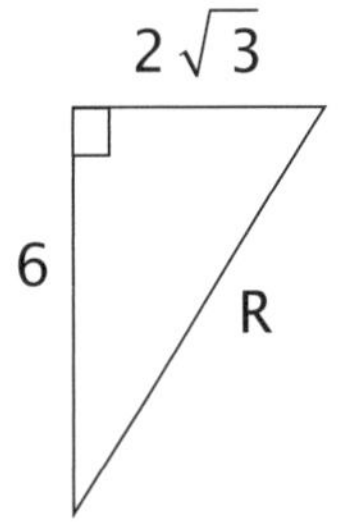

2. Write the equation using the Pythagorean theorem.

3. Solve the equation.

4. Simplify the radical if possible.

5. Estimate T.

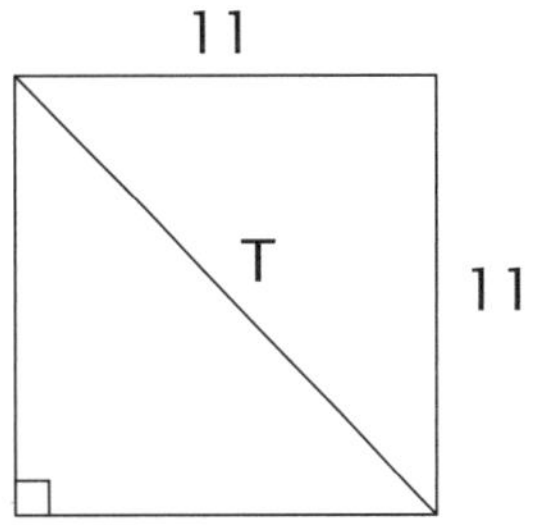

6. Write the equation using the Pythagorean theorem.

7. Solve the equation.

8. Use your calculator to get an approximate value for the radical.

Answer the questions.

9. Could there be a right triangle with sides $2\sqrt{7}$, $2\sqrt{3}$, $2\sqrt{10}$?

10. Explain the reason for your answer in #9.

11. Is it possible to have a right isosceles triangle? Explain.

Answer the questions.

12. What is the volume of the entire cylinder?

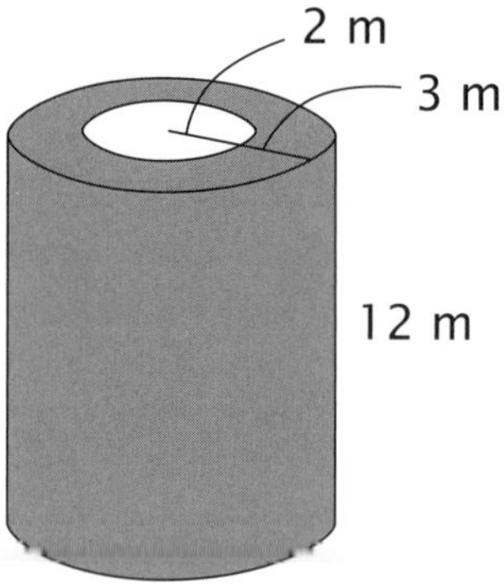

13. What is the volume of the smaller center cylinder?

14. What is the volume of the shaded part of the cylinder?

Simplify if possible.

15. $5\sqrt{2} - 4\sqrt{3} =$

16. $(5\sqrt{6})(2\sqrt{10}) =$

17. $\dfrac{\sqrt{100}}{\sqrt{25}} =$

Sharpen your algebra skills!

When factoring polynomials with negative numbers, carefully watch the signs of the factors.

EXAMPLE 1 $X^2 + X - 2 = (X + 2)(X - 1)$

EXAMPLE 2 $X^2 - 3X - 4 = (X - 4)(X + 1)$

Factor the polynomials.

18. $X^2 + 3X - 10 =$ 19. $X^2 - 2X - 3 =$ 20. $X^2 + X - 6 =$

The Pythagorean theorem can be used to find the distance from a given point above the earth to the farthest visible point on the surface of the earth. For these problems, assume that the sky is clear and that there are no inconvenient hills or mountains in the way.

Follow the directions.

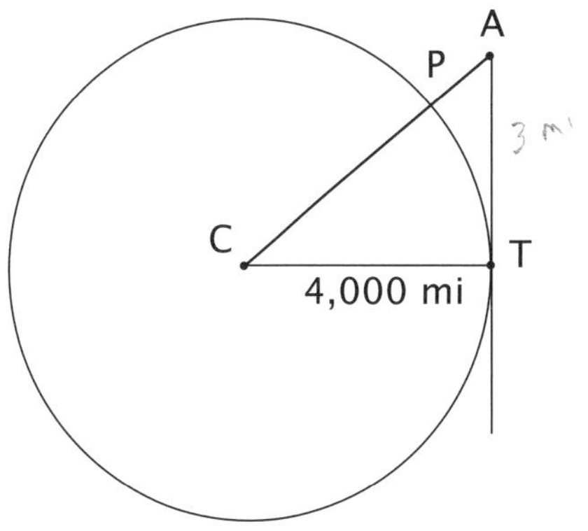

1. We will use a rounded value of 4,000 miles for the radius of the earth. An airplane is flying three miles above the earth at point A. How long is the line segment CA?

2. A passenger in the airplane can see along the tangent represented by line AT all the way to point T. What is the angle between line segment CT and line segment AT? How do you know?

3. Use the Pythagorean theorem to find the distance between point A and point T. Your answers for these kinds of problems will usually not come out as perfect squares. Use your calculator to find the value of the square root, and round the answer to the nearest mile.

4. The top of Mount Everest is 29,035 feet above the surface of the earth. To the nearest whole mile, how many miles high is Mt. Everest?

5. How many miles away is the furthest point on earth that a climber should be able to see from the top of Mount Everest?

6. The Washington Monument is 555 feet tall. How far away is the furthest point that an observer should be able to see from the top of the monument? (In this case, use tenths of a mile for the height.)

A man looks across the flat prairie to a mountain that he knows is 150 miles away. He can just see the top of the mountain and wants to know the height of the mountain.

7. Set up an equation using the Pythagorean theorem. Use X + 4000 for the length of the hypotenuse.

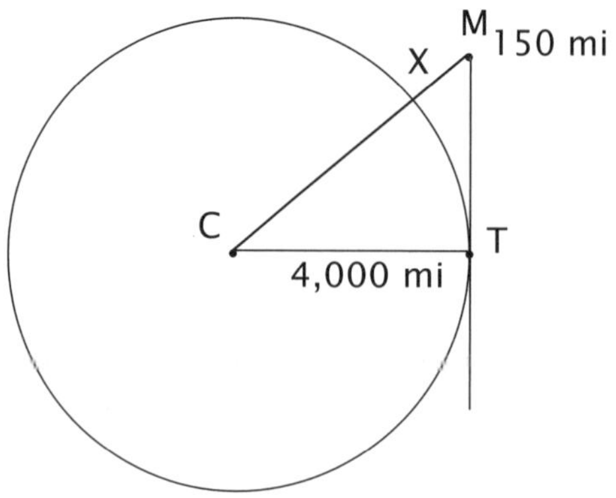

8. Expand the polynomial that represents the hypotenuse.

9. Simplify the equation, so that you have zero on one side and a polynomial on the other. A little examination will show you that the polynomial cannot be factored. In *Algebra 2*, you will learn how to use the quadratic formula to solve unfactorable equations.

10. In this case, we know that the value of X^2 is actually very small in comparison to the radius of the earth. For a good estimate of the height of the mountain, just drop X^2 and solve the resulting equation to the nearest tenth of a mile.

19A

Simplify the radical expressions.

1. $\frac{9}{\sqrt{2}} =$

2. $\frac{10}{\sqrt{5}} =$

3. $\frac{6}{\sqrt{3}} =$

4. $\frac{8}{\sqrt{3}} =$

5. $\frac{15}{\sqrt{5}} =$

6. $\frac{9}{\sqrt{3}} =$

7. $\frac{3}{\sqrt{2}} + \frac{6}{\sqrt{5}} =$

8. $\frac{4}{\sqrt{5}} + \frac{2}{\sqrt{6}} =$

9. $\frac{4}{\sqrt{2}}+\frac{9}{\sqrt{5}}=$

10. $\frac{5}{\sqrt{10}}-\frac{3}{\sqrt{8}}=$

11. $\frac{5}{\sqrt{7}}+\frac{6}{\sqrt{2}}=$

12. $\frac{5\sqrt{2}}{\sqrt{3}}-\frac{4\sqrt{3}}{\sqrt{5}}=$

Fill in the blanks.

13. Radicals should not be left in the _______________ of a fraction.

14. We can multiply the numerator and denominator by the same number because this is the same as multiplying by _______________ .

15. When adding numbers with radicals, first eliminate the radicals in the _______________ , and then find the _______________ denominator.

19B

Simplify the radical expressions.

1. $\frac{11\sqrt{5}}{\sqrt{5}} =$

2. $\frac{18}{\sqrt{2}} =$

3. $\frac{12}{\sqrt{6}} =$

4. $\frac{7}{\sqrt{2}} =$

5. $\frac{6}{\sqrt{3}} =$

6. $\frac{9\sqrt{6}}{\sqrt{5}} =$

7. $\frac{4\sqrt{7}}{\sqrt{2}} + \frac{3\sqrt{7}}{\sqrt{2}} =$

8. $\frac{\sqrt{12}}{9} - \frac{\sqrt{18}}{4} =$

9. $\frac{5}{\sqrt{2}} + \frac{7}{\sqrt{8}} =$

10. $\frac{8\sqrt{3}}{\sqrt{2}} - \frac{5\sqrt{6}}{\sqrt{5}} =$

11. $\frac{3}{\sqrt{5}} + \frac{7}{\sqrt{2}} =$

12. $\frac{4\sqrt{11}}{\sqrt{3}} + \frac{2\sqrt{5}}{\sqrt{7}} =$

Fill in the blanks.

13. Fractions may be simplified by multiplying them by a number equal to ________________ .

14. The denominator of a fraction should not contain a ________________ sign.

15. Find the ________________ ________________ before adding two fractions.

Simplify the radical expressions as completely as possible.

1. $\frac{6}{\sqrt{7}} =$

2. $\frac{8}{\sqrt{2}} =$

3. $\frac{6\sqrt{2}}{\sqrt{3}} =$

4. $2\sqrt{3} + 6\sqrt{2} =$

5. $(4\sqrt{3})(7\sqrt{15}) =$

6. $\frac{\sqrt{36}}{\sqrt{6}} =$

7. $\frac{10\sqrt{10}}{\sqrt{7}} - \frac{2\sqrt{6}}{\sqrt{11}} =$

8. $\frac{24\sqrt{13}}{\sqrt{3}} + \frac{3\sqrt{2}}{\sqrt{3}} =$

Follow the directions.

9. Estimate Q.

10. Write the equation using the Pythagorean theorem.

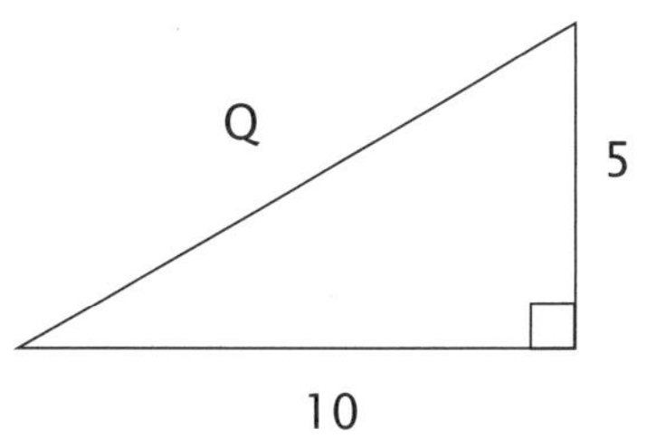

11. Solve the equation. Simplify as needed.

Follow the directions.

12. Estimate X.

13. Write the equation using the Pythagorean theorem.

14. Solve the equation. Simplify as needed.

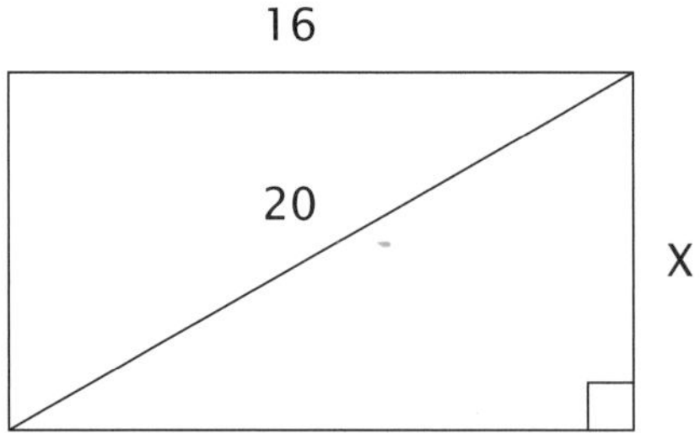

15. Find the volume of a cone with a radius of 11" and a height of 14.3".

16. Construct a rhombus with sides each measuring five centimeters long and one pair of opposite interior angles each measuring 60°.

17. What are the measures of the other two opposite angles in #16?

Follow the steps below to find the area of the regular polygon.

18. Find the area of one triangle with a base of 5". How many triangles of the same size will fit in the octagon?

19. Multiply to find the area of the octagon.

20. What is the perimeter of the octagon?

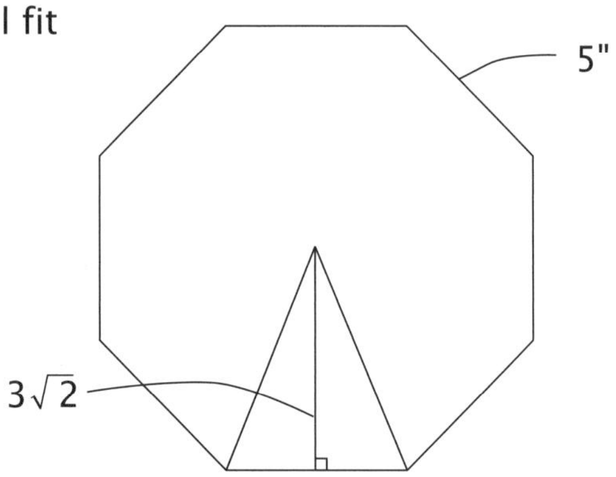

The length of each side is 5".
The apothem (⊥ line from side to center) is $3\sqrt{2}$ ".

Simplify the radical expressions as completely as possible.

1. $\frac{9}{\sqrt{5}} =$

2. $\frac{6}{\sqrt{2}} =$

3. $\frac{5\sqrt{10}}{\sqrt{6}} =$

4. $5\sqrt{6} + 2\sqrt{10} =$

5. $(3\sqrt{8})(2\sqrt{5}) =$

6. $\frac{2\sqrt{14}}{\sqrt{7}} =$

7. $\frac{2\sqrt{5}}{\sqrt{6}} + \frac{2\sqrt{2}}{\sqrt{3}} =$

8. $\frac{5\sqrt{11}}{\sqrt{2}} - \frac{3\sqrt{5}}{\sqrt{2}} =$

Follow the directions.

9. Write the equation to find X.

10. Find the length of the unknown side.

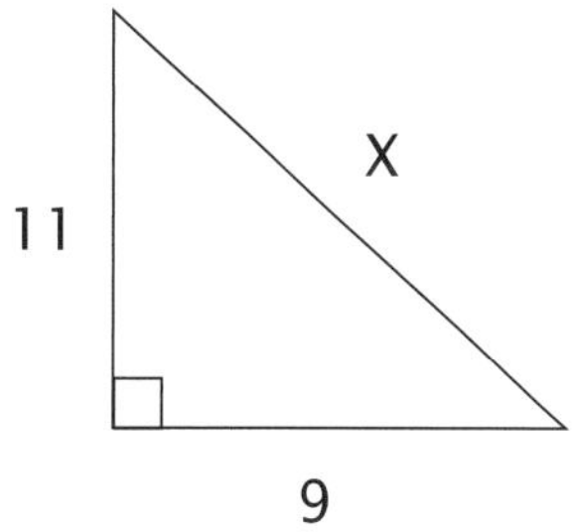

11. Find the area of the triangle.

Follow the directions.

12. Write the equation to find X.

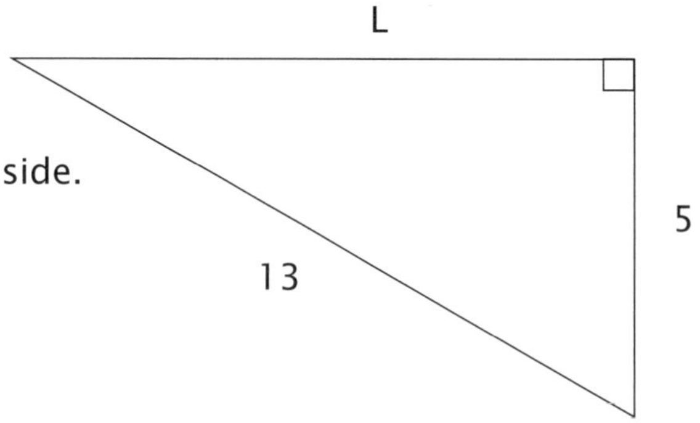

13. Find the length of the unknown side.

14. Find the area of the triangle.

15. Construct a 90° angle and bisect it using a compass.

16. What is the measure of each resulting angle in #15?

17. Find the area of an ellipse with a long axis of seven meters and a short axis of five meters.

Follow the steps below to find the area of a sector of the circle.

18. Find the area of the circle.

19. What fraction of the circle is the sector if it has a measure of 90°?
Hint: a full circle has 360°, so write a fraction with 90 over 360 and reduce.

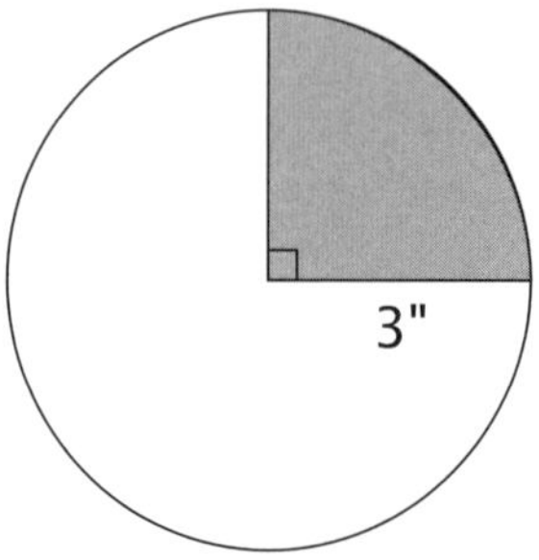

Given: The radius of the circle is 3".

20. Use your answers to #18 and #19 to find the area of the sector. Round to the nearest hundredth.

Simplify the radical expressions as completely as possible.

1. $\frac{2\sqrt{6}}{2\sqrt{5}} =$

2. $\frac{\sqrt{5}}{\sqrt{10}} =$

3. $\frac{12\sqrt{13}}{2\sqrt{13}} =$

4. $8\sqrt{2} + 2\sqrt{14} =$

5. $(2\sqrt{7})(5\sqrt{8}) =$

6. $\frac{14}{\sqrt{7}} =$

7. $\frac{15}{\sqrt{5}} + \frac{20}{\sqrt{2}} =$

8. $\frac{5\sqrt{2}}{\sqrt{14}} - \frac{3\sqrt{2}}{\sqrt{14}} =$

Follow the directions.

9. Write the equation to find X.

10. Find the length of the unknown side.

11. Find the area of the triangle.

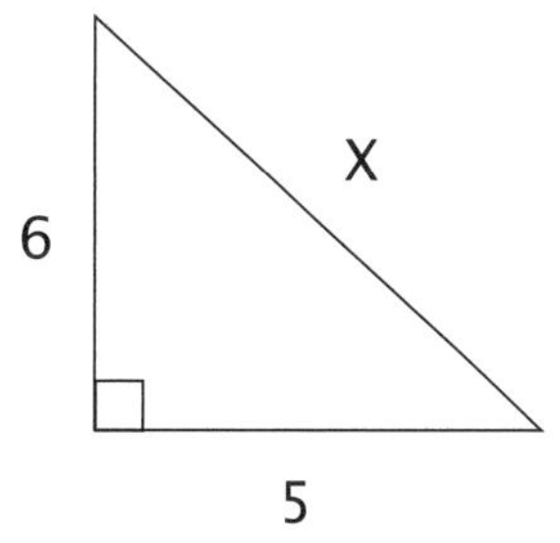

12. Write the equation to find X.

13. Find the length of side X.

14. Find the area of the triangle.

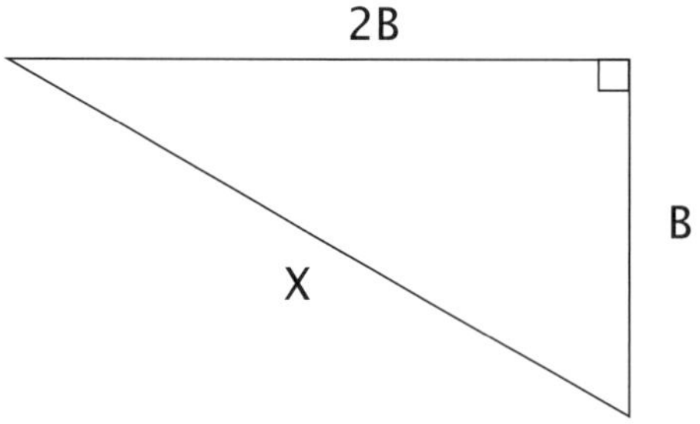

Follow the steps below to find the area of a sector of the circle.

15. Find the area of the circle.

16. Since the sector has a measure of 45°, what fraction of the circle is it?

17. Use your answers to #15 and #16 to find the area of the sector. Round to the nearest hundredth.

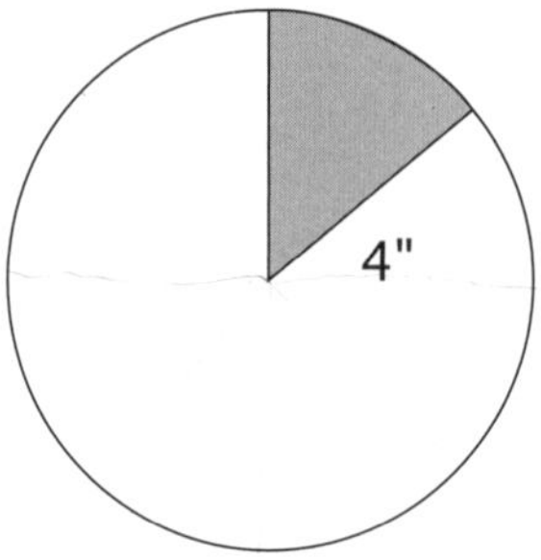

Given: The radius of the the circle is 4".

Sharpen your algebra skills!
When using exponential notation, roots are indicated with fractional exponents.

EXAMPLE 1 $\quad 8^{\frac{1}{3}} = \sqrt[3]{8} = 2 \quad (2 \times 2 \times 2 = 8)$

EXAMPLE 2 $\quad 9^{\frac{3}{2}} = \sqrt{9}^{\,3} = 3^3 = 27$

Simplify.

18. $9^{1/2}$

19. $1{,}000^{2/3}$

20. $4^{3/2}$

In lesson 15 in your text, you learned how to find the volume of a right prism. If the lateral surfaces of a prism do not form right angles with the bases, the prism is an oblique prism. In an oblique prism, at least two faces are parallelograms, not rectangles. The bases are still parallel to each other.

The procedure for finding the volume of an oblique prism is similar to that used to find the volume of a pyramid. The altitude is not the length of one of the edges but the length of a line perpendicular to the bases.

Follow the directions.

1. Find the volume of the oblique prism shown on the right. The bases of the prism are squares, and the other four faces are parallelograms.

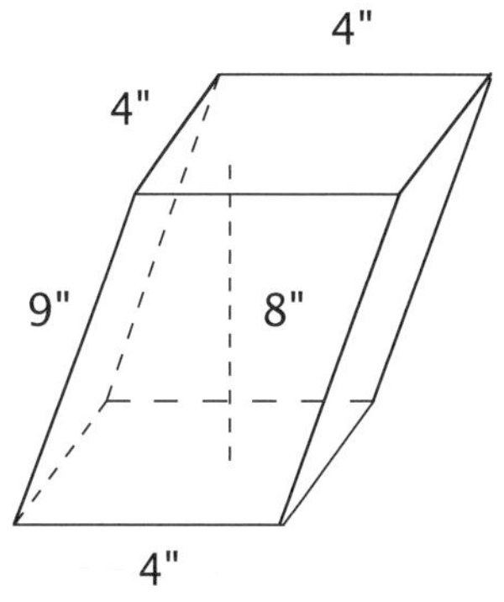

2. Find the surface area of the same oblique prism. Assume all four faces to be parallelograms, and use the altitude, or height, to find their areas.

3. Find the volume of an oblique prism whose bases are 3-4-5 right triangles. The length of the lateral edges is 15 and the altitude of the prism is 10. All measurements are in feet.

4. Find the surface area of the oblique prism described in #3. Assume all three faces to be parallelograms.

Here are some more volume and surface-area problems that may challenge you.

5. A cubic foot of copper is drawn into a wire .2 inches in diameter. What is the length of the wire in feet?

6. A rectangular piece of sheet metal containing 625 square inches is bent to form the sides of a cylinder nine inches in diameter. What is the height of the cylinder? What is the volume of the space enclosed by the cylinder? (Do not worry about the thickness of the sheet metal.)

7. An artist made a spherical Christmas-tree ornament four inches in diameter. She wants to make a cylindrical cardboard container in which the ornament will just fit. How many square inches of cardboard will be used? Do not worry about the thickness of the cardboard or the waste that results from cutting circles.

8. How many square inches of cardboard would be needed to make a cube-shaped box exactly the right size for the ornament in #8? Which would use the least cardboard, the cylinder or the cube?

Fill in the blanks.

1. If a right triangle has one 45° angle, the other angles will have measures of _______° and _______°.

2. Since a 45° right triangle has two congruent legs, it can be named an _________________ triangle.

3. The longest side of a right triangle is called the _________________ .

4. The sides opposite two 45° angles are _________________ in length.

5. To find the unknown side of any right triangle, use the _________________ theorem.

6. If a triangle is a 45°–45°–90° triangle, the longer side is always ________ times the leg.

Find the unknown sides of these right triangles.

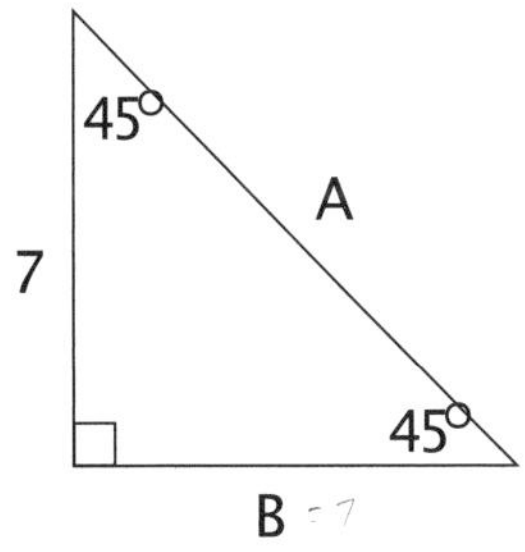

7. A = _________________

8. B = _________________

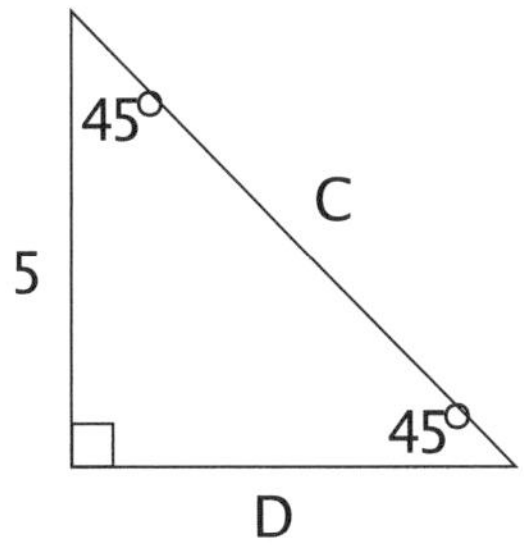

9. C = _________________

10. D = _________________

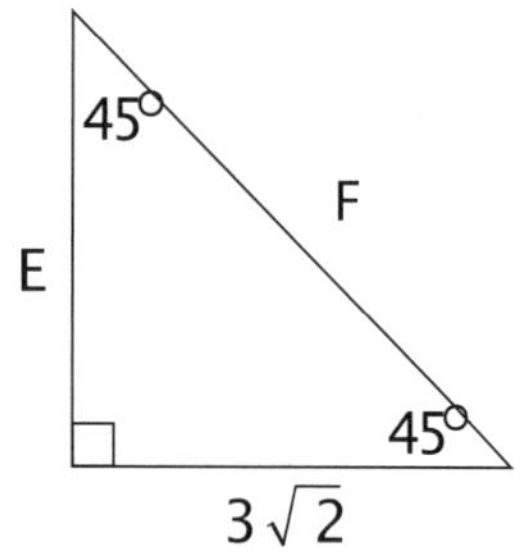

11. E = ____________

12. F = ____________

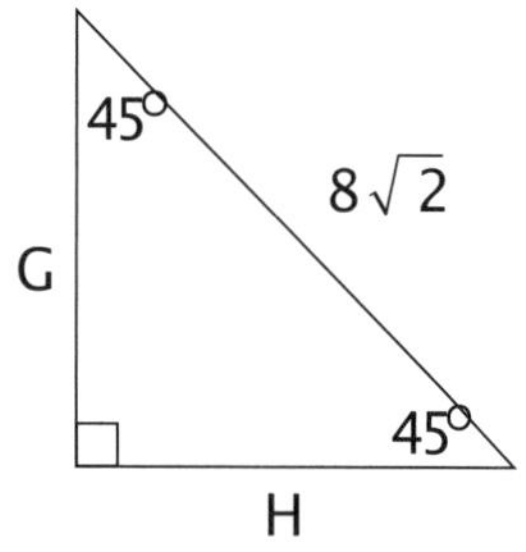

13. G = ____________

14. H = ____________

15. If ABCD is a square with one side equal to 10 cm, what is the length of $\overline{BD}$?

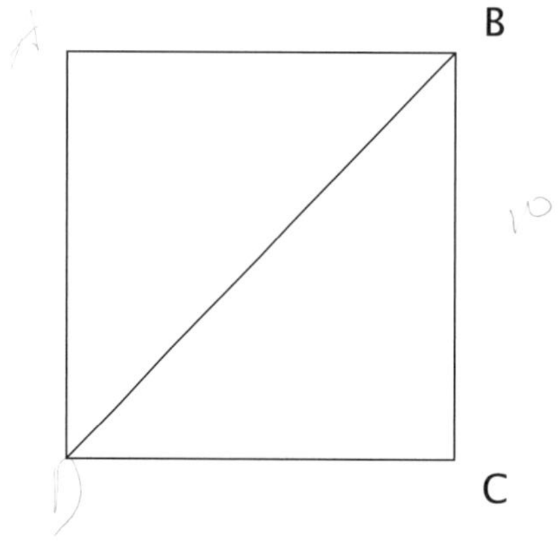

20B

True or false.

1. The side of a triangle opposite the smallest angle is called the hypotenuse.

2. The leg of a 45°–45°–90° triangle is always $\sqrt{2}$ times the hypotenuse.

3. It is possible to find the length of a leg of a 45°–45°–90° triangle if the hypotenuse is known.

4. The rule for the length of the sides of a 45°–45°–90° triangle is based on the Pythagorean theorem.

5. A 45°–45°–90° triangle is an equilateral triangle.

6. The hypotenuse of a 45°–45°–90° triangle is always $\sqrt{2}$ times the leg.

Find the unknown sides of these right triangles.

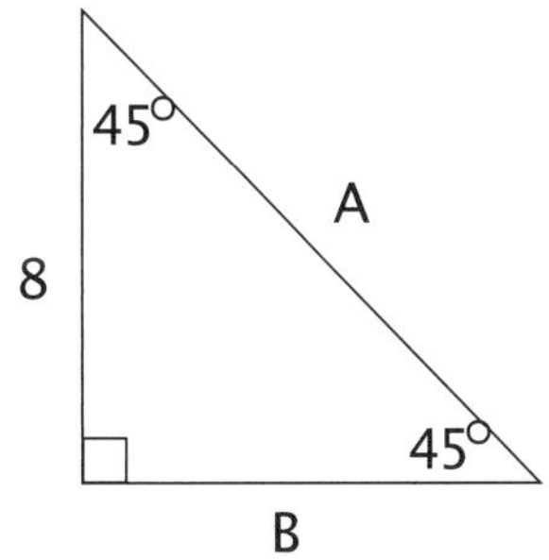

7. A = ________________

8. B = ________________

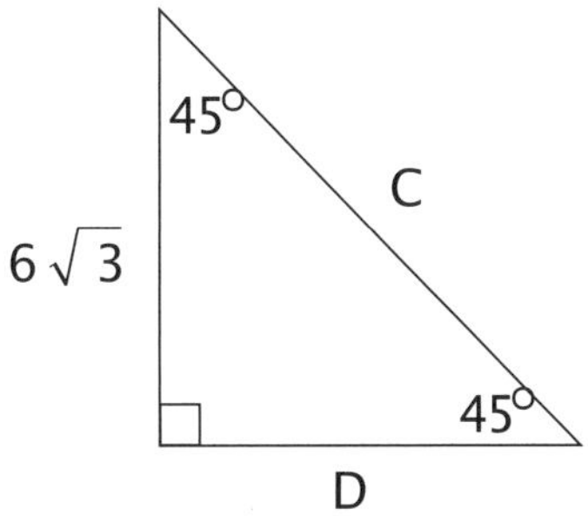

9. C = ________________

10. D = ________________

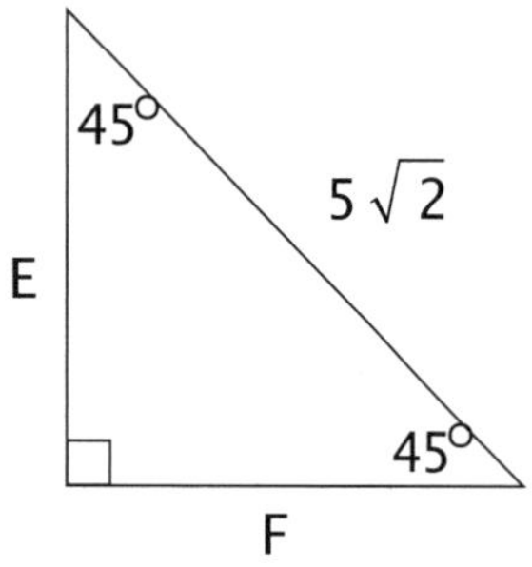

11. E = ________________

12. F = ________________

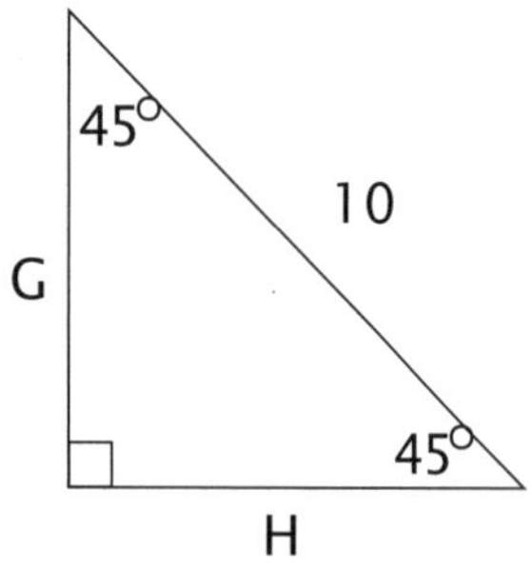

13. G = ________________

14. H = ________________

15. If ABCD is a square with $\overline{BD}$ equal to 14 cm, what is the length of $\overline{BC}$?

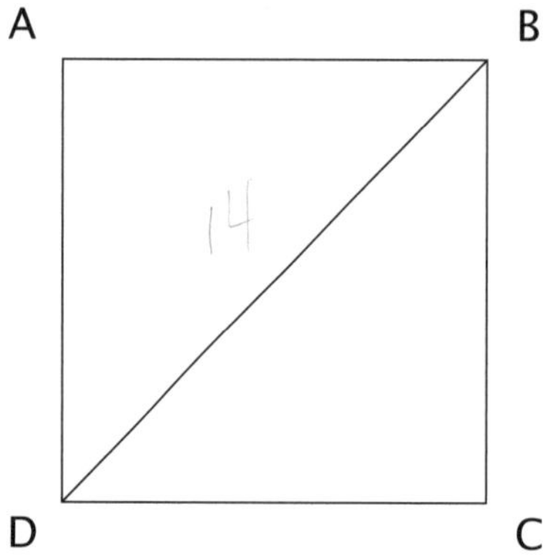

Find the unknown sides of the right triangles.

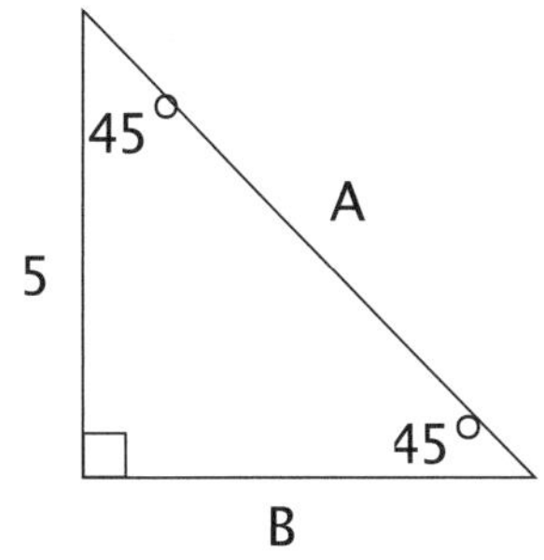

1. A = ______________

2. B = ______________

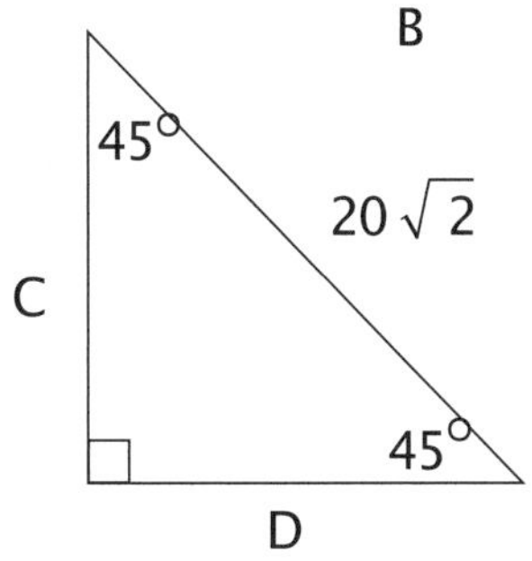

3. C = ______________

4. D = ______________

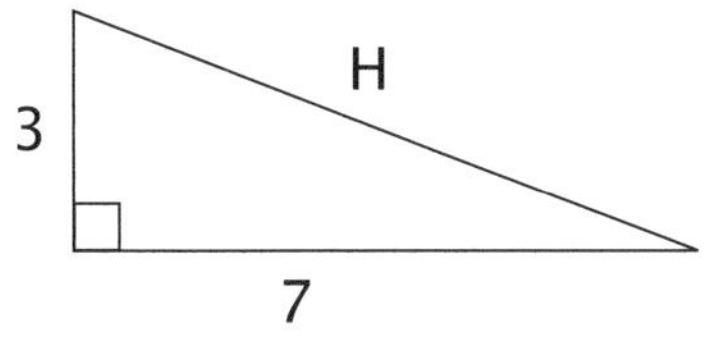

5. H = ______________

Simplify the radical expressions.

6. $(11\sqrt{40})(9\sqrt{5}) =$

7. $(2\sqrt{6})(10\sqrt{8}) =$

8. $\dfrac{5\sqrt{6}}{\sqrt{7}} - \dfrac{\sqrt{5}}{\sqrt{6}} =$

Follow the directions.

9. Construct a quadrilateral with two pairs of parallel sides of length 4 cm and 6 cm and one pair of opposite angles each measuring 123°.

10. What are the measures of the other two angles in #9?

11. What is the area of the figure in #9 if the height is 3.5 cm? (Use the longer side for the base.)

Follow the directions.

12. What is the measure of each interior angle in a pentagon?

13. A cone has a radius of 62 mm and a height of 52 mm. What is the area of its base?

14. What is the circumference of the base of the cone in #13?

15. Find the volume of a sphere with a radius of one meter.

16. What fraction of a circle is a sector with a 120° measure?

17. If the circle in #16 has a radius of three, what is the area of the sector?

Follow the steps below to find the area of the regular polygon.

18. Find the area of one triangle. How many triangles of the same size will fit in the pentagon?

19. Multiply to find the area of the pentagon.

20. What is the perimeter of the pentagon?

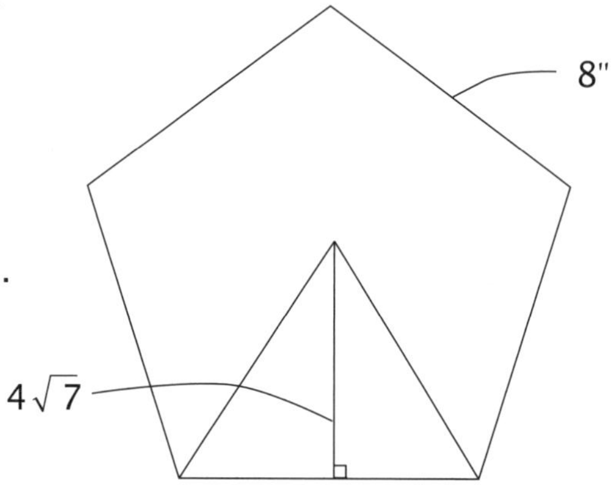

The length of each side is 8". The apothem (⊥ line from side to center) is $4\sqrt{7}$ ".

20D

Find the unknown sides of the right triangles.

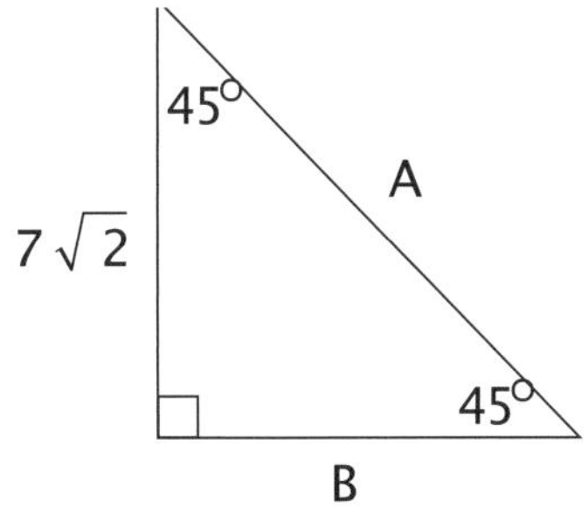

1. A = ______________

2. B = ______________

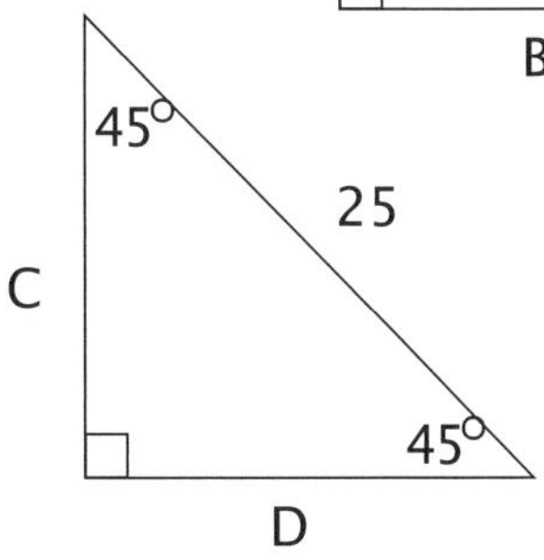

3. C = ______________

4. D = ______________

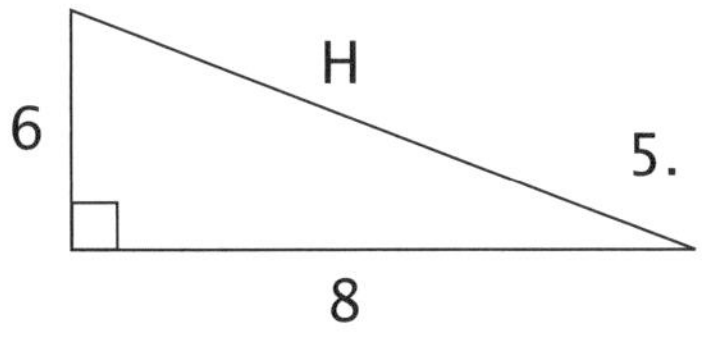

5. H = ______________

Simplify the radical expressions.

6. $(12\sqrt{3})(4\sqrt{18}) =$

7. $(4\sqrt{5})(20\sqrt{2}) =$

8. $\frac{2\sqrt{25}}{\sqrt{5}} + \frac{\sqrt{5}}{\sqrt{25}} =$

Follow the directions.

9. Construct a quadrilateral with four right angles, one pair of opposite sides each measuring 1¾ inches and the other pair of sides one-half as long.

10. What is the perimeter of the figure in #9?

Follow the directions.

11. Give the formula for the volume of a sphere.

12. What is the measure of each interior angle in an octagon?

13. A cone has a radius of 8.3 cm and a height of 12.4 cm. What is its volume?

14. What is the name of a chord that goes through the center of a circle?

15. Find the volume of a cylinder with a radius of 8 cm and a height of 12 cm.

16. What is the surface area of the figure in #15?

17. What fraction of a circle is a sector with a 60° measure?

18. If the circle in #17 has a radius of four units, what is the area of the sector?

Find the area and perimeter of the figure.

19. A = ______________

20. P = ______________

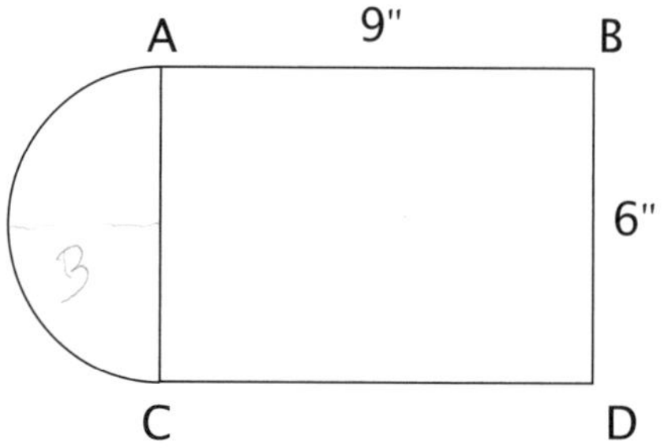

Given: $\overline{AC}$ is a diameter.

Find the unknown sides of the right triangles.

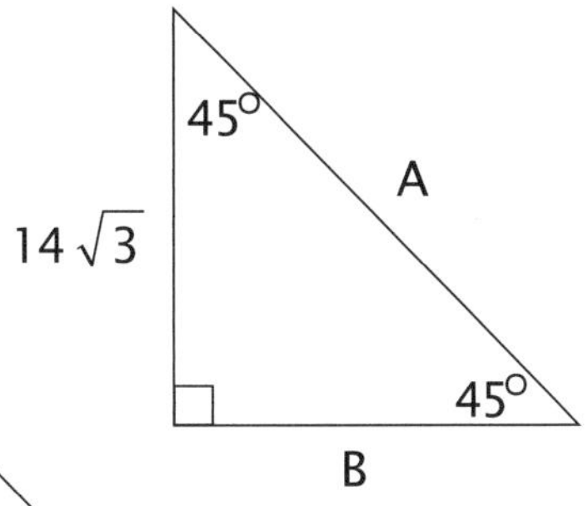

1. A = ______________

2. B = ______________

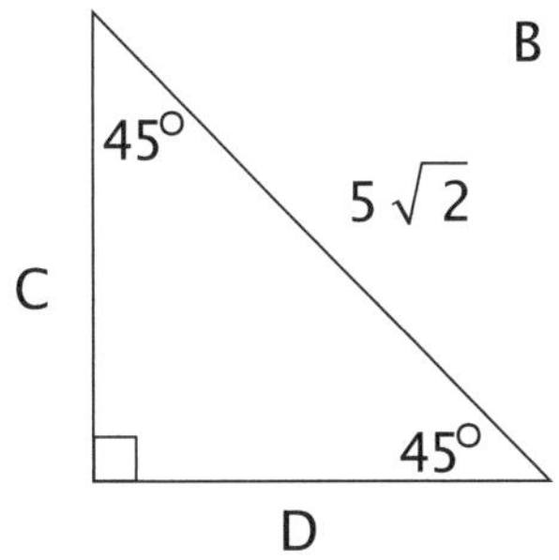

3. C = ______________

4. D = ______________

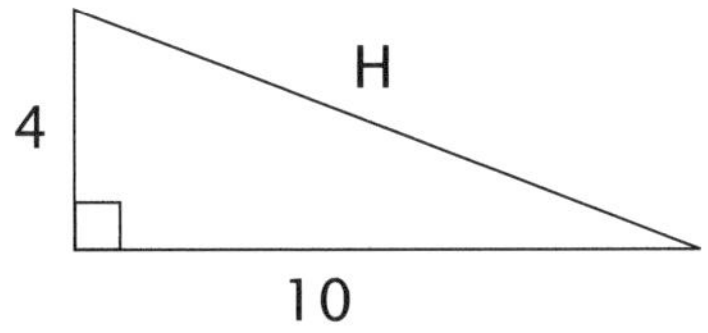

5. H = ______________

Simplify the radical expressions.

6. $(10\sqrt{2})(3\sqrt{8}) =$

7. $(4\sqrt{7})(6\sqrt{3}) =$

8. $\frac{2\sqrt{16}}{\sqrt{2}} + \frac{\sqrt{2}}{\sqrt{16}} =$

Follow the directions.

9. Draw an arc with a measure of 210°.

10. Name a solid with two congruent, parallel bases and lateral surfaces that are parallelograms.

11. What is the area of a trapezoid with bases of 10 and 12 and a height of 13?

12. What is the measure of each interior angle in a decagon?

Follow the directions.

13. A one-dimensional figure with length but no width is a ____________ .

14. Complete: If two parallel lines are cut by a transversal, corresponding . . .

15. In the figure at right, a circle with center O is circumscribed about a square. What is the circumference of the circle?

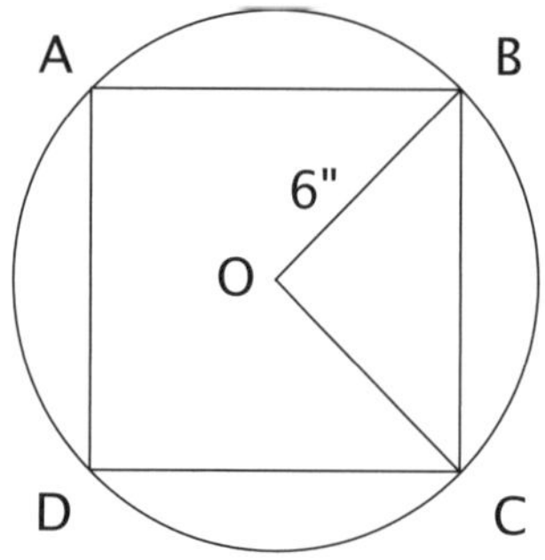

16. Given your answer for #15, find the length of minor arc BC.

17. How long is the major arc BC?

Sharpen your algebra skills!

When factoring polynomials with coefficients, first look for a greatest common factor (GCF).

EXAMPLE 1 $2X^2 + 4X + 2 = 2(X^2 + 2X + 1) = 2(X + 1)(X + 1)$

EXAMPLE 2 $4X^2 + 11X + 6 = (4X + 3)(X + 2)$
No GCF—examine carefully to find the pattern.

Factor the polynomials.

18. $7X^2 + 28X + 28 =$

19. $3X^2 + 15X - 18 =$

20. $2X^2 + 11X + 5 =$

A vector is a line that shows both direction and speed. Vectors are used in navigation of airplanes and ships, as well as in physics problems involving force and direction. In more advanced math courses, you will learn how to work with vectors using trigonometric functions. For now, we will use your geometry skills to solve simple vector problems.

Follow the directions.

1. Imagine that a man sets out to fly his small plane in a straight line to a city that is 300 miles east of his starting point. (This is called due east.) If he flies at a speed of 150 miles an hour, how long should the trip take?

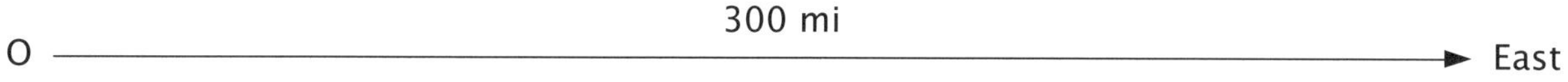

2. The man in #1 flew for the computed length of time, but when he looked for the airport, it was nowhere in sight. Assume his math was correct, and see whether you can guess what caused the problem.

As you may have guessed, the plane was blown off course by the wind. The pilot could have adjusted for the wind by drawing a vector before starting and changing the heading of the plane.

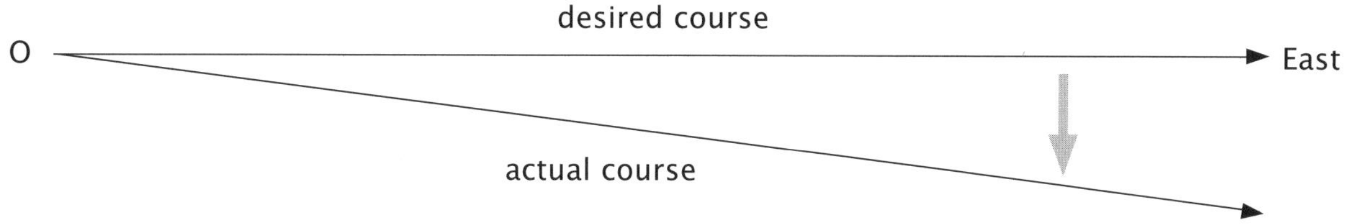

Vector lines are drawn to a chosen scale and always point in a given direction. We will use millimeters because it is easier than working with fractions of an inch. For this lesson, let one millimeter equal two miles per hour.

3. The wind was blowing south at 30 miles an hour. The letter O represents the pilots starting point. The direction of the line OW represents the direction of the wind, and the length of segment OW represents the speed of the wind. Since the line represents both direction and speed, it is a vector. At 1 mm = 2 mph, how long should the vector OW be?

4. The pilot plans to fly at 150 miles an hour. How long should you make the vector that represents his speed? (This is the distance from O to P.)

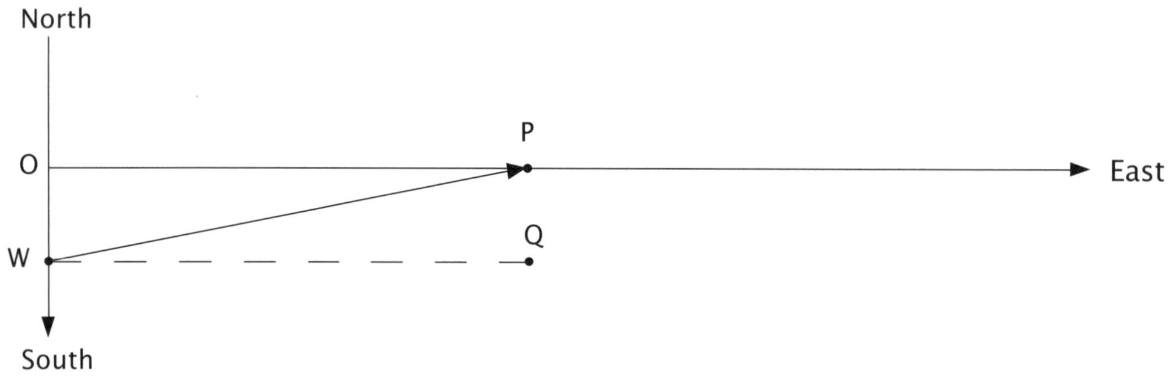

The vector OP represents the route the pilot wishes to travel. The vector OW represents where the wind wants to take the plane. The addition of the two vectors is vector WP. This represents the direction the pilot should set his compass to in order to end up at his desired destination.

5. Measure angle OWP on the drawing above. (Angle PWQ represents the number of degrees north of due east the pilot should set his course, so without drawing line WQ, we could express this number as 90° minus the measure of angle OWP. If the pilot sets his course correctly, the wind will blow him back to his destination at P, as shown below.)

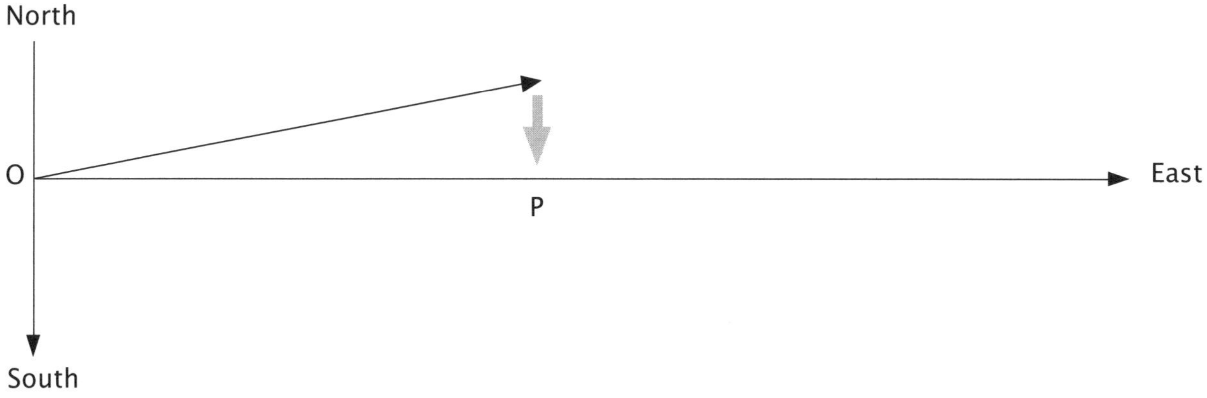

6. A pilot wishes to fly due east to a city that is 560 miles away. The wind is blowing south at 40 miles an hour, and the pilot plans to fly at an airspeed of 150 miles an hour. Use the procedure above to find how many degrees north of due east he should set his course. (Let 1 mm = 2 mph.)

21A

Fill in the blanks.

1. If a right triangle has one 30° angle, the other angles will have measures of _______° and _______°.

2. Since a 30°-60°-90° triangle has sides of three different lengths, it can be named a(n) __________________ triangle.

3. The hypotenuse of a 30°-60°-90° triangle is _________ times the short leg.

4. The long leg of a 30°-60°-90° triangle is _________ times the short leg.

5. To find the unknown side of any right triangle, use the __________________ theorem.

6. If the hypotenuse of a 30°-60°-90° triangle is known, divide by _________ to find the short leg, and then __________________ that answer by _________ to find the long leg.

Find the unknown sides of these right triangles.

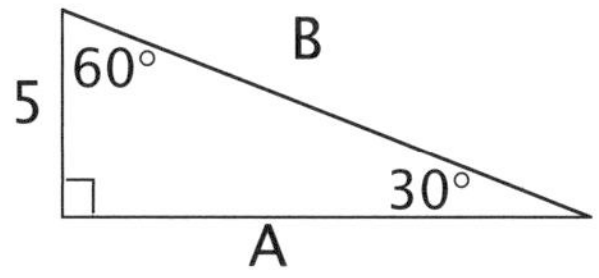

7. A = ______________

8. B = ______________

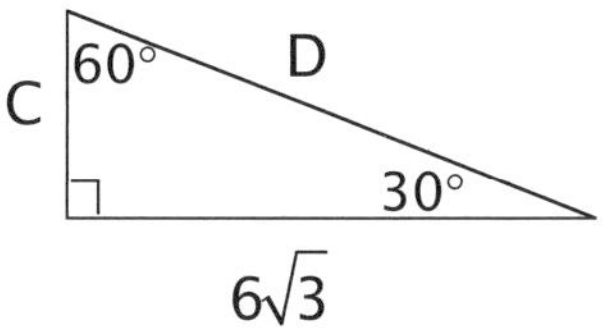

9. C = ______________

10. D = ______________

Find the unknown sides of these right triangles.

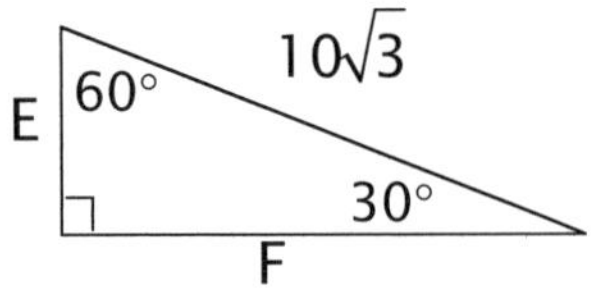

11. E = ______________

12. F = ______________

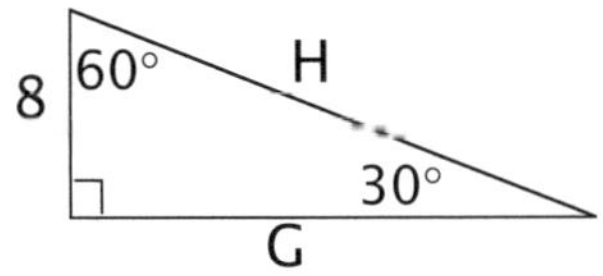

13. G = ______________

14. H = ______________

15. ABCD is a rectangle. $\overline{BC} = 3$, $\overline{BD} = 6$, and $\overline{DC} = 3\sqrt{3}$. What are the measures of angles 1 and 2?

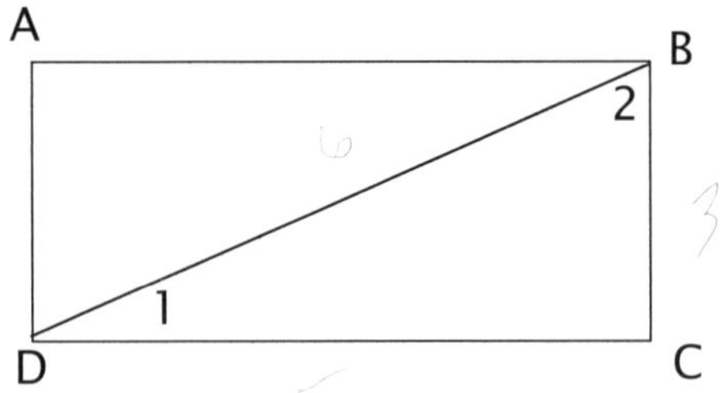

LESSON PRACTICE

21B

True or false.

1. The hypotenuse is always opposite a 30° angle.

2. The long leg of a 30°-60°-90° triangle is always two times the hypotenuse.

3. If the length of one side of a 30°-60°-90° triangle is known, it is possible to find the lengths of both of the other sides.

4. The long leg of a 30°-60°-90° triangle is $\sqrt{2}$ times the short leg.

5. The Pythagorean theorem works for all right triangles.

6. The side opposite the 90° angle is the longest side of a right triangle.

Find the unknown sides of these right triangles.

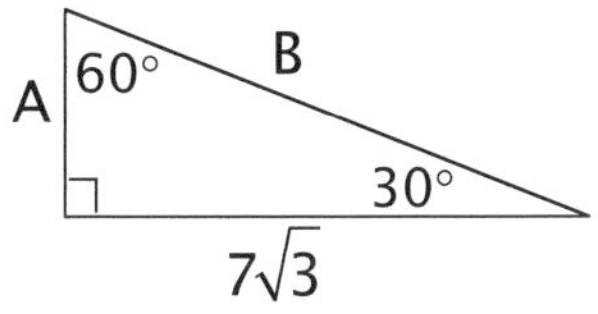

7. A = ______________

8. B = ______________

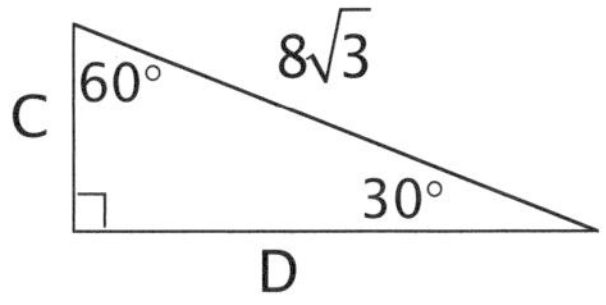

9. C = ______________

10. D = ______________

Find the unknown sides of these right triangles.

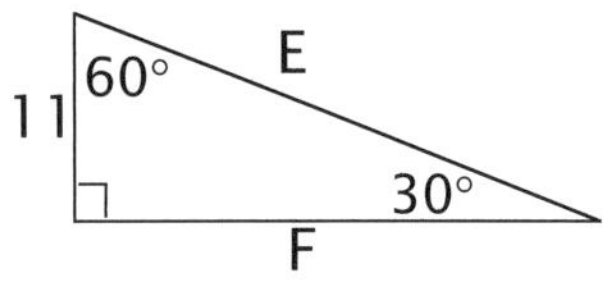

11. E = ______________

12. F = ______________

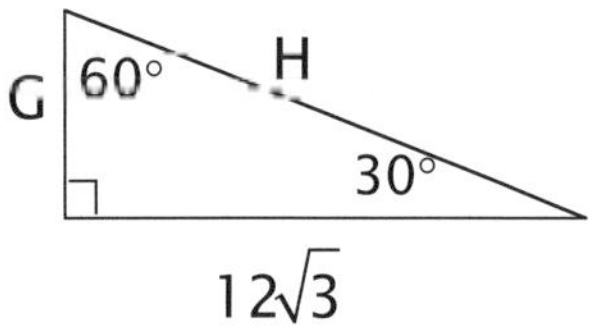

13. G = ______________

14. H = ______________

15. What is the length of the radius $\overline{AB}$ of the circle?

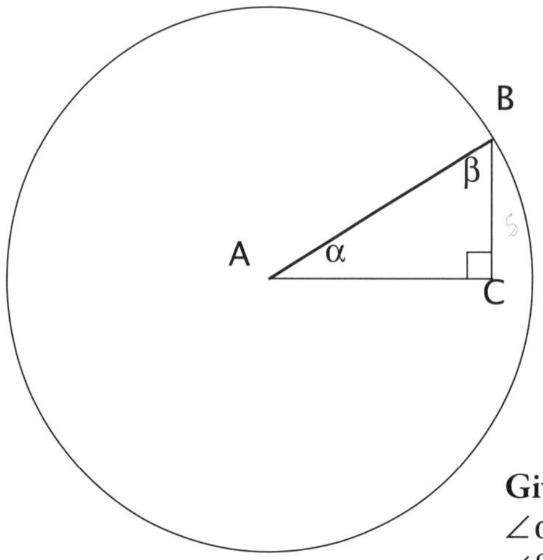

Given:
$\angle\alpha = 30°$
$\angle\beta = 60°$

$\overline{BC} = 5$ cm

21C

Find the unknown sides of the right triangles.

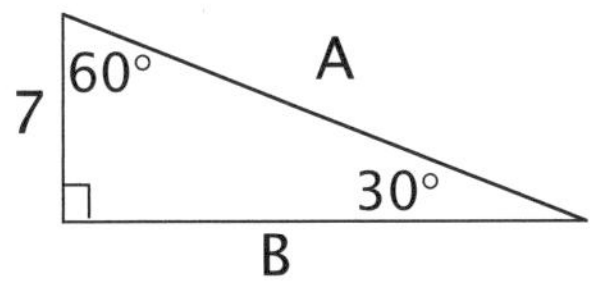

1. A = ______________

2. B = ______________

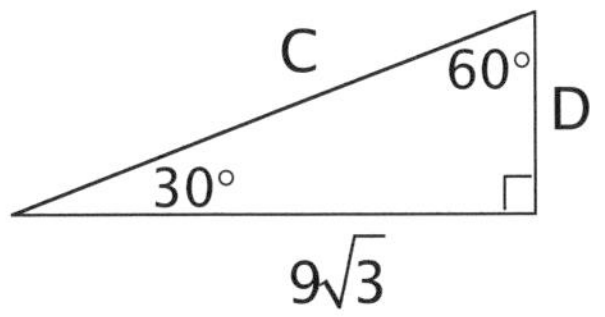

3. C = ______________

4. D = ______________

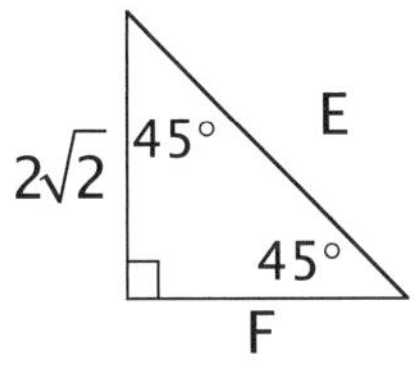

5. E = ______________

6. F = ______________

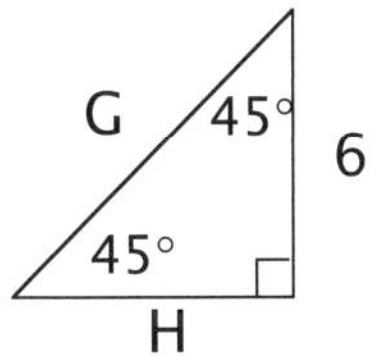

7. G = ______________

8. H = ______________

Simplify the radical expressions.

9. $\left(10\sqrt{20}\right)\left(2\sqrt{7}\right) =$

10. $3\sqrt{5} + 4\sqrt{5} =$

11. $\dfrac{4\sqrt{8}}{\sqrt{4}} + \dfrac{\sqrt{5}}{\sqrt{16}} =$

Follow the directions.

12. A right triangle has legs of lengths 22 and 16. Find the length of the hypotenuse.

13. The formula for the surface area of a sphere is $4\pi r^2$. What is the surface area of a sphere with a radius of 1.5 inches?

14. Draw a circle with two parallel tangents.

15. Find the number of sides of a regular polygon if the measure of each interior angle is 140°.

16. What is the circumference of a circle with a radius of seven inches?

17. What fraction of a circle is a 180° arc?

18. Use your answers to #16 and #17 to find the length of an 180° arc if the radius of the circle is seven inches.

For #19–20: Figures include semicircles, and lines that appear parallel are parallel.

19. Find the area of figure 1.

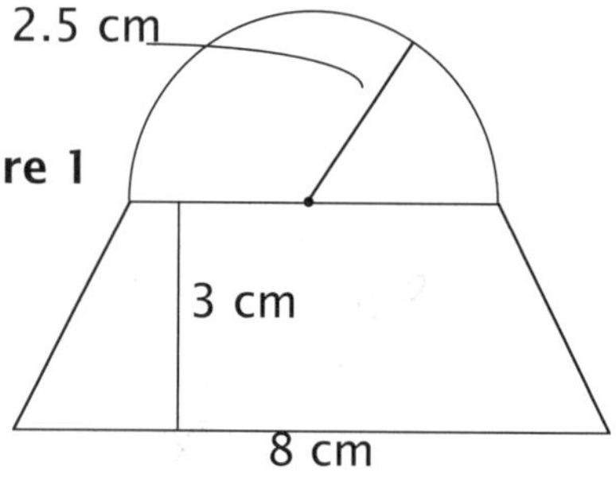

Figure 1

20. Find the perimeter of figure 2.

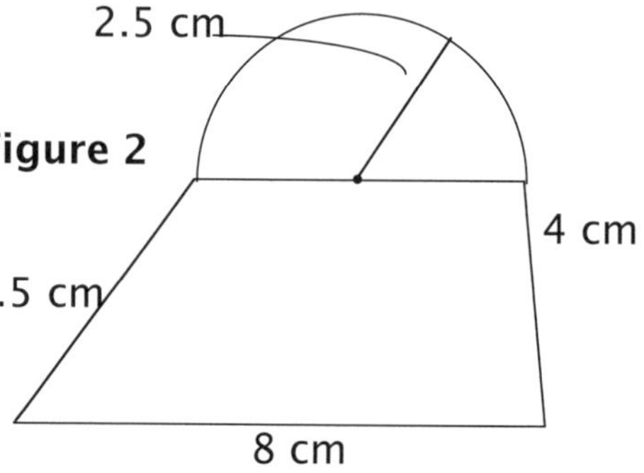

Figure 2

SYSTEMATIC REVIEW 21D

Find the unknown sides of the right triangles.

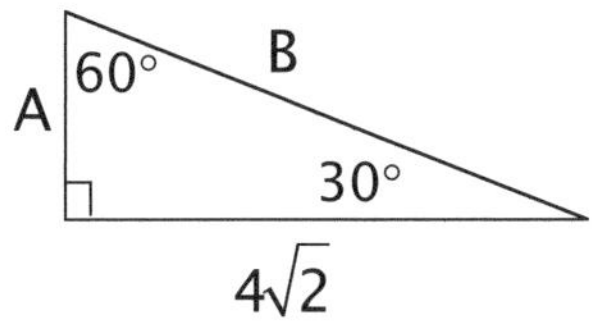

1. A = ________________

2. B = ________________

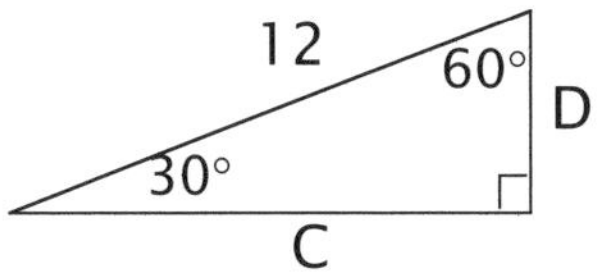

3. C = ________________

4. D = ________________

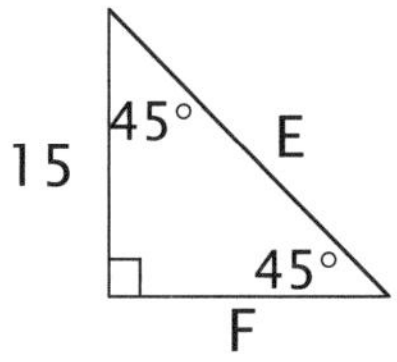

5. E = ________________

6. F = ________________

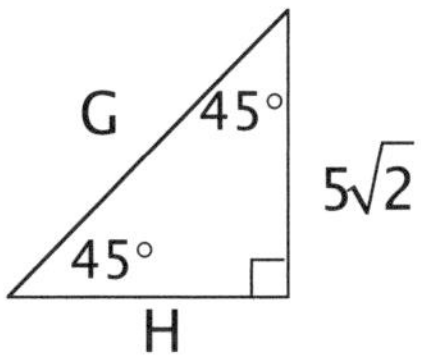

7. G = ________________

8. H = ________________

Simplify the radical expressions.

9. $\left(4\sqrt{4}\right)\left(2\sqrt{4}\right) =$

10. $2\sqrt{18} + 5\sqrt{9} =$

11. $\dfrac{3\sqrt{6}}{\sqrt{7}} + \dfrac{4\sqrt{6}}{\sqrt{5}} =$

12. A right triangle has a leg with a measure of 13 and a hypotenuse with a measure of 17. What is the measure of the other leg?

13. The formula for the surface area of a sphere is $4\pi r^2$. What is the surface area of a sphere with a diameter of four inches?

14. Draw a circle intersected by a secant.

15. Find the number of sides of a regular polygon if the measure of each interior angle is 150º.

16. What is the circumference of a circle with a radius of four inches?

17. What fraction of a circle is a 270º arc?

18. Use your answers to #16 and #17 to find the length of a 270º arc if the radius of the circle is four inches.

19. Find the volume of the prism.

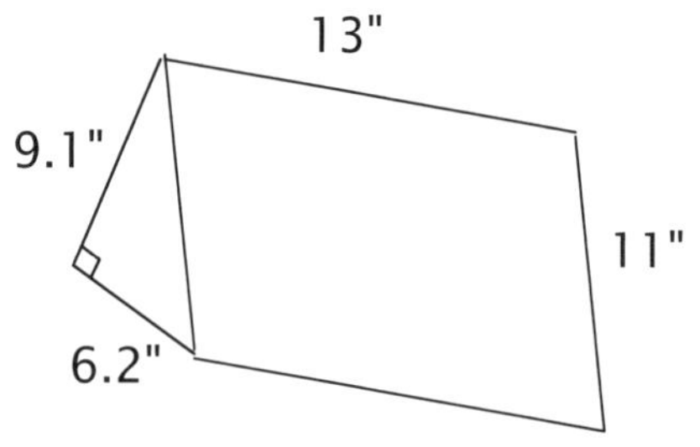

20. Find the area of the figure to the right.

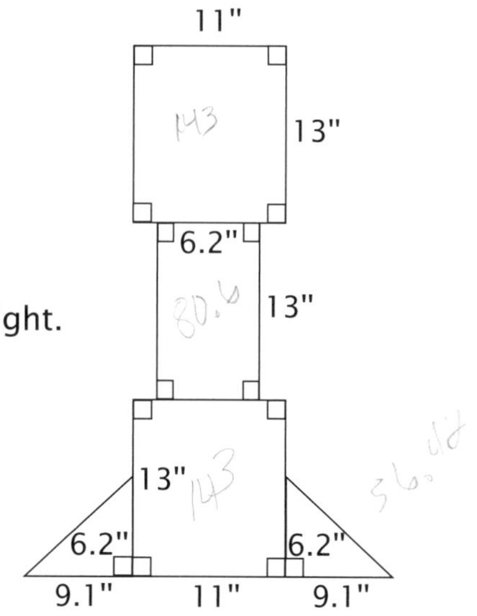

SYSTEMATIC REVIEW 21E

Find the unknown sides of the right triangles.

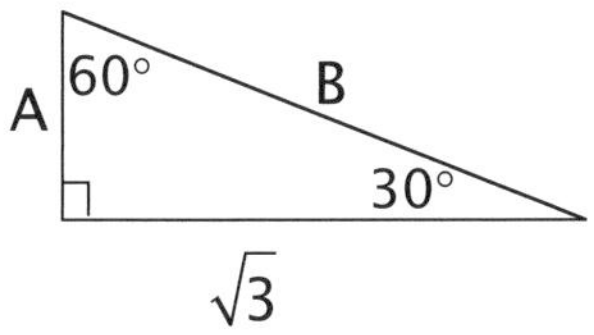

1. A = ______________

2. B = ______________

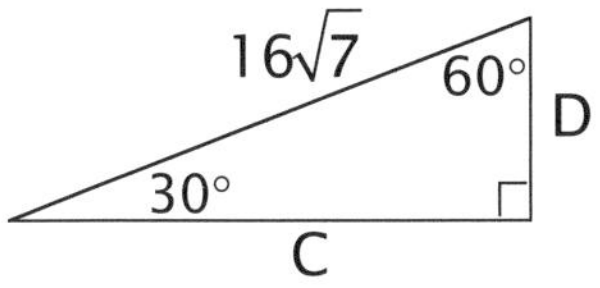

3. C = ______________

4. D = ______________

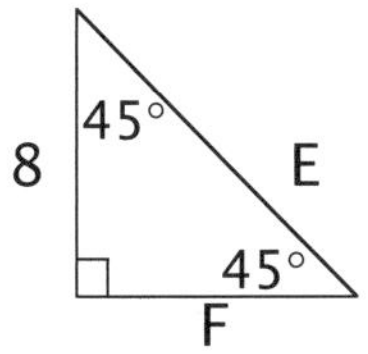

5. E = ______________

6. F = ______________

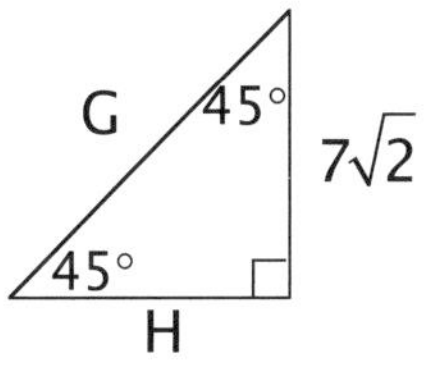

7. G = ______________

8. H = ______________

Simplify the radical expressions.

9. $\left(3\sqrt{10}\right)\left(7\sqrt{10}\right) =$

10. $5\sqrt{7} + 4\sqrt{3} =$

11. $\dfrac{10\sqrt{18}}{2\sqrt{6}} =$

Follow the directions.

12. A right triangle has a leg with a measure of 11 and a hypotenuse with a measure of 22. What is the measure of the other leg?

13. What is the area of the triangle described in #12?

14. Find the area of a regular hexagon with an apothem of 14 inches and a side length of $5\sqrt{11}$ inches.

15. Find the volume of a swimming pool with a diameter of 12 ft and a height of 4 ft. (Think of the pool as a cylinder.)

16. If a cubic foot of water weighs 62 pounds, what would the water weigh if the pool in #15 was full to the brim?

17. Use your answer from #16 to find how much the water in the pool described in #15 weighs in tons. (1 ton = 2,000 lb)

Sharpen your algebra skills!

Use your algebra and geometry skills to find the unknown sides of these triangles.

EXAMPLE

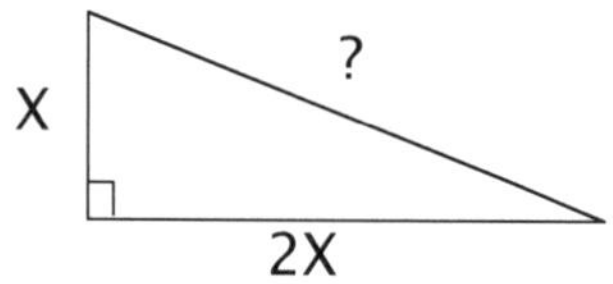

$(2X)^2 + X^2 = H^2$ (Pythagorean theorem)

$4X^2 + X^2 = H^2$

$5X^2 = H^2$

$X\sqrt{5} = H$

18.

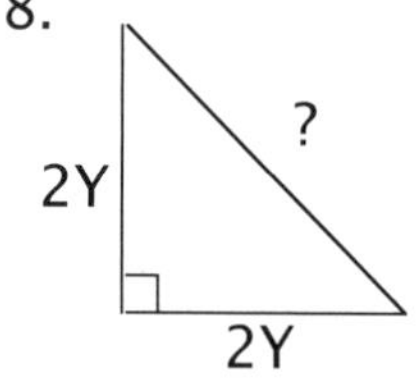

19.

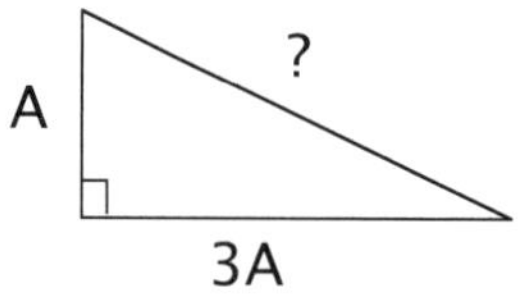

20.

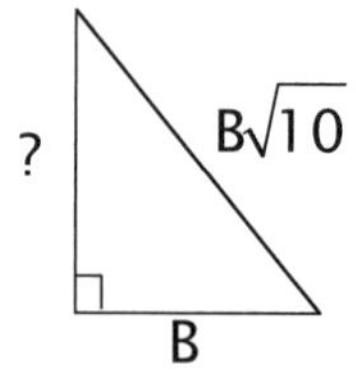

We can often use what we already know about geometry, along with our algebra skills, to find useful shortcuts for practical problems. For example, to find the area of the ring shown below, you would probably want to know the radius of each circle. Then you could find the area of each circle, and subtract the area of the smaller from the larger to find the area of the ring.

You might be surprised to know that you can compute the area of the ring from the length of the chord of the large circle that is tangent to the small circle. Follow the directions below to see how this works.

Follow the directions. Be sure to read all the given statements under the drawing.

1. The area of the larger circle can be written as πx^2. Write the area of the smaller circle.

2. Write the area of the ring as the difference between the areas of the two circles: A =

3. A tangent line is perpendicular to the radius at the point at which it touches a circle, so we know that CDF is a right triangle. The hypotenuse is the radius of the large circle, so we know it has a length of x. The short leg of the triangle has a length of y. Use what you know about the Pythagorean theorem to express z^2 in terms of x and y.

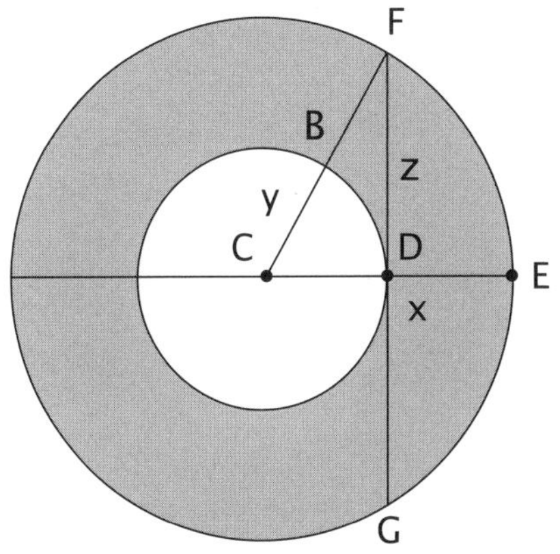

Given:
C is the center of both circles.
$\overline{FG}$ is tangent to the smaller circle at D.
$\overline{CE}$ is a radius of the larger circle. We will call its length x.
$\overline{CB}$ is a radius of the smaller circle. We will call its length y.
z is the length of $\overline{FD}$.

4. Go back to your answer to #2, and use the distributive property to rewrite the area of the ring as times a quantity in parentheses.

5. Compare your answers to #3 and #4. Rewrite the formula for the area of the ring in terms of z. You may want to check your results in the answer key before working the following problems.

6. The length of the chord in the drawing on the right is 10 inches. What is the area of the shaded ring? (Remember that z is one-half the length of the chord.)

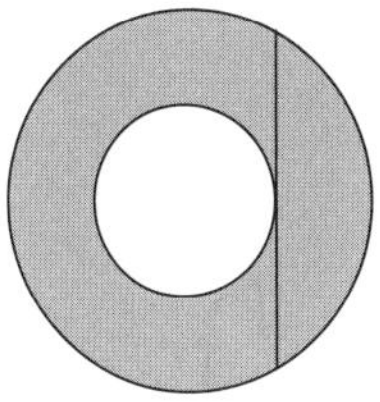

Peter has a roll of tickets on a spool. The paper is .007" thick and the tickets are each two inches long. The length of a chord tangent to the spool is eight inches. Peter wants to find out how many tickets are left on the roll.

7. Use the formula you learned above to find the surface area of the ring made by the edges of the tickets.

8. Imagine unrolling the tickets to form a very long, very thin rectangle. We found the area of the edge of the tickets in #7. Divide the area by the width (the thickness of the tickets) to find the length of the unrolled tickets. Round your answer to the nearest inch.

9. Now you only need to divide by the length of one ticket to find about how many tickets are on the roll.

Note: In real life, accuracy will be affected by factors such as how tightly the tickets are wound on the roll.

LESSON PRACTICE 22A

Fill in the blanks.

1. An observation that one assumes to be true is called an ________________ or a ________________ .

2. Statements that can be proven true are called ________________ .

3. All of the statements listed in this lesson also have ________________ that are true.

4. Vertical angles are ________________ .

5. A ________________ divides an angle into two congruent parts.

6. If two parallel lines are cut by a transversal, corresponding angles are ________________ .

7. If two angles have equal measures, they are ________________ .

8. The measures of the interior angles of a triangle add up to ________________ .

9. Two lines that are coplanar and don't intersect are ________________.

10. The measures of the exterior angles of a regular polygon add up to ________________ .

Write the converses of the following:

11. If two parallel lines are cut by a transversal, alternate interior angles are congruent.
    Converse:

12. A parallelogram has two pairs of parallel sides.
    Converse:

13. If a figure is a right triangle, leg squared plus leg squared equals hypotenuse squared.
    Converse:

14. Two lines that intersect and form a right angle are perpendicular.
    Converse:

15. A trapezoid has only one pair of parallel sides.
    Converse:

State the property being described.

16. If A = B, then B = A.

17. A = A.

18. If A = B and B = C, then A = C.

22B

Fill in the blanks.

1. An axiom or postulate is an observation that one ________________ to be true.

2. Statements that can be ________________ true are called "theorems."

3. If the order of a statement can be reversed successfully, then its ________________ is also true.

4. A(n) ________________ triangle has two congruent sides.

5. If two parallel lines are cut by a ________________ , alternate interior angles are ________________ .

6. Two angles whose measures add up to 90° are ________________ .

7. The measures of the ________________ angles of a regular polygon add up to 360°.

8. A ________________ divides a line segment into two congruent segments.

9. A ________________ has four right angles and two pairs of parallel sides.

10. A ________________ has four right angles, four congruent sides, and two pairs of parallel sides.

Write the converses of the following:

11. Two angles whose measures add up to 180° are supplementary
    Converse:

12. A parallelogram has two pairs of parallel sides.
    Converse:

13. If two parallel lines are cut by a transversal, alternate exterior angles are congruent.
    Converse:

14. If two line segments have equal lengths, they are congruent.
    Converse:

15. A rhombus has four congruent sides and two pairs of parallel sides.
    Converse:

State the property being described.

16. If A = B and B = C, then A = C.

17. If A = B, then B = A.

18. A = A.

Fill in the blanks or complete the statements.

1. Postulates are ________________ assumptions.

2. Vertical angles are ________________ .

3. If two parallel lines are cut by a transversal, then...

4. If a triangle has sides A, B, and C, and A ≤ B ≤ C, then...

5. The measures of the ________________ ________________ of a triangle add up to 180º.

6. The property of symmetry states...

Find the unknown sides of the right triangles.

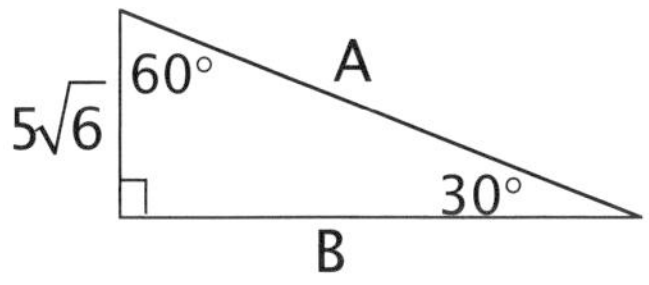

7. A = ______________

8. B = ______________

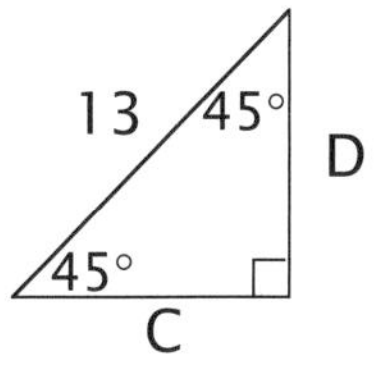

9. C = ______________

10. D = ______________

Follow the directions.

11. Write in numerical form and simplify: two times the square root of three, divided by the square root of five.

12. A right triangle has a leg with length 13 and a hypotenuse with length 17. Find the length of the other leg.

13. Find the number of sides of a regular polygon if the measure of each interior angle is 120°.

14. Find the length of a 150° arc in a circle with a radius of 10".

15. Find the area of a 150° sector in a circle with a radius of 10".

16. Find the area of a regular octagon with an apothem of 10" and a side length of $3\sqrt{13}$". (Remember that the apothem is a line segment drawn from the center that is perpendicular to one side of the polygon.)

17. Find the volume of a swimming pool with a diameter of 15' and a height of 4'.

18. Find the weight of the water in the pool in #17 if the pool is full of water. (62 lb per ft^3)

19. How many tons does the water in the pool weigh?

20. Find the volume of the rocket. The radius is 14', the height of the cylinder is 17' and the height of the cone is 16.5'.

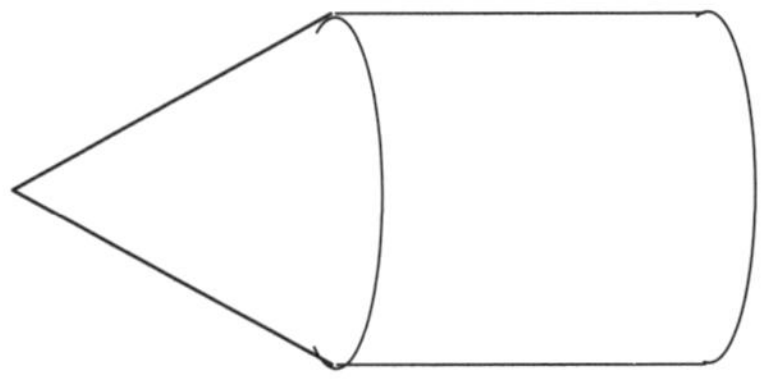

22D

Fill in the blanks or complete the statements.

1. Theorems are ________________ using axioms and postulates.

2. Two angles that have equal measures are ________________ .

3. If a triangle has two congruent sides, then it is a(n) ________________ triangle.

4. A quadrilateral with four right angles and four congruent sides is a ________________ .

5. The measures of the exterior angles of a polygon add up to ______°.

6. The reflexive property states that ...

Find the unknown sides of the right triangles.

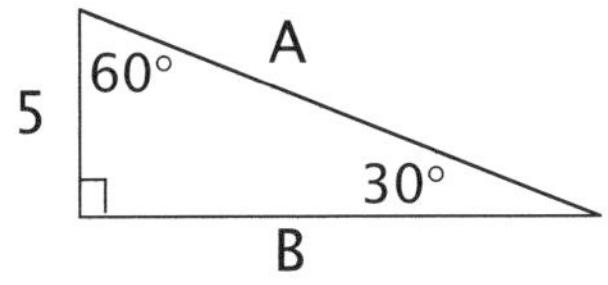

7. A = ______________

8. B = ______________

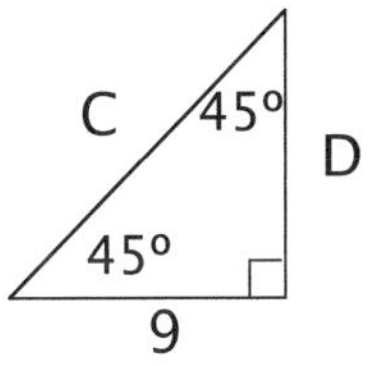

9. C = ______________

10. D = ______________

Follow the directions.

11. A right triangle has sides of 16 and 12. What is the length of its hypotenuse?

12. Find the area of the triangle in #11.

13. Find the number of sides of a regular polygon if the measure of each interior angle is 150°.

Follow the directions.

14. Draw a circle with a chord which is not its diameter.

15. Find the area of a regular decagon with an apothem of 25" and a side length of $6\sqrt{13}$".

16. Find the volume of a swimming pool with a diameter of 18' and a height of 4'.

17. Find the weight of the water in the pool in #16 if the pool is full of water. (62 lb per ft^3)

18. How many tons does the water weigh in the pool in #16?

19. Find the surface area of the figure shown.

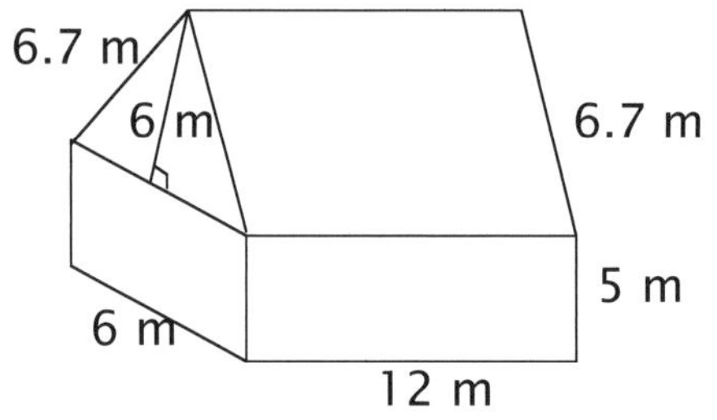

20. Find the volume of the figure shown.

Fill in the blanks or complete the statements.

1. A quadrilateral with four right angles is a _______________ .

2. Two lines that intersect and form a _______________ _______________ are perpendicular.

3. If a parallelogram has four congruent sides, then it is a _______________ .

4. Two angles whose measures add up to 180° are said to be _______________ .

5. Two angles with _______________ _______________ are congruent.

6. The transitive property states ...

Find the unknown sides of the right triangles.

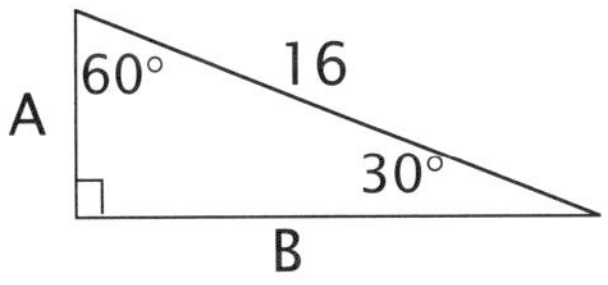

7. A = _______________

8. B = _______________

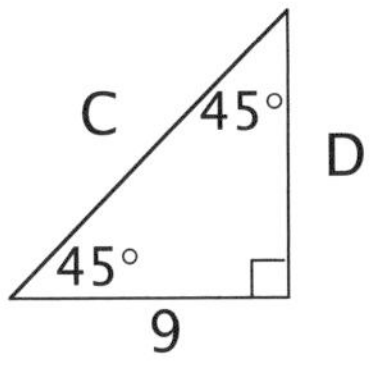

9. C = _______________

10. D = _______________

Follow the directions.

11. Write in numerical form and simplify: the square root of six, divided by four times the square root of eight.

12. A right triangle has a leg with length 48 and a hypotenuse with length 50. Find the length of the other leg.

Follow the directions.

13. Find the length of a 360° arc of a circle with a radius of 6".

14. Find the area of a 360° sector of a circle with a radius of 6".

15. Find the area of a regular pentagon with an apothem of 22" and a side length of $8\sqrt{10}$".

16. Find the volume of a swimming pool with a diameter of 24' and a height of 4'.

17. Find the weight of the water in the pool in #16 in pounds and tons. (62 lb per ft^3)

Sharpen your algebra skills!

Binomials involving the difference of two squares may be factored as in example 1 below. This works with the *difference* of two perfect squares, but the *sum* of two perfect squares cannot be factored in this way. Sometimes an expression may be factored more than once (repeated factoring), as in example 2.

EXAMPLE 1 $X^2 - 4 = (X - 2)(X + 2)$

EXAMPLE 2 $X^4 - 16 = (X^2 - 4)(X^2 + 4) = (X - 2)(X + 2)(X^2 + 4)$

Find all possible factors.

18. $X^4 - 81 =$

19. $X^3 - 9X =$

20. $X^4 - 25X^2 =$

Logical thinking is very important in proving geometric theorems. The ancient Greeks developed rules for thinking logically that are still used today. Although your text does not stress the formal rules of logic, you may come across them in advanced courses. Here is an introduction to some of the most important concepts.

A person may reach a conclusion based on either inductive or deductive reasoning. Inductive reasoning starts with general observations and comes to a specific conclusion based on those observations. The conclusion may or may not be true.

EXAMPLE 1 I have only observed red roses. Therefore, all roses are red. Why is my conclusion faulty? There may be roses of a different color that I have not seen.

Note that some inductive reasoning may produce true results. If I visit my uncle's home many times over the years and only see or hear about girl cousins, it is fairly safe to conclude that my uncle has no boys. However, I have not proved it conclusively.

Deductive reasoning starts with a known fact and reaches a conclusion step by step, using the rules of logic. This is the kind of reasoning you will use when doing geometric proofs. The formal reasoning process is called a syllogism. It consists of a major premise, a minor premise, and a conclusion.

EXAMPLE 2 - A syllogism: Everyone in the Smith family has red hair. (major premise)
Rose is in the Smith family. (minor premise)
Rose has red hair.(conclusion)

EXAMPLE 3 - Geometric syllogism: A rectangle has four right angles. (major premise)
ABCD is a rectangle. (minor premise)
ABCD has four right angles. (conclusion)

Sometimes the argument is in the form of if/then statements. Be sure the minor premise references the first part of the major premise with a positive statement.

Valid

EXAMPLE 4
If it snows, then I will stay home.
It snowed.
I stayed home.

Not valid

EXAMPLE 5
If it snows, then I will stay home.
It did not snow.
I did not stay home.

Example 4 is a valid argument or conclusion. Example 5 is not valid because the major premise says nothing about what I will do if it does not snow. A conclusion can be false because one of the premises is false or because the reasoning process is faulty.

Write a conclusion for each of the syllogisms. Do not worry about whether the major premise is true or false.

1. All cardinals are red.

   This bird is a cardinal.

   ____

2. Vertical angles are congruent.

   $\angle A$ and $\angle B$ are vertical angles.

   ____

3. If I study, I will get 100% on my math test.

   I studied.

   ____

4. If a triangle is isosceles, it has two congruent sides.

   This triangle is isosceles.

   ____

23A

Find the corresponding parts of the corresponding triangles.

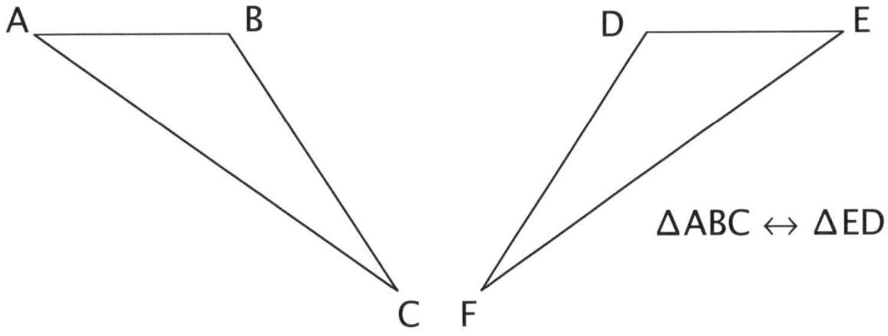

$\Delta ABC \leftrightarrow \Delta EDF$

1. $\angle B$ corresponds to __________.
2. ΔBCA corresponds to __________.
3. ΔBAC corresponds to __________.
4. $\angle E$ corresponds to __________.
5. $\overline{EF}$ corresponds to __________.
6. $\overline{BC}$ corresponds to __________.

$\Delta RST \leftrightarrow \Delta XYT$

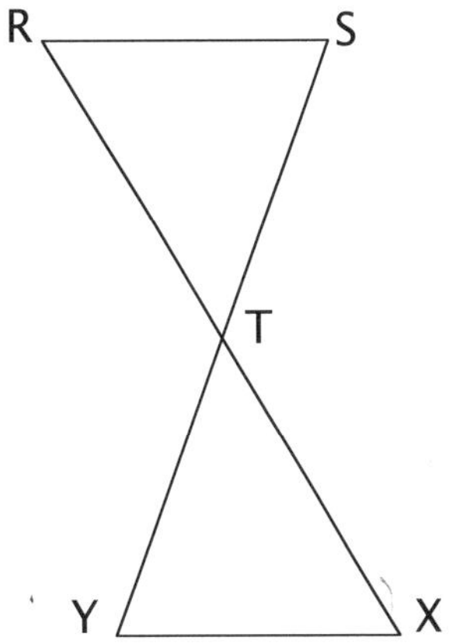

7. $\angle RTS$ corresponds to __________.
8. $\angle XYT$ corresponds to __________.
9. $\overline{ST}$ corresponds to __________.
10. $\overline{TX}$ corresponds to __________.
11. ΔSTR corresponds to __________.
12. $\overline{RT}$ corresponds to __________.

Fill in the blanks.

13. If two triangles are congruent, then the sides and angles of one ____________________ to the sides and angles of the other.

14. The 120° angle in the figure below is a(n) ____________________ angle.

15. From the perspective of ∠C, ∠A and ∠B are ____________________ ____________________ angles.

Find the measure of each angle named below.

16. m∠C =

17. m∠B =

18. m∠D =

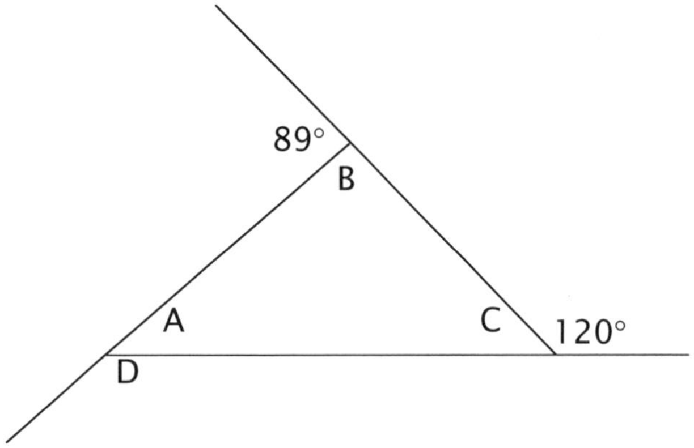

23B

Find the corresponding parts of the corresponding triangles.

$\triangle AEC \leftrightarrow \triangle BFD$

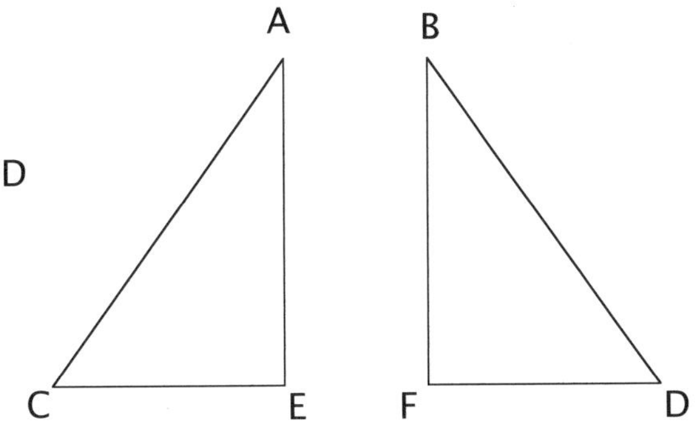

1. $\overline{AC}$ corresponds to ____________.

2. $\overline{AE}$ corresponds to ____________.

3. $\triangle ACE$ corresponds to ____________.

4. $\angle D$ corresponds to ____________.

5. $\angle BFD$ corresponds to ____________.

6. $\overline{BD}$ corresponds to ____________.

Find the corresponding parts for the corresponding triangles.

7. $\overline{DC}$ corresponds to ____________.

8. $\overline{CA}$ corresponds to ____________.

9. $\triangle DCE$ corresponds to ____________.

10. $\angle D$ corresponds to ____________.

11. $\angle A$ corresponds to ____________.

12. $\overline{BA}$ corresponds to ____________.

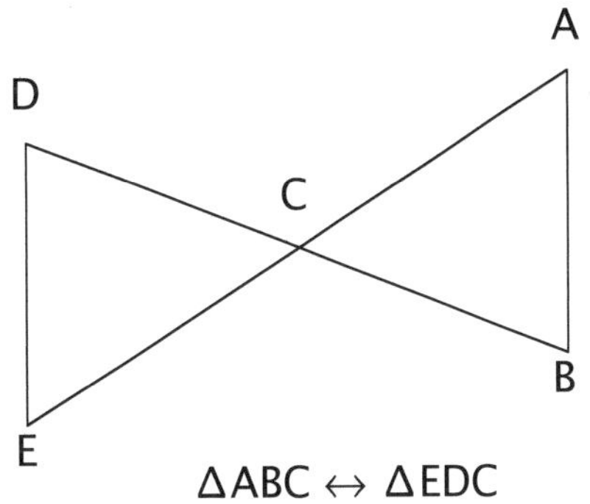

$\triangle ABC \leftrightarrow \triangle EDC$

Find the corresponding parts for the corresponding triangles.

13. Two supplementary angles add up to _______°.

14. The 84° angle in the figure below is a(n) ____________________ angle.

15. From the perspective of ∠D, ∠ ____ and ∠ ____ are remote interior angles.

Find the measure of each angle named below.

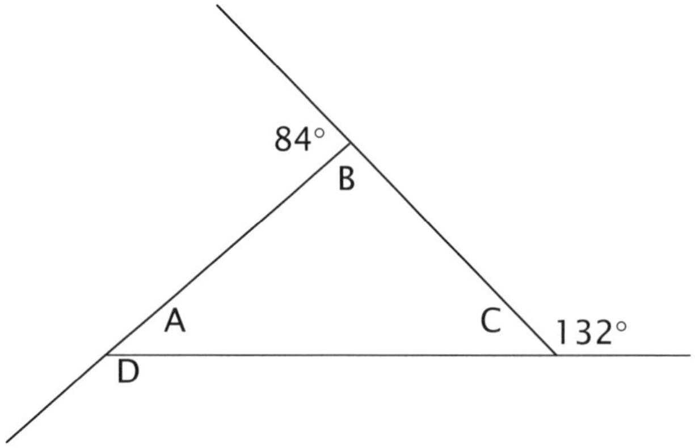

16. m∠B =

17. m∠C =

18. m∠D =

Find the corresponding parts of the corresponding triangles.

1. $\overline{GH}$ corresponds to _____.

2. $\overline{KL}$ corresponds to _____.

3. ΔKML corresponds to _____.

4. ∠HJG corresponds to _____.

5. ∠GHJ corresponds to _____.

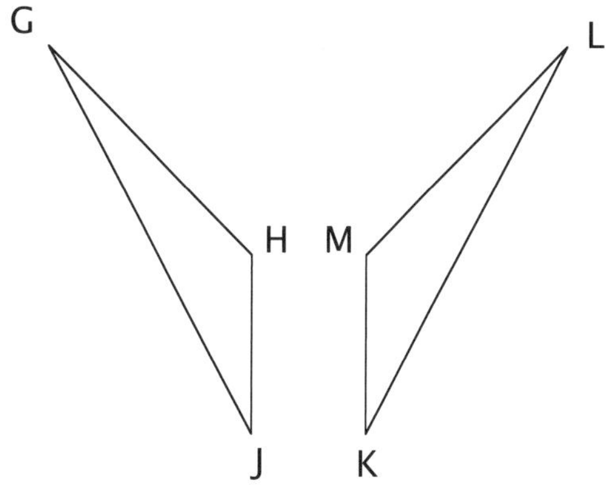

Given: ΔGHJ ↔ ΔLMK

Find the unknown angles.

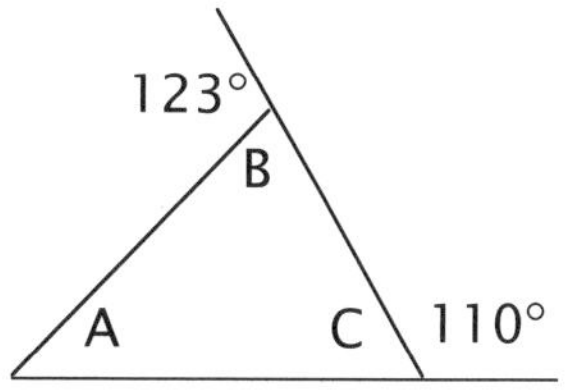

6. m∠B =

7. m∠C =

8. m∠A =

Find the unknown sides.

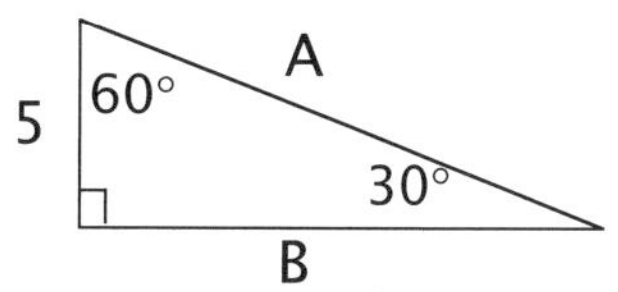

9. A =

10. B =

Fill in the blanks.

11. A quadrilateral with only one pair of ___________ ___________ is a trapezoid.

12. A polygon with all sides congruent and all angles congruent is a ___________ polygon.

13. If the measures of two angles add up to 90°, they are ___________ ___________.

14. A ___________ has two pairs of parallel sides.

15. If a triangle is a right triangle, then ___________ + ___________ = hypotenuse squared.

Follow the directions.

16. If the measure of each exterior angle is 120°, tell how many sides the regular polygon has. What kind of shape is this?

17. Find the volume of a sphere with a radius of 4.3 cm.

18. What is the surface area of the sphere in #17? (SA = $4\pi r^2$)

19. Find the volume of a section of a cylinder with a radius of 4', an arc of 45°, and a height of 5.2'. (First find the area of the sector that is the base of the section, and then multiply the area by the height of the cylinder.

20. In pounds, find the weight of water that would fill the section in #19. (62 lb per ft^3)

Find the corresponding parts of the corresponding triangles.

1. $\overline{YA}$ corresponds to _____.

2. $\overline{ZX}$ corresponds to _____.

3. ∠XAY corresponds to _____.

4. ΔYAX corresponds to _____.

5. ΔAXY corresponds to _____.

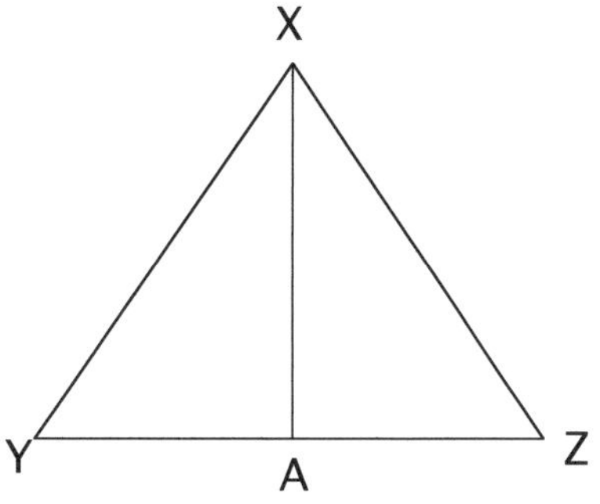

Given: ΔXYA ↔ ΔXZA

Find the unknown angles.

6. m∠C = ________________

7. m∠X = ________________

8. m∠Y = ________________

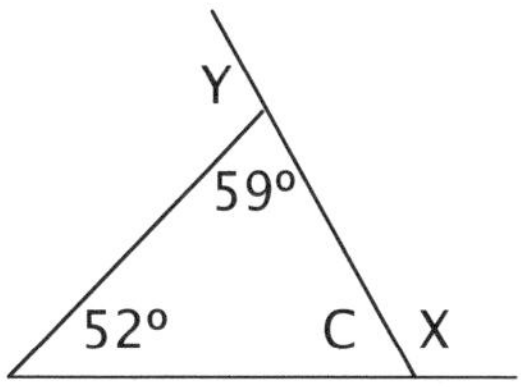

Find the unknown sides.

9. A = ________________

10. B = ________________

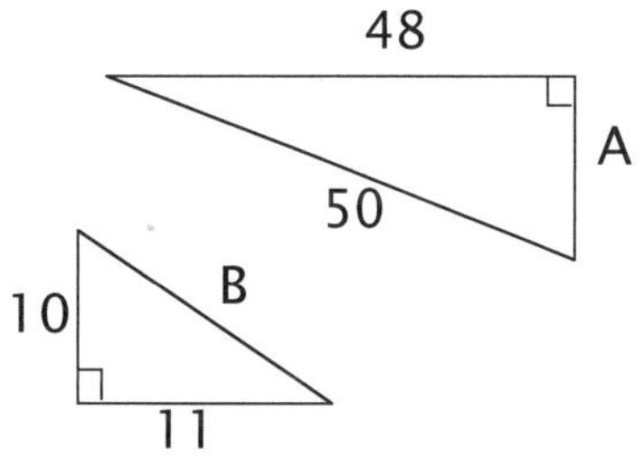

Fill in the blanks.

11. A ________________ with four right angles is a rectangle.

12. Two lines that intersect and form a right angle are ________________ .

Fill in the blanks.

13. If a parallelogram has four _______________ sides, then it is a rhombus.

14. Two angles whose measures add up to ______° are said to be supplementary.

15. Two angles with the same measures are _______________ .

Follow the directions.

16. If the measure of each exterior angle is 60°, tell how many sides the regular polygon has. What kind of shape is this?

17. Find the area of an ellipse with a short axis of 10 m and a long axis of 15 m.

18. Find the volume of a cone with a radius of 42 inches and a height of 15 feet. (Hint: first convert the radius to feet.)

19. Find the volume of a section of a cylinder with a radius of 7', an arc of 60°, and a height of 2'.

20. In pounds, find the weight of water that would fill the section in #19. (62 lb per ft^3)

23E

Find the corresponding parts of the corresponding triangles.

1. $\overline{ST}$ corresponds to ______.

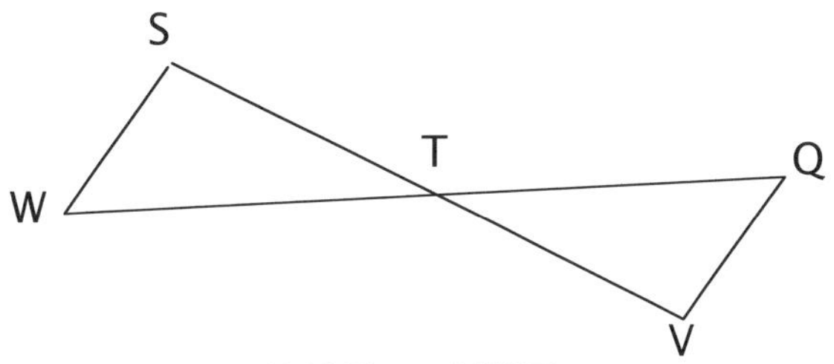

2. ∠WTS corresponds to ______.

Given: ΔVQT ↔ ΔSWT

3. ∠TSW corresponds to ______.

4. ΔTVQ corresponds to ______.

5. ΔVQT corresponds to ______.

Find the unknown angles.

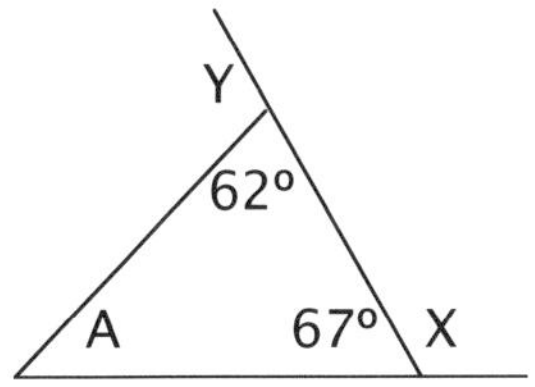

6. m∠A =

7. m∠X =

8. m∠Y =

Find the unknown sides.

9. A =

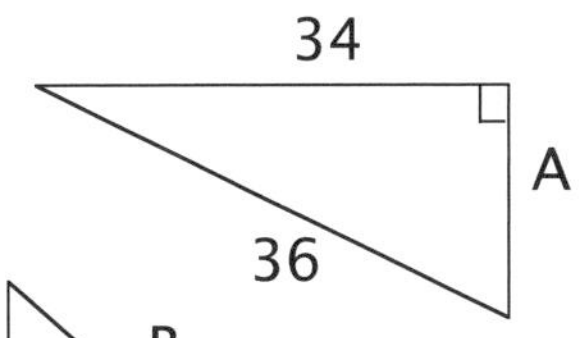

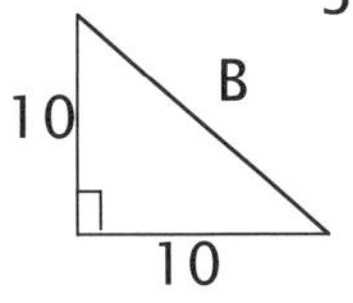

10. B =

Fill in the blanks.

11. An inscribed angle has its ________________ on the circle.

12. The measure of an inscribed angle is ________________ of the intercepted arc.

13. If two parallel lines are cut by a transversal, ________________ interior angles are ________________ .

14. The measures of the interior angles of a triangle add up to _______°.

15. If a triangle has sides A, B, and C, and $A \le B \le C$, then A + B _____ C.

16. The measure of each interior angle in an octagon is ________________ .

17. The volume of a cone with a radius of .33 feet and a height of 7 inches is ________________ .

Sharpen your algebra skills!
Factoring can be used to solve some equations.

EXAMPLE $X^2 + 5X + 6 = 20$

$X^2 + 5X - 14 = 0$	Rewrite so the polynomial equals zero.
$(X + 7)(X - 2) = 0$	Factor the polynomial.
$(X + 7) = 0$ or $(X - 2) = 0$	One of the factors must equal zero.
$X = -7$ or $X = 2$	There are two possible solutions.

Use factoring to solve.

18. $X^2 + 6X + 8 = 0$

19. $X^2 + 5X = -6$

20. $X^2 - 3X + 2 = 30$

The original statement, or first premise, of an argument is called the conditional. In formal logic, there are several different ways in which the conditional may be rearranged. In this lesson, we will focus on forming the converse. To form the converse, simply reverse the original statement.

	Conditional	Converse
EXAMPLE A:	If it snows, then I will stay home.	If I stay home, it will snow.

Notice that the converse of a true statement may be false. In the example above, it may be true that I will stay home if it snows. My staying home, however, does not make it snow.

	Conditional	Converse
EXAMPLE B	If a triangle is equilateral, it is equiangular.	If a triangle is equiangular, it is equilateral.

In this example, the converse is true. It is very important when learning mathematical rules or postulates to also learn whether or not the converse is true. Here is another example.

	Conditional	Converse
EXAMPLE C:	If a figure is a square, it has two pairs of parallel sides.	If a figure has two pairs of parallel sides, it is a square.

The conditional is true, but the converse is not because there is the possibility that the figure is a rectangle.

Write the converse of each statement, and tell whether it is always true. Assume that the original statement is true.

1. If I touch a hot stove, I get burned.

   Converse:

2. If two line segments have equal length, they are congruent.

   Converse:

3. If a bird is a cardinal, it is red.

   Converse:

4. If a triangle is a right triangle, then the leg squared plus the leg squared equals the hypotenuse squared.

   Converse:

5. If I stop watering my plants, they will wilt.

   Converse:

If you find this interesting, you may do some research to find the meanings of the inverse and the contrapositive.

Complete the following proofs using SSS or SAS postulates.

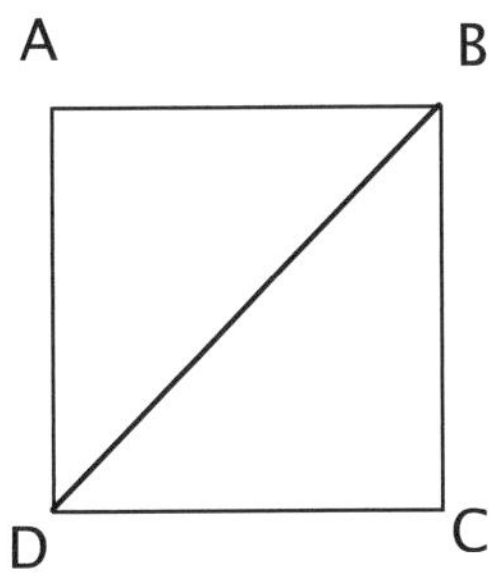

Given: ABCD is a square.
Prove: $\Delta ABD \cong \Delta CDB$

STATEMENTS	*REASONS*
ABCD is a square.	1. ________
$\overline{AB} \cong \overline{DC}$	2. ________
$\overline{AD} \cong \overline{BC}$	definition of a square
$\overline{BD} \cong \overline{BD}$	3. ________
$\Delta ABD \cong \Delta CDB$	4. ________

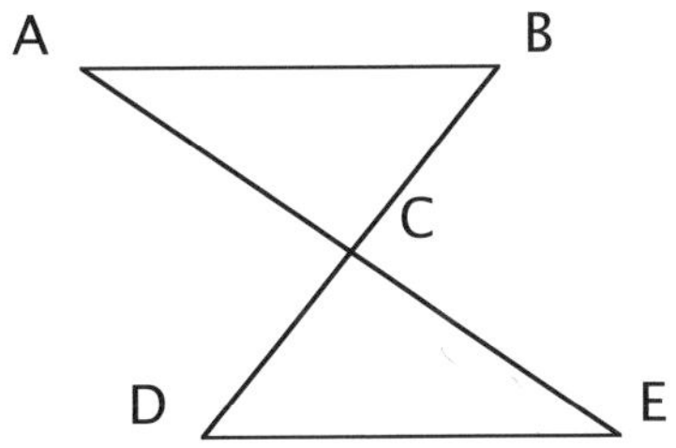

Given: $\overline{AB} \cong \overline{ED}$
C is the midpoint of $\overline{BD}$.
$\overline{AB} \parallel \overline{DE}$
Prove: $\Delta ABC \cong \Delta EDC$

STATEMENTS	*REASONS*
$\overline{AB} \cong \overline{ED}$	5. ________
C is the midpoint of $\overline{BD}$.	6. ________
$\overline{BC} \cong \overline{DC}$	definition of midpoint
$\angle ABC \cong \angle EDC$	7. If 2 $\parallel$ lines are cut by a __________, the alternate interior angles are ________.
$\Delta ABC \cong \Delta EDC$	8. ________ postulate

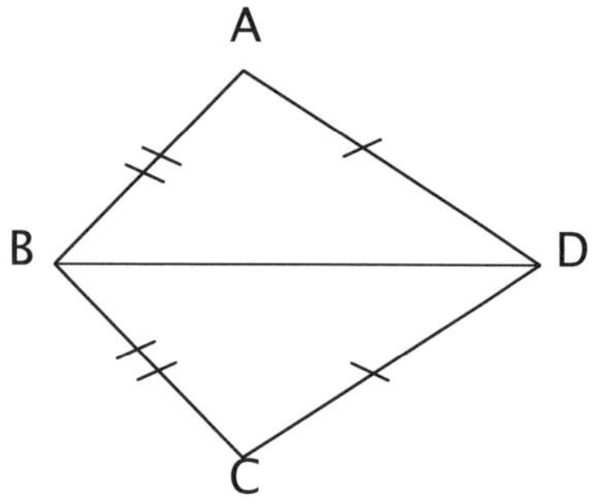

Given: $\overline{AB} \cong \overline{CB}$
$\overline{AD} \cong \overline{CD}$
Prove: $\Delta ABD \cong \Delta CBD$

STATEMENTS	*REASONS*
9. ______ ≅ ______	13.__________
10. ______ ≅ ______	14.__________
11. ______ ≅ ______	reflexive
12. ______ ≅ ______	SSS postulate

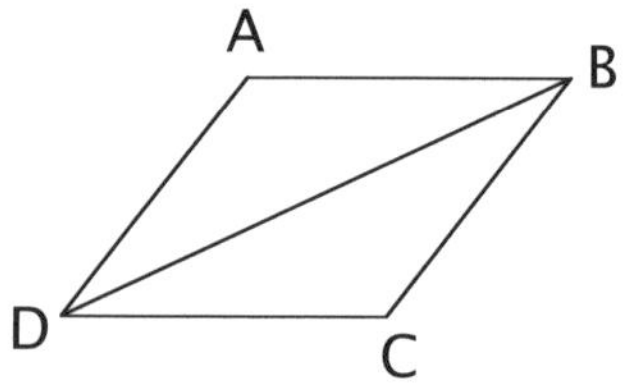

Given: ABCD is a rhombus
Prove: $\Delta ABD \cong \Delta CDB$

STATEMENTS	*REASONS*
15. ____________	given
16. ____________	definition of a rhombus
17. ____________	definition of a rhombus
18. ____________	reflexive property
19. ____________	SSS postulate

Complete the following proofs using SSS or SAS postulates.

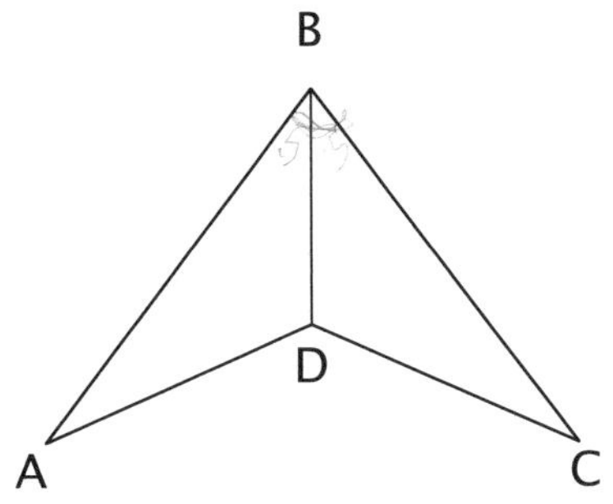

Given: $\overline{BD}$ bisects ∠ABC.
$\overline{AB} \cong \overline{CB}$
Prove: ΔABD ≅ ΔCBD

STATEMENTS	REASONS
$\overline{BD}$ bisects ∠ABC.	1. ________
$\overline{AB} \cong \overline{CB}$	2. ________
3. ____ ≅ ____	reflexive property
∠ABD ≅ ∠CBD	4. ________
ΔABD ≅ ΔCBD	SAS postulate

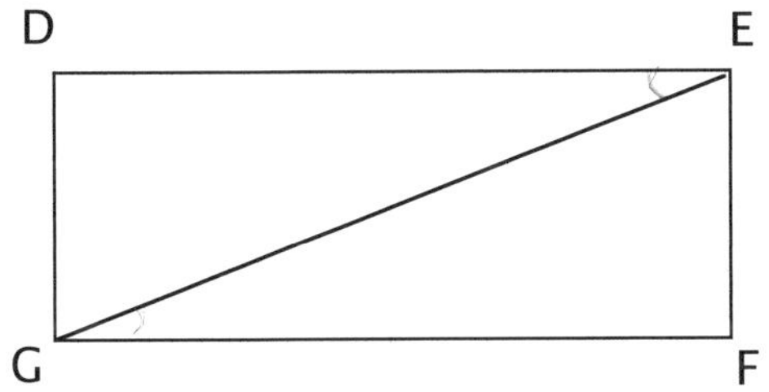

Given: DEFG is a rectangle.
$\overline{DE} \cong \overline{FG}$
Prove: ΔDEG ≅ ΔFGE

STATEMENTS	REASONS
DEFG is a rectangle.	5. ________
$\overline{DE} \parallel \overline{FG}$	6. ________
∠DEG ≅ ∠FGE	7. ________
$\overline{EG} \cong \overline{EG}$	8. ________
ΔDEG ≅ ΔFGE	9. ________

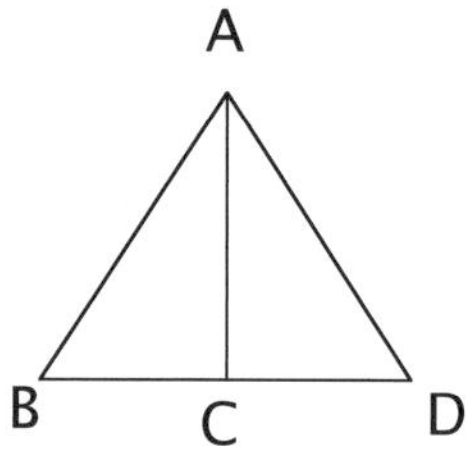

Given: $\overline{AC} \perp \overline{BD}$

C is the midpoint of $\overline{BD}$.

Prove: $\Delta ACB \cong \Delta ACD$

STATEMENTS	*REASONS*
$\overline{AC} \perp \overline{BD}$	10. ________
$\angle ACB$ and $\angle ACD$ are right angles.	11. ________
$\angle ACB \cong \angle ACD$	12. ________
C is the midpoint of BD.	13. ________
$\overline{BC} \cong \overline{DC}$	14. ________
$\overline{AC} \cong \overline{AC}$	15. ________
$\Delta ACB \cong \Delta ACD$	16. ________

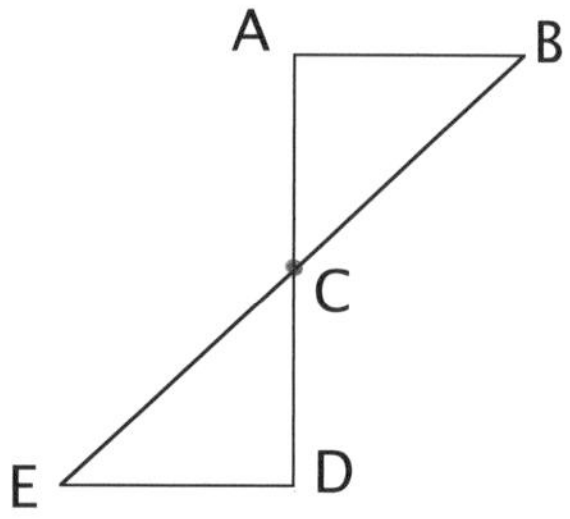

Given: C is the midpoint of $\overline{BE}$ and $\overline{AD}$.

$\overline{ED} \cong \overline{BA}$

Prove: $\Delta ABC \cong \Delta DEC$

STATEMENTS	*REASONS*
C is the midpoint of $\overline{BE}$ and $\overline{AD}$.	17. ________
$\overline{ED} \cong \overline{BA}$	18. ________
19. ____ ≅ ____	definition of midpoint
20. ____ ≅ ____	definition of midpoint
21. ____ ≅ ____	SSS postulate

Complete the following proof using SSS or SAS postulates.

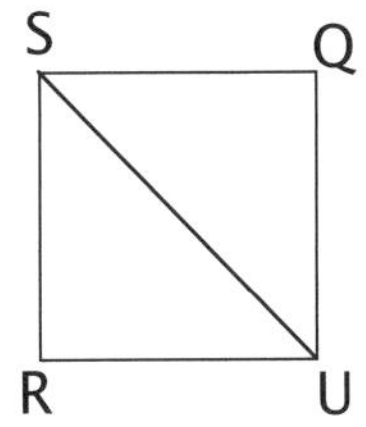

Given: □SQUR is a square.
Prove: ΔSQU ≅ ΔURS

STATEMENTS	*REASONS*
□SQUR is a square.	given
$\overline{SQ} \cong \overline{UR}$	1. ________
$\overline{QU} \cong \overline{RS}$	2. ________
$\overline{SU} \cong \overline{SU}$	3. ________
4. ________	SSS postulate

5. Is ∠QUS ≅ ∠RSU?

Find the unknown angles.

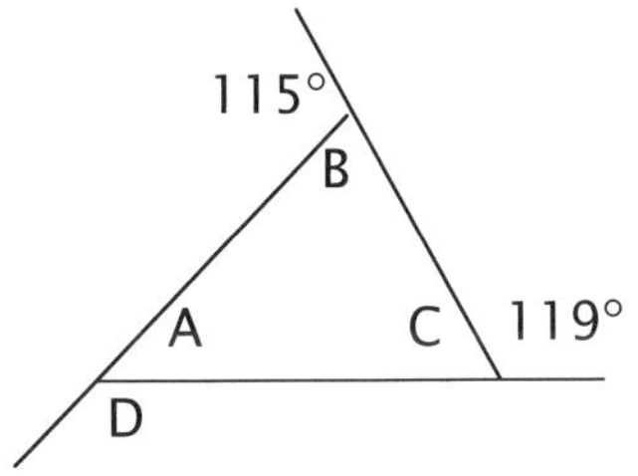

6. m∠D =

7. m∠B =

8. m∠A =

9. m∠C =

Find the corresponding parts of the corresponding triangles.

10. ∠GDE ↔ ∠ _____

11. $\overline{DE}$ ↔ _____

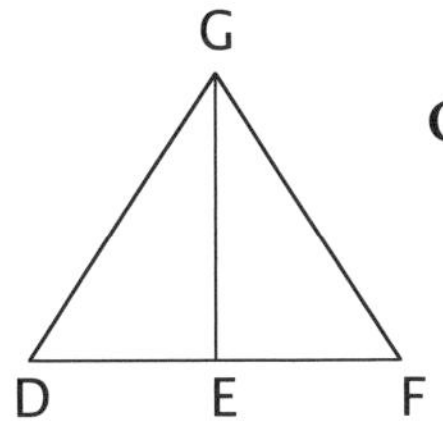

Given: ΔGDE ↔ ΔGFE

Find the unknown sides.

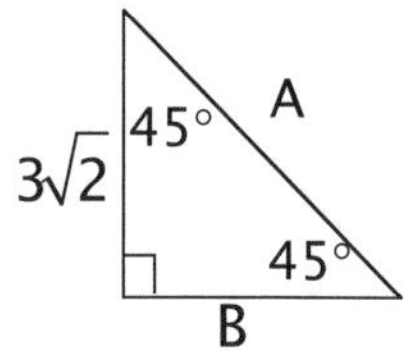

12. A =

13. B =

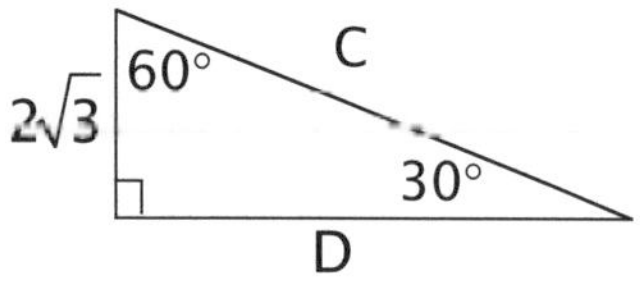

14. C =

15. D =

Follow the directions.

16. Name a quadrilateral with only one pair of parallel sides.

17. What is the sum of the measures of two supplementary angles?

18. A parallelogram has how many pairs of parallel sides?

19. Find the volume of a section of a cylinder that has a radius of four feet. The section has an arc of 90° and a height of eight feet.

20. In pounds, find the weight of water that would fill the section in #19. (62 lb per ft^3)

24D

Complete the following proof using SSS or SAS postulates.

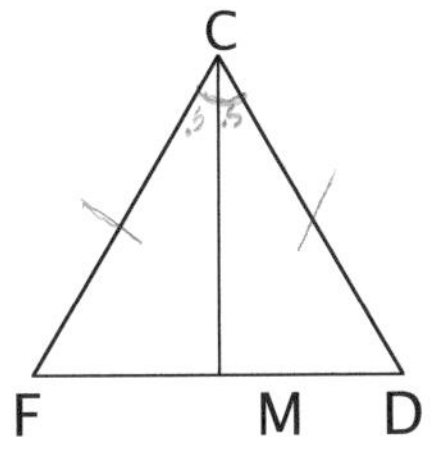

Given: ΔCDF is an isosceles triangle whose shortest side is $\overline{FD}$.
$\overline{CM}$ bisects ∠FCD

Prove: ΔCDM ≅ ΔCFM

STATEMENTS	*REASONS*
Δ CDF is an isosceles triangle	given
$\overline{CM}$ bisects ∠FCD	given
$\overline{CF} \cong \overline{CD}$	1. ________
∠FCM ≅ ∠DCM	2. ________
$\overline{CM} \cong \overline{CM}$	3. ________
4. ________	SAS postulate

5. Is ∠CFM ≅ ∠CDM?
If so, then you have proven that in an isosceles triangle, not only are the two sides congruent, but also the angles opposite those two sides.

Find the unknown angles.

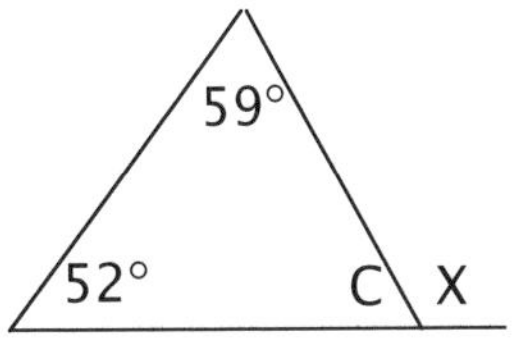

6. m∠C =

7. m∠X =

Find the corresponding parts of the corresponding triangles.

8. ∠FGE ↔ ∠______

9. $\overline{GE}$ ↔ ______

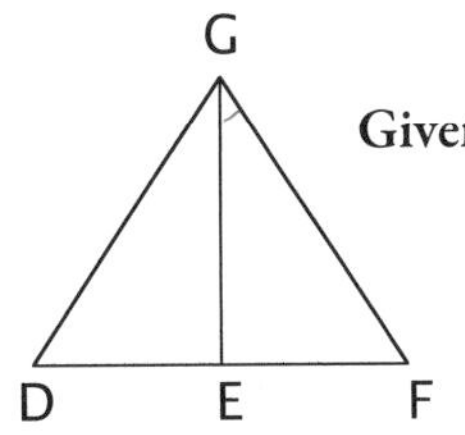

Given: ΔGDE ↔ ΔGFE

Find the unknown sides.

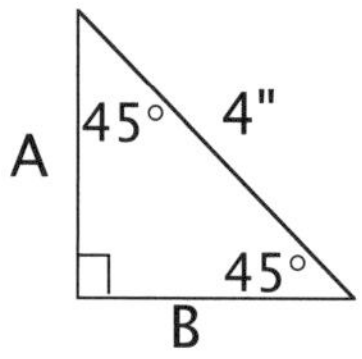

10. A =

11. B =

Find the area and perimeter.

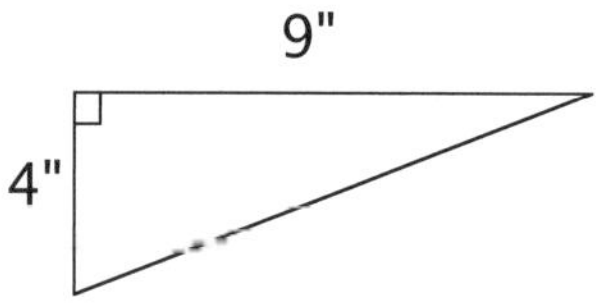

12. A =

13. P =

Follow the directions.

14. Write the Pythagorean theorem.

15. Theorems are proven using axioms and __________________.

16. Two angles with equal measures are said to be __________________.

17. Give the term for a triangle with two congruent sides.

18. What is a quadrilateral with four right angles and four congruent sides?

19. Find the volume of a section of a cylinder with a radius of 10', an arc of 120°, and a height of 12'.

20. In pounds, find the weight of water that would fill the section in #19. (62 lb per ft^3)

Complete the following proof using SSS or SAS.

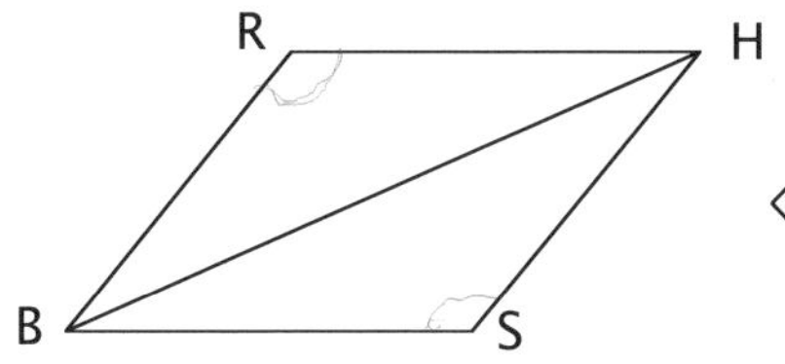

Given: ◇ RHSB is a rhombus.
Prove: $\Delta HSB \cong \Delta BRH$

STATEMENTS	*REASONS*
◇ RHSB is a rhombus	given
1. ________	definition of a rhombus
2. ________	definition of a rhombus
3. ________	reflexive property
$\Delta HSB \cong \Delta BRH$	4. ________

5. Is $\angle HSB \cong \angle BRH$? Why?

Find the unknown angles.

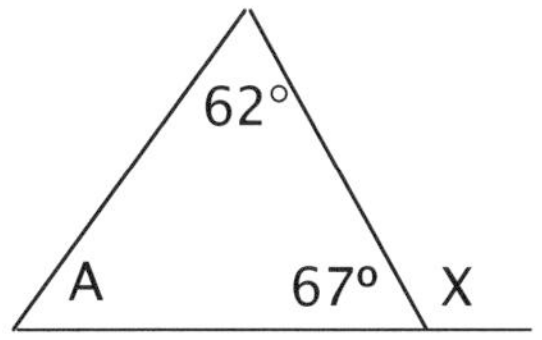

6. $m\angle A =$ _____
7. $m\angle X =$ _____

Find the corresponding parts of the corresponding triangles.

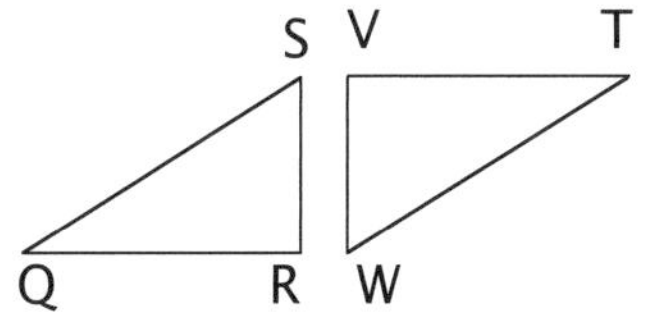

Given: $\Delta SRQ \leftrightarrow \Delta WVT$

8. $\angle QSR \leftrightarrow$ _____
9. $\overline{RQ} \leftrightarrow$ _____

Use drawing for #10–14. Find the unknown parts.

10. LL = _____
11. a = _____
12. b = _____

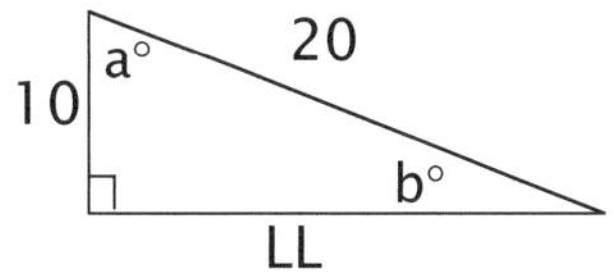

Find the area and perimeter of the triangle above.

13. A =
14. P =

Follow the directions.

15. What is the measure of each interior angle of a decagon?

16. In the circle shown, arc BAC = 264°.
What is the m∠BAC?

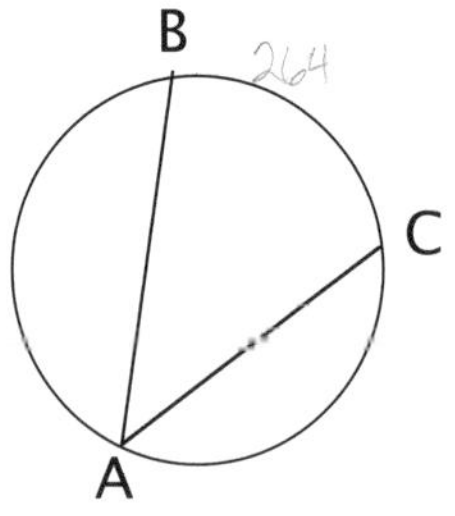

17. Simplify: $\frac{3}{\sqrt{5}}+\frac{7}{\sqrt{2}}=$

Sharpen your algebra skills!

Scientific notation uses exponents to simplify the handling of very large and very small numbers.

EXAMPLE 1 $62,700,000 = 6.27 \times 10^7$

EXAMPLE 2 $.000054 = 5.4 \times 10^{-5}$

Write each number in scientific notation.

18. 1,450,000 19. .0076 20. 640,000,000,000

Here are some questions that require you to use what you know about geometric figures to find new information. Don't forget the properties of inscribed angles and remote interior angles when solving these.

Use the given information to find the measures of the numbered angles and arcs.

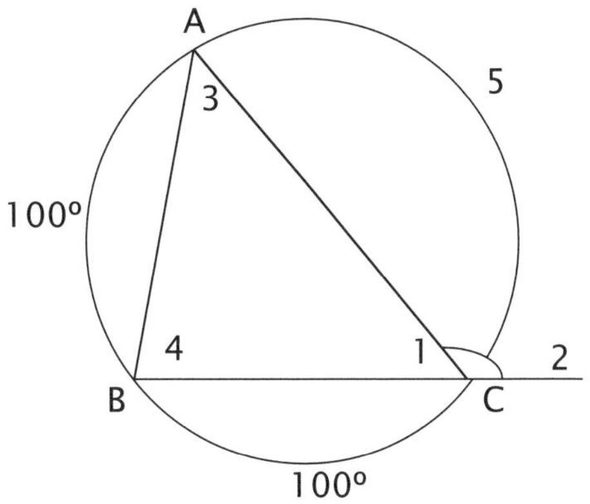

1. m∠1 =

2. m∠2 =

3. m∠3 =

4. m∠4 =

5. m arc 5 =

Find the measures of the lettered angles. Use what you know about remote interior angles to check your results.

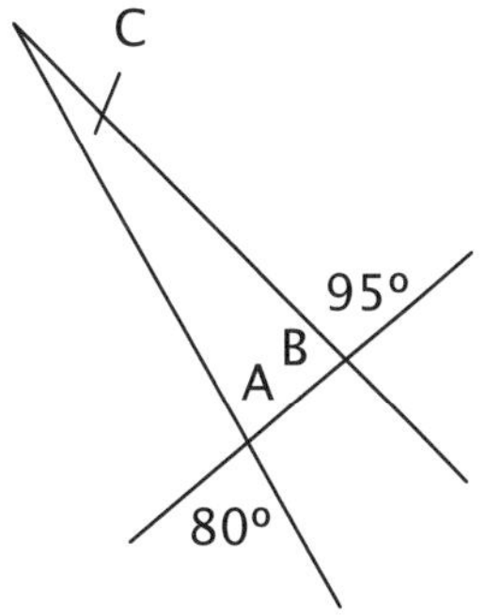

6. m∠A =

7. m∠B =

8. m∠C =

Find the measures of the numbered angles. Lines a and b are parallel.

9. m∠1 =

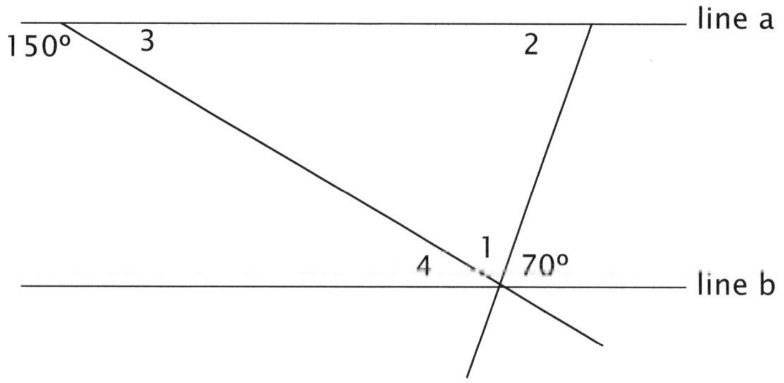

10. m∠2=

11. m∠3=

12. m∠4=

Complete the following proofs using ASA or AAS postulates.

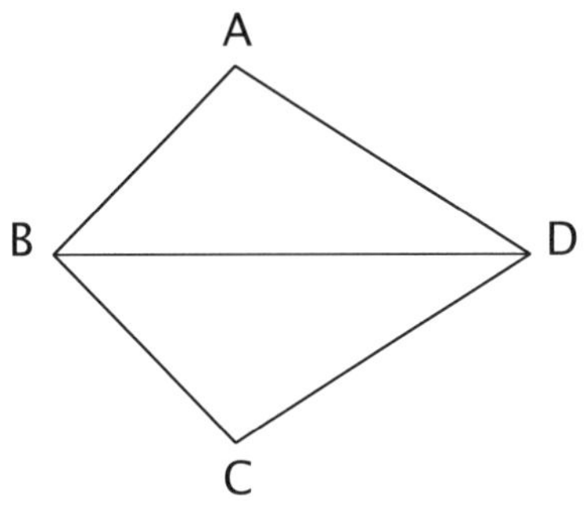

Given: $\overline{AB} \cong \overline{CB}$

$\overline{DB}$ bisects $\angle ABC$.

$\angle BAD \cong \angle BCD$

Prove: $\Delta ABD \cong \Delta CBD$

STATEMENTS	***REASONS***
$\overline{AB} \cong \overline{CB}$	1. ________
2. ___ ≅ ___	3. ________
4. ________	given
$\angle ABD \cong \angle CBD$	5. ________
6. ___ ≅ ___	7. ________

8. Is $\overline{AD} \cong \overline{CD}$? Why?

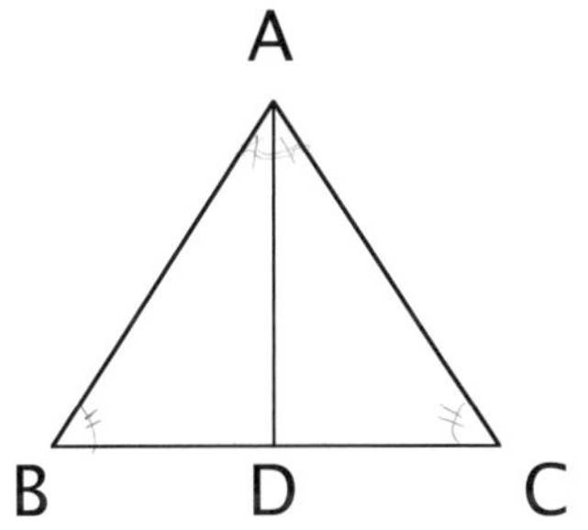

$\overline{AD}$ bisects $\angle BAC$.

$\angle ABD \cong \angle ACD$

Prove: $\Delta ADB \cong \Delta ADC$

STATEMENTS	***REASONS***
9. ___ ≅ ___	10. ________
11. ________	given
$\angle BAD \cong \angle CAD$	12. ________
13. ___ ≅ ___	reflexive property
14. ___ ≅ ___	15. ________

16. Is $\overline{AB} \cong \overline{AC}$? Why?

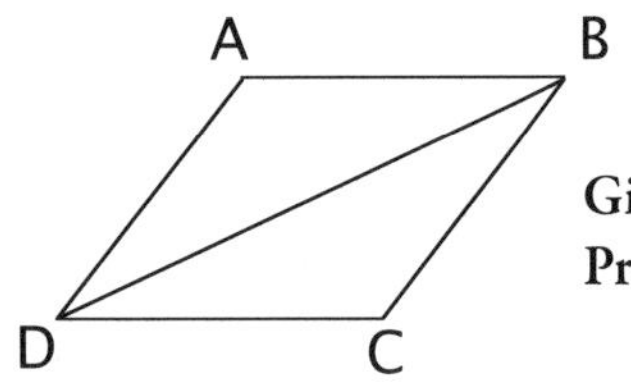

Given: $\overline{BD}$ bisects $\angle ABC$ and $\angle ADC$.
Prove: $\angle BAD \cong \angle BCD$

STATEMENTS	*REASONS*
17. ________	given
18. ___ ≅ ___	definition of a bisector
19. ___ ≅ ___	definition of a bisector
20. ___ ≅ ___	reflexive property
21. ___ ≅ ___	ASA postulate
22. ___ ≅ ___	CPCTRC

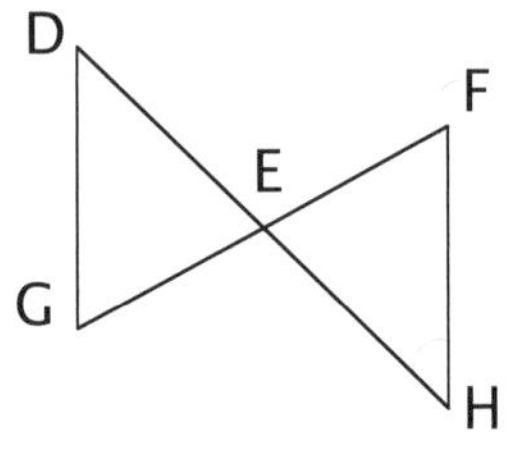

Given: E is the midpoint of $\overline{FG}$
$\overline{DG} \parallel \overline{HF}$
Prove: $\angle GDE \cong \angle FHE$

STATEMENTS	*REASONS*
23. ________	given
24. ___ ≅ ___	25. ____________
26. ___ ∥ ___	given
27. ___ ≅ ___	alternate interior angles
28. ___ ≅ ___	vertical angles
29. ___ ≅ ___	ASA postulate
30. ___ ≅ ___	CPCTRC

25B

Complete the following proofs using ASA or AAS postulates.

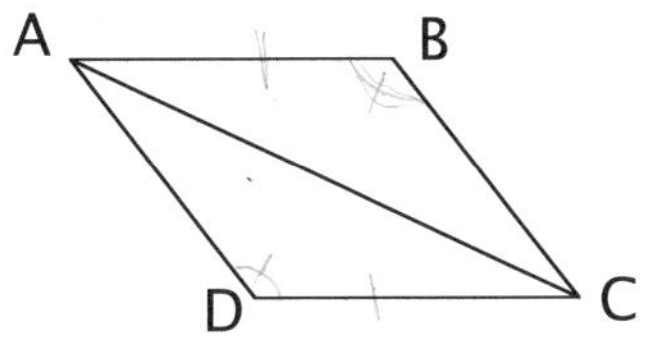

Given: ∠ADC ≅ ∠ABC
$\overline{AB} \parallel \overline{DC}$
$\overline{AB} \cong \overline{CD}$
Prove: ΔABC ≅ ΔADC

STATEMENTS	REASONS
∠ADC ≅ ∠ABC	1. ________
2. ____ ≅ ____	given
3. ____ ∥ ____	given
∠BAC ≅ ∠DCA	alternate interior angles
4. ____ ≅ ____	ASA postulate

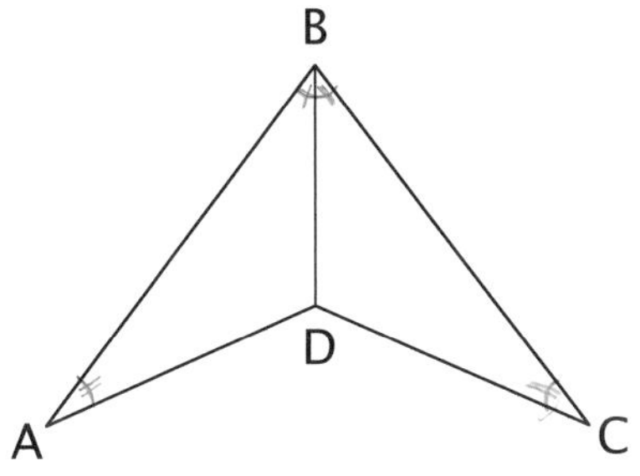

Given: $\overline{BD}$ bisects ∠ABC.
∠BAD ≅ ∠BCD
Prove: ΔABD ≅ ΔCBD

STATEMENTS	REASONS
5. ________	6. ________
∠ABD ≅ ∠CBD	7. ________
8. ___ ≅ ____	given
9. ___ ≅ ____	reflexive property
10. ___ ≅ ____	AAS postulate

11. Is $\overline{AB} \cong \overline{CB}$? Why?

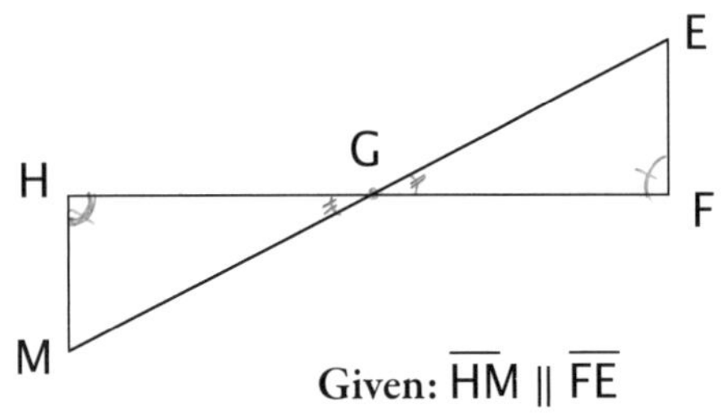

Given: $\overline{HM} \parallel \overline{FE}$
$\overline{ME}$ bisects $\overline{HF}$.
Prove: $\Delta HGM \cong \Delta FGE$

STATEMENTS	REASONS
$\overline{HM} \parallel \overline{FE}$	12. ________
$\angle MHF \cong \angle EFG$	13. ________
$\overline{ME}$ bisects $\overline{HF}$.	14. ________
15. ___ ≅ ____	16. ________
17. ____ ≅ ____	vertical angles
18. ____ ≅ ____	ASA postulate

19. Is $\angle HMG \cong \angle FEG$? Why?

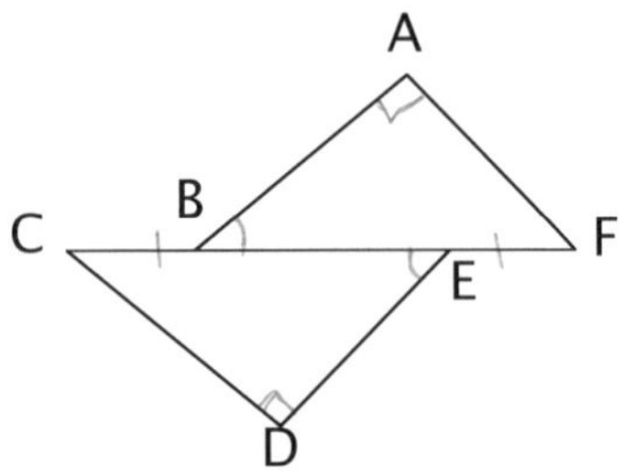

Given: $\overline{AB} \parallel \overline{DE}$
$\angle BAF$ and $\angle EDC$ are right angles.
$\overline{CE} \cong \overline{FB}$
Prove: $\Delta CDE \cong \Delta FAB$

STATEMENTS	REASONS
$\overline{AB} \parallel \overline{DE}$	20. ________
$\angle ABF \cong \angle DEC$	21. ________
22. ________	given
23. ___ ≅ ____	definition of right angles
24. ____ ≅ ____	given
25. ____ ≅ ____	26. ________

27. Is $\overline{ED} \cong \overline{AB}$? Why?

SYSTEMATIC REVIEW

25C

Complete the following proof.

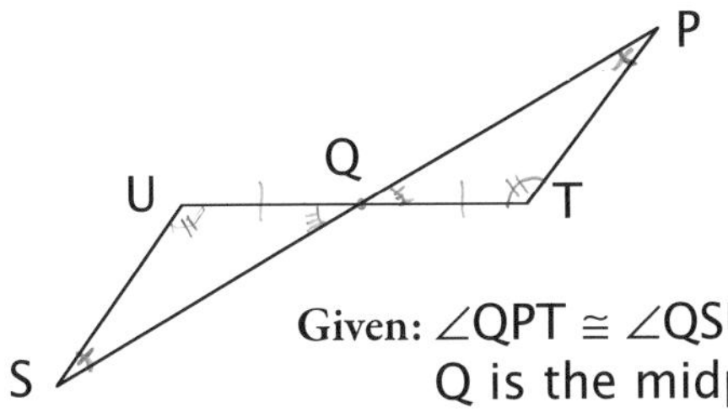

Given: ∠QPT ≅ ∠QSU
Q is the midpoint of $\overline{UT}$.
Prove: ΔQSU ≅ ΔQPT

STATEMENTS	*REASONS*
1. ________	given
2. ________	given
3. ________	4. ________
5. ________	6. ________
7. ________	8. ________

9. Is ∠QUS ≅ ∠QTP? Why?

Find the unknown angles.

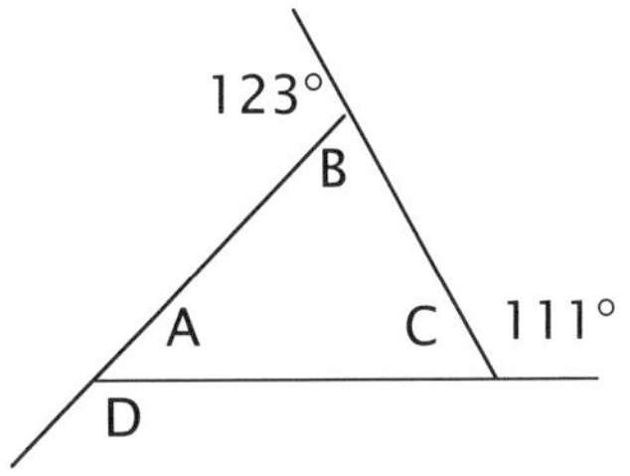

10. m∠B =

11. m∠C =

12. m∠A =

Find the corresponding parts of the corresponding triangles.

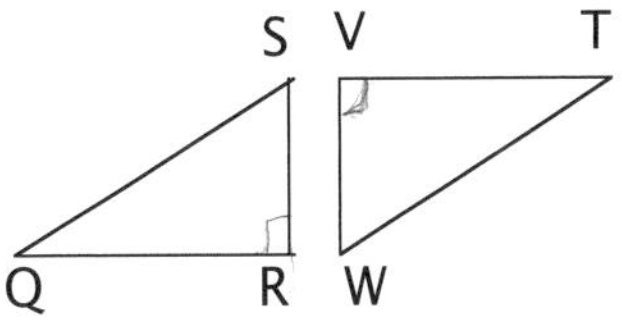

Given: ΔSRQ ↔ ΔWVT

13. ∠TVW ↔ ∠______

14. $\overline{VW}$ ↔ ______

Follow the directions.

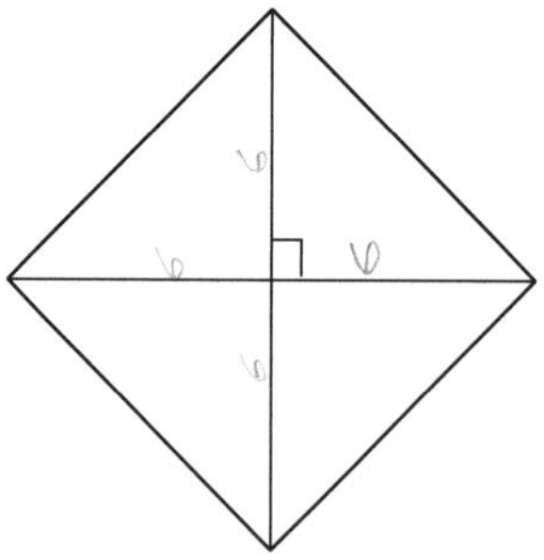

15. Both diagonals are 12" long, and they bisect each other. What is the area of the figure?

16. Using the information in #15, find the perimeter of the figure.

17. Find the area of a sector with a radius of 8" and a measure of 36°.

18. Find the length of an arc with a radius of 8" and a measure of 36°.

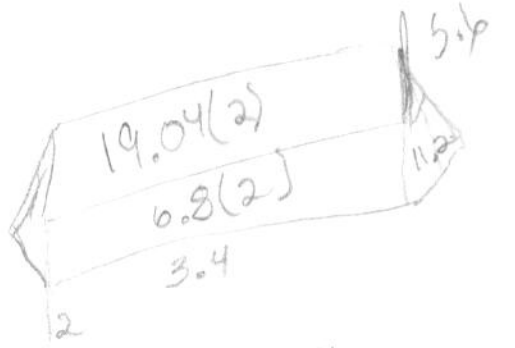

3.4 5.6

19. Find the volume of a rectangular solid that is 2 m by 340 cm by 560 cm. (100 cm = 1 m)

2 × 3.4 × 5.6

20. Find the surface area of the rectangular solid in #19.

25D

Complete the following proof.

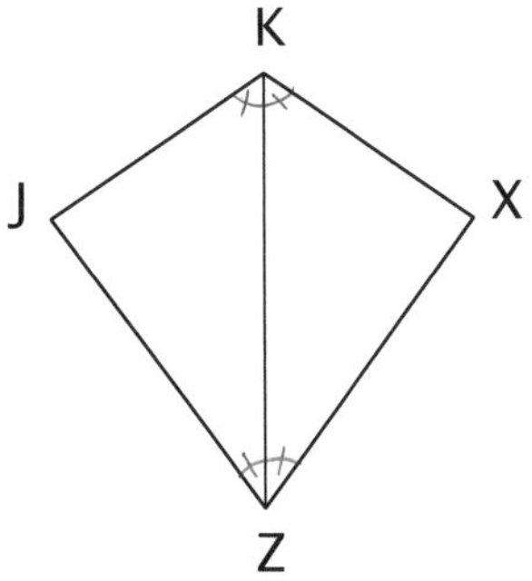

Given: $\overline{KZ}$ bisects $\angle JKX$ and $\angle XZJ$.
Prove: $\overline{KJ} \cong \overline{KX}$
(Hint: first prove the triangles congruent.)

STATEMENTS	*REASONS*
1. ________	given
2. ________	given
3. ________	4. ________
5. ________	6. ________
7. ________	8. ________
9. ________	10. ________
11. ________	CPCTRC

Find the unknown angles.

12. $m\angle a =$

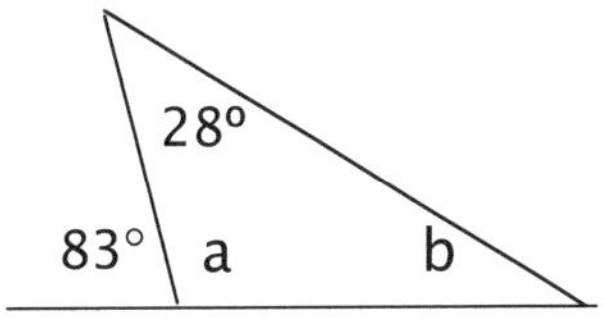

13. $m\angle b =$

Find the unknown side.

14. S =

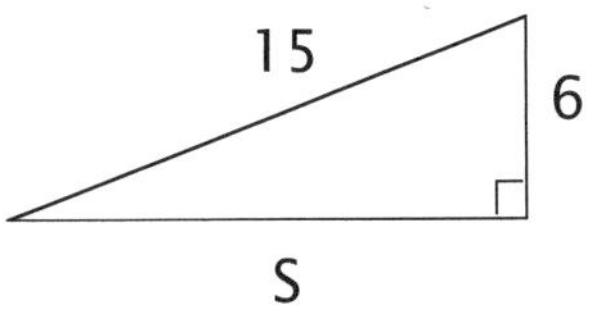

Follow the directions.

15. The vertical diagonal is 8 cm long, and the horizontal diagonal is 6 cm long. They bisect each other. What is the area of the figure?

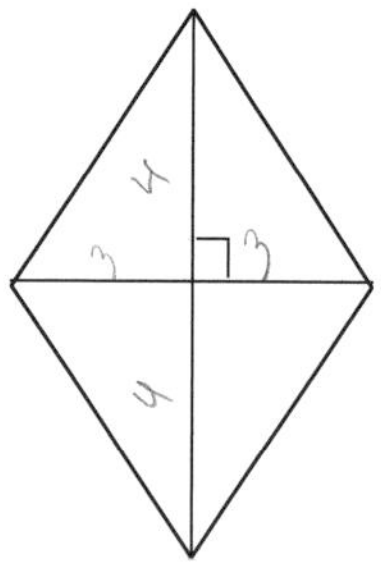

16. Using the information in #15, find the perimeter of the figure.

17. Find the volume of a section of a cylinder with a radius of 4 cm, a height of 3.3 cm, and a measure of 10°.

18. Find the length of an arc with a radius of 4 cm and a measure of 10°.

19. Give the volume of the prism using yards.

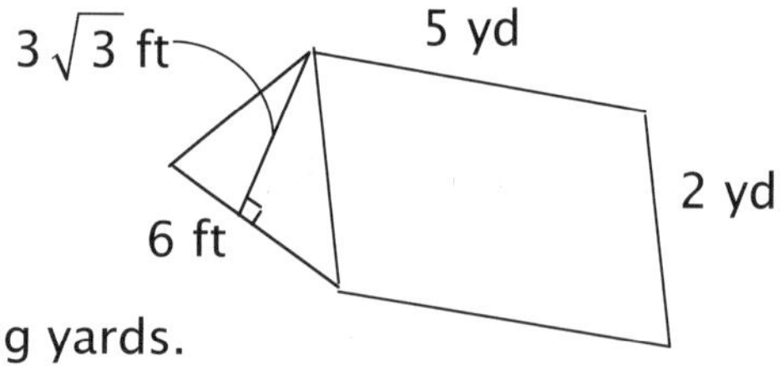

20. Give the surface area of the prism using yards.

Complete the following proof.

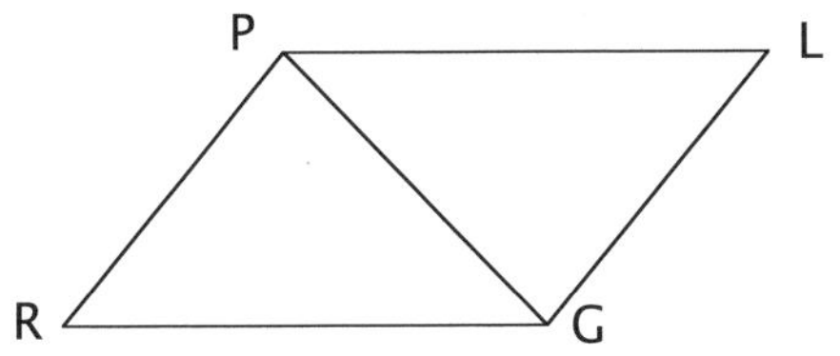

Given: ▱ PLGR is a parallelogram

Prove: $\Delta PLG \cong \Delta GRP$.

STATEMENTS	***REASONS***
PLGR is a parallelogram.	given
$\overline{PL} \parallel \overline{GR}$, $\overline{PR} \parallel \overline{LG}$	def. of a parallelogram
1. ________	2. ________
3. ________	4. ________
5. ________	6. ________
7. ________	8. ________

9. Is $\angle PLG \cong \angle GRP$? Why?

Find the unknown angles.

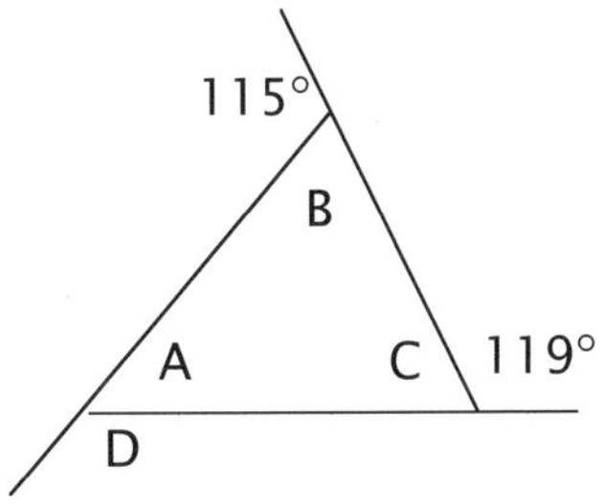

10. $m\angle D =$

11. $m\angle B =$

12. $m\angle A =$

13. $m\angle C =$

Follow the directions.

14. What is the area of the figure shown?

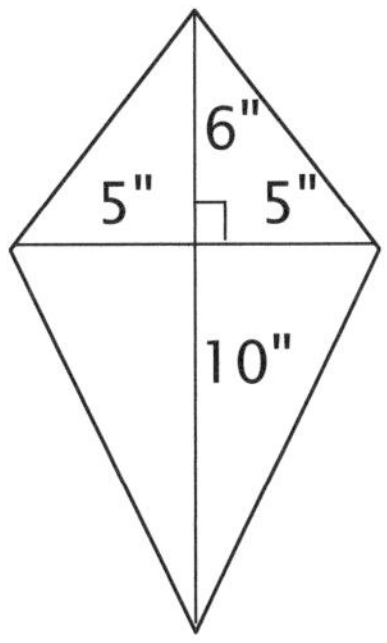

15. What is the perimeter of the figure?

Follow the directions.

16. Find the area of a sector with a radius of 7 mm and a measure of 240°.

17. Find the length of an arc with a radius of 7 mm and a measure of 240°.

Sharpen your algebra skills!

When using scientific notation to multiply or divide, compute the numbers and the exponents separately.

EXAMPLE 1 $1900 \times 50 = (1.9 \times 10^3)(5.0 \times 10^1) = (1.9 \times 5.0)(10^3 \times 10^1) =$
$(9.5)(10^4) = 9.5 \times 10^4$

EXAMPLE 2 $60{,}000 \div 120 = (6.0 \times 10^4) \div (1.2 \times 10^2) =$
$(6.0 \div 1.2)(10^4 \div 10^2) = 5 \times 10^2$

Use scientific notation to solve the following:

18. $5{,}000 \times 8{,}000{,}000 =$

19. $18{,}000 \times .007 =$

20. $1{,}400{,}000 \div 290 =$

Geometric proofs can be used to prove many things by deductive reasoning. Here are some examples that are a little different from those in your text.

Write the missing reasons for each statement.

1. For the diagram below, prove that ∠CDE ≅ ∠CBA. Sides and angles are marked by slashes to show which ones are already known to be congruent. Begin by drawing a straight line from point C to point E and one from point C to point A.

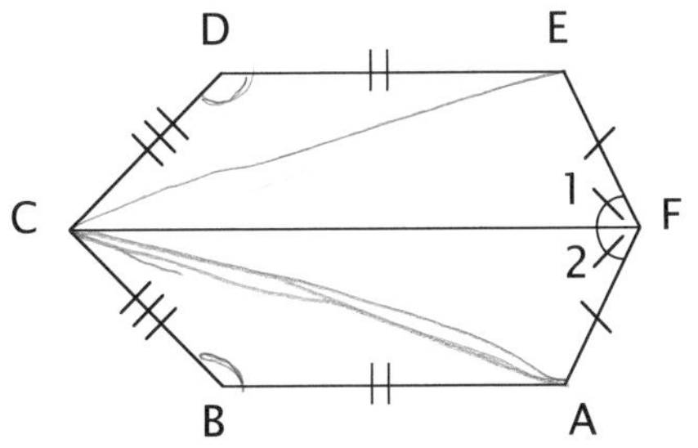

Statements	Reasons
AF ≅ EF	Given
∠1 ≅ ∠2	
CF ≅ CF	
ΔCEF ≅ ΔCAF	
CE ≅ CA	because they are corresponding parts of congruent triangles
Now look at the outer triangles formed by the lines you drew.	
ΔCDE ≅ ΔCBA	
∠CDE ≅ ∠CBA	because they are corresponding parts of congruent triangles

This is a variation on the proof above. See whether you can do this one by yourself.

2. For the diagram marked below, prove that ∠TSV ≅ ∠RSV.

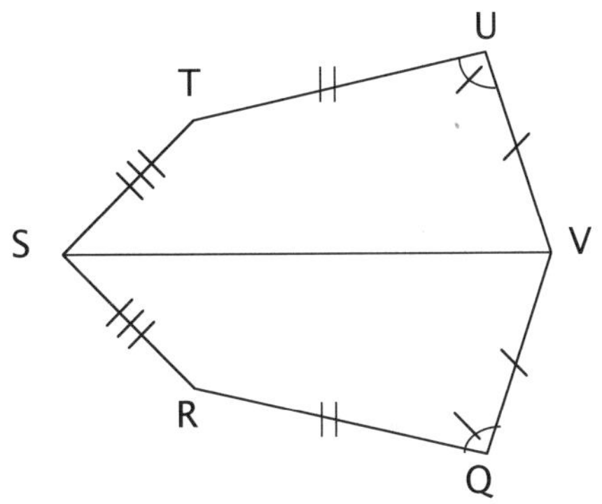

Statements	Reasons

This proof is easy if you first redraw the triangles you are interested in as two separate figures.

3. **Given:** $\overline{FE} \cong \overline{GH}$, $\overline{FH} \cong \overline{GE}$
Prove: $\Delta FEH \cong \Delta GHE$

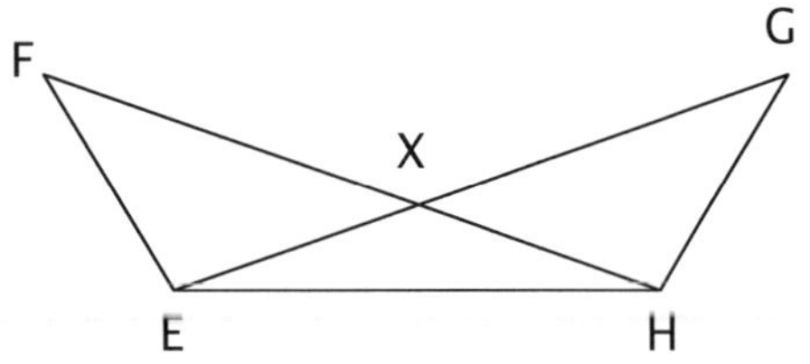

Statements	Reasons

LESSON PRACTICE 26A

Complete the following proofs using HL, LL, HA, or LA theorems.

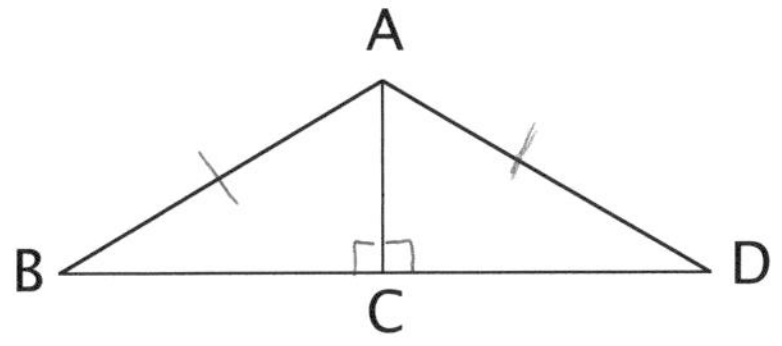

Given: ΔABD is isosceles with long side $\overline{BD}$.
$\overline{AC} \perp \overline{BD}$

Prove: C is midpoint of $\overline{BD}$.

STATEMENTS	*REASONS*
1. ________	given
$\angle ACB$ is right $\angle$.	2. ________
$\angle ACD$ is a right $\angle$.	3. ________
4. ________	given
5. ________	def. of isosceles triangle
6. ________	reflexive property
7. ________	HL theorem
$\overline{BC} \cong \overline{DC}$	8. ________
9. ________	10. ________

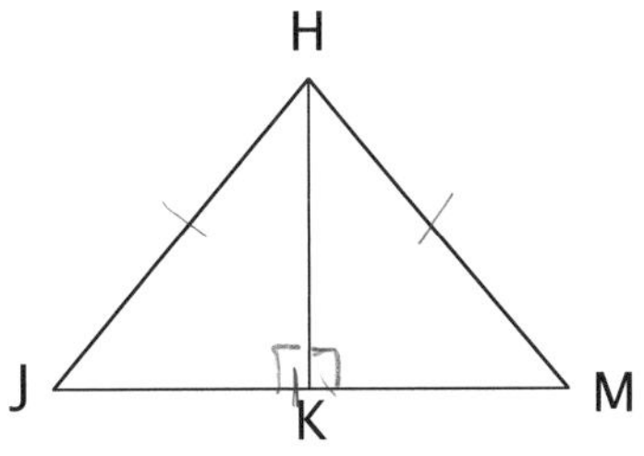

Given: ΔHJM is equilateral.
$\overline{HK} \perp \overline{JM}$

Prove: $\Delta HJK \cong \Delta HMK$

STATEMENTS	*REASONS*
11. ________	given
$\angle HJK \cong \angle HMK$	12. ________
13. ________	given
$\angle HKJ$ is a right $\angle$	14. ________
$\angle HKM$ is a right $\angle$	15. ________
16. ___ $\cong$ ___	reflexive property
17. ___ $\cong$ ___	LA

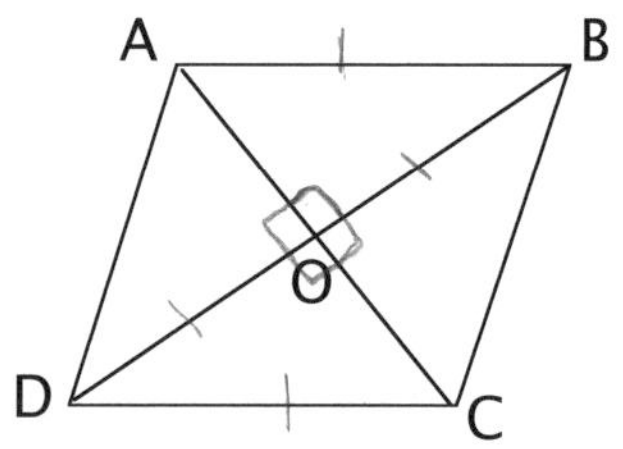

Given: ABCD is a rhombus.
$\overline{AC} \perp \overline{DB}$
O is midpoint of $\overline{BD}$.
Prove: $\Delta ABO \cong \Delta CDO$

STATEMENTS	*REASONS*
18. ________	given
19. ________	definition of a rhombus
20. ________	21. ________
22. ∠______	definition of perpendicular
23. ∠______	definition of perpendicular
24. ________	given
25. ___≅___	26. ________
27. ___≅___	28. ________

26B

Complete the following proofs using HL, LL, HA, or LA theorems.

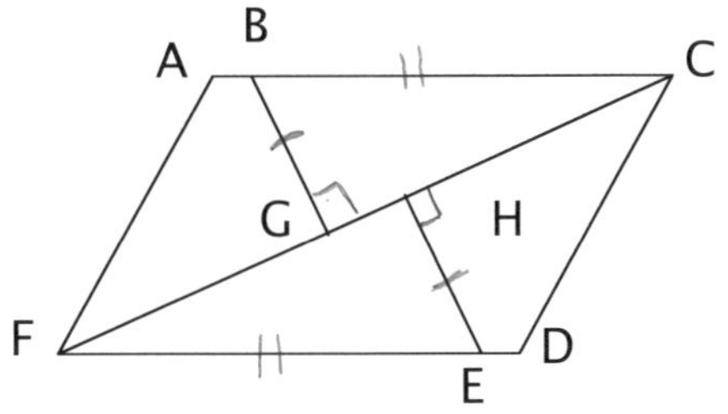

Given: $\overline{HE} \perp \overline{FC}$
$\overline{BG} \perp \overline{FC}$
$\overline{BG} \cong \overline{EH}$
$\overline{BC} \cong \overline{EF}$
Prove: $\Delta FHE \cong \Delta CGB$, using HL.

STATEMENTS	***REASONS***
1. ________	given
2. ________	given
3. ________	def. of perpendicular
4. ________	def. of perpendicular
5. ________	6. ________
7. ________	8. ________
9. ___ ≅ ___	10. ________

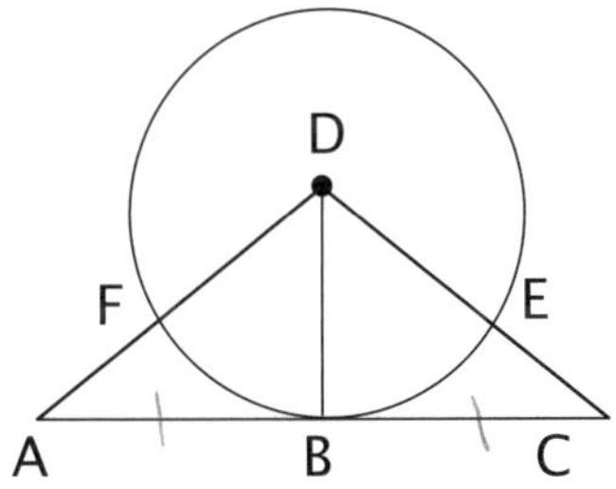

Given: Figure is circle with center at D.
$\overline{AC}$ is tangent to circle at B.
B is midpoint of $\overline{AC}$.
Prove: $\Delta ABD \cong \Delta CBD$, using LL.

STATEMENTS	***REASONS***
11. ________	given
12. ________	13. ________
14. ________	15. ________
16. ________	given
17. ________	18. ________
19. ________	20. ________
21. ___ ≅ ___	22. ________

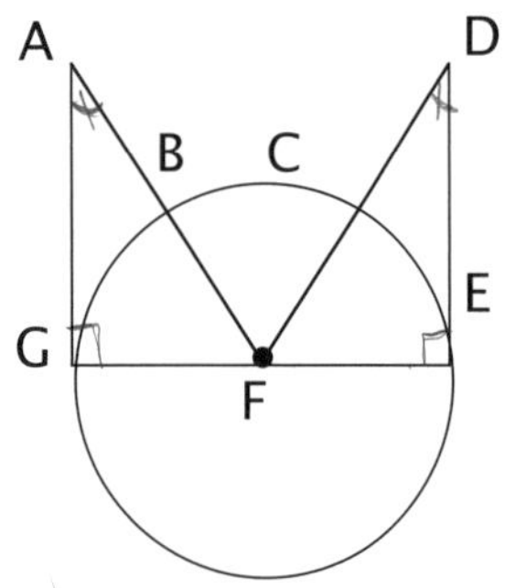

Given: Figure is circle with center at F.
$\overline{AG}$ is tangent to circle at G.
$\overline{DE}$ is tangent to circle at E.
$\angle GAF \cong \angle EDF$

Prove: $\overline{AF} \cong \overline{DF}$, using LA to prove triangles congruent.

STATEMENTS	*REASONS*
23. ________	given
24. ________	given
25. ___⊥___	26.________
27. ___⊥___	28.________
29. ________	definition of perpendicular
30. ________	definition of perpendicular
31. ________	32.________
33. ________	34.________
35. ___≅___	36.________
37. ___≅___	38.________

26C

Complete the following proof.

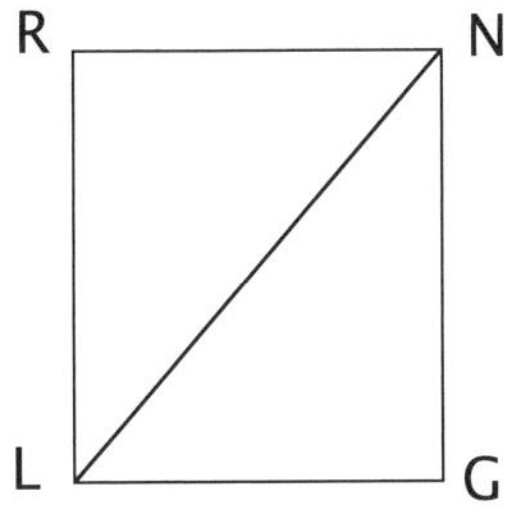

Given: ▭ RNGL is a rectangle.
Prove: $\Delta RNL \cong \Delta GLN$, using HL.

STATEMENTS	***REASONS***
RNGL is a rectangle.	given
1. ________	2. ________
3. ________	4. ________
5. ________	6. ________
7. ________	8. ________

Find the unknown side.

9. L =

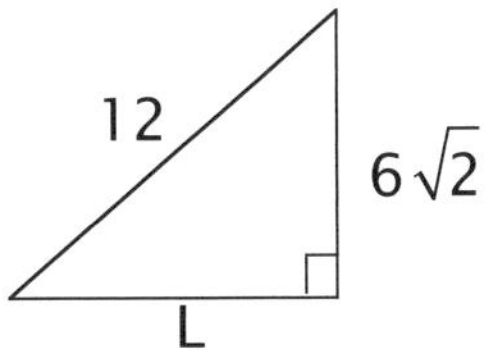

10. H =

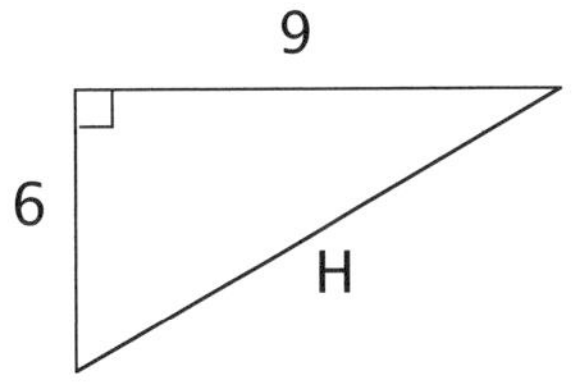

Follow the directions.

11. What is the sum of two supplementary angles?

12. Give the number of congruent sides in an isosceles triangle.

13. In a 45° right triangle, what is multiplied by the length of one leg to find the length of the hypotenuse?

Follow the directions.

14. Simplify: $\frac{2}{\sqrt{5}} \times \frac{5}{\sqrt{2}} =$

15. Find the circumference of a circle with a radius of 2.3 cm.

16. Find the area of a circle with a radius of 2.3 cm.

17. What is the measure of each interior angle of a fifteen-sided regular polygon?

18. Name a geometric figure with no length or width.

19. What is the measure of ∠A in the drawing? (The horizontal lines are parallel.)

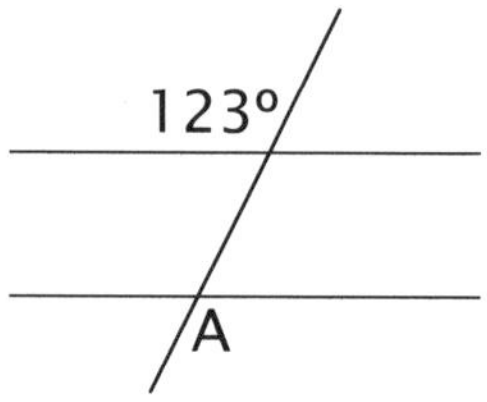

20. Give the reason for your answer to #19.

Complete the following proof.

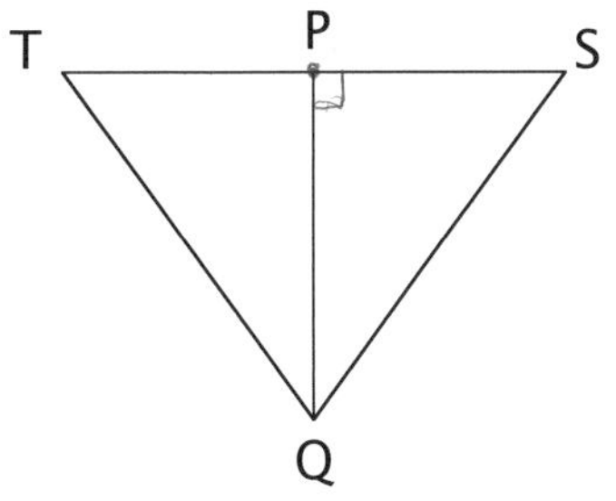

Given: $\overline{QP} \perp \overline{ST}$, and P is the midpoint of $\overline{ST}$.

Prove: $\overline{SQ} \cong \overline{TQ}$, using LL.

STATEMENTS	***REASONS***
P is the midpoint of $\overline{ST}$.	given
$\overline{QP} \perp \overline{ST}$	given
$\angle SPQ$ and $\angle TPQ$ are right angles.	def. of $\perp$ lines
ΔPTQ and ΔPSQ are right triangles.	def. of right triangles
1. ________	2.________
3. ________	4.________
5. ________	6.________
7. ________	8.________

Answer the questions about each triangle.

9. What is the height (if it is a perpendicular bisector) when each side is 8" long?

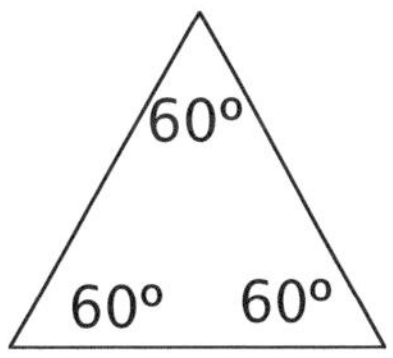

10. What is the area of the triangle?

11. What is the perimeter of the triangle?

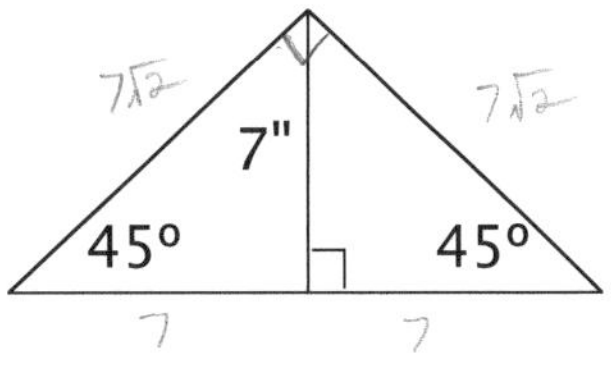

12. What is the area of the triangle?

Follow the directions.

13. An octagon is inscribed in a circle. In how many points does the octagon touch the circle?

14. Simplify: $\frac{\sqrt{5}}{3\sqrt{2}} \times \frac{\sqrt{3}}{4\sqrt{2}} =$

15. Find the volume of a sphere with a radius of 4".

16. What is the surface area of the sphere in #15? ($SA = 4\pi r^2$)

17. What is the measure of each interior angle of an eighteen-sided regular polygon?

18. Name a geometric figure with length, but no width.

19. What is the measure of ∠A? (The horizontal lines are parallel.)

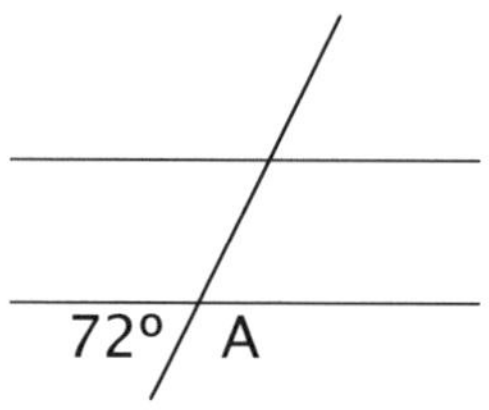

20. Give the reason for your answer to #19.

26E

Complete the following proof.

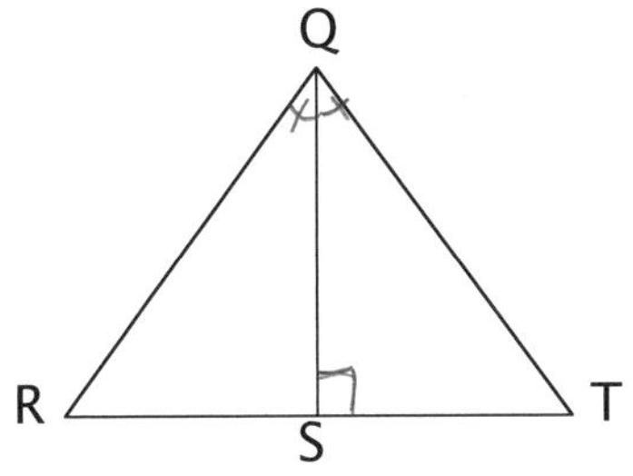

Given: $\overline{QS} \perp \overline{RT}$, and bisects $\angle RQT$.

Prove: $\overline{RQ} \cong \overline{TQ}$, using LA.

STATEMENTS	***REASONS***
$\overline{QS}$ bisects $\angle RQT$.	given
$\overline{QS} \perp \overline{RT}$	given
$\angle RSQ$ and $\angle TSQ$ are right angles.	def. of $\perp$ lines
ΔRSQ and ΔTSQ are right triangles.	def. of right triangles
1. ________	2.________
3. ________	4.________
5. ________	6.________
7. ________	8.________

Find volume and surface area using meters.

9. V =

10. SA =

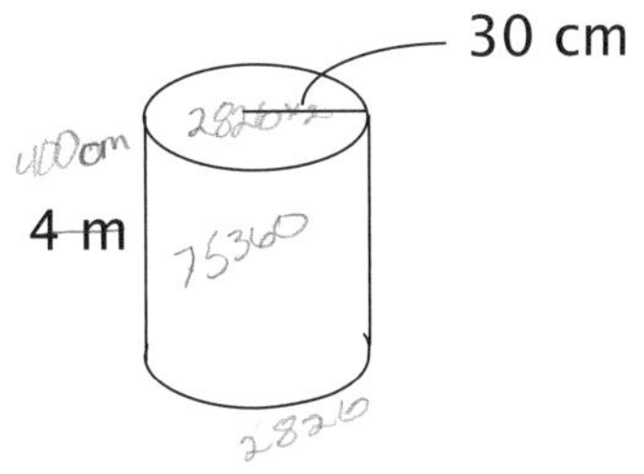

Write out the names of the following postulates or theorems.

11. SSS

12. SAS

13. ASA

14. AAS

15. HL

16. LL

17. HA

18. LA

Sharpen your algebra skills!

For the next few lessons, this section will have problems combining algebra and geometry skills.

EXAMPLE 1 Find the unknown side.

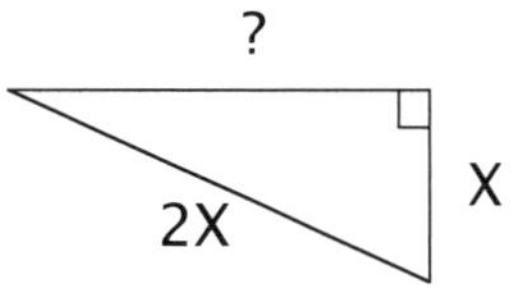

Use the Pythagorean theorem.

$L^2 + X^2 = (2X)^2$

$L^2 = 4X^2 - X^2 = 3X^2 \quad L = X\sqrt{3}$

This must be a 30°-60°-90° triangle.

Solve.

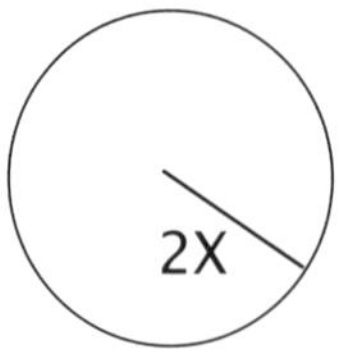

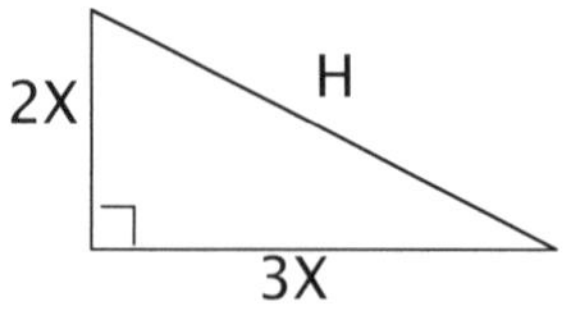

19. Area =

20. H =

Here are some more proofs to try.

There are two ways in which you could separate overlapping triangles from the drawing. You will have to decide which way is most useful to you.

1. **Given:** $\overline{AB} \cong \overline{AC}$, $\overline{CQ} \perp \overline{AB}$, $\overline{BR} \perp \overline{AC}$
   Prove: $\overline{CQ} \cong \overline{BR}$

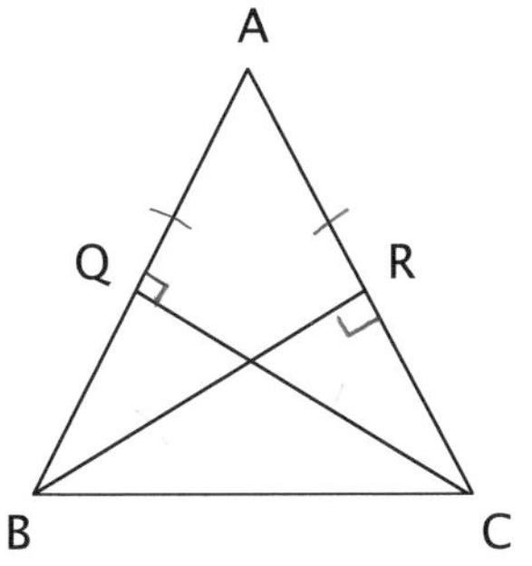

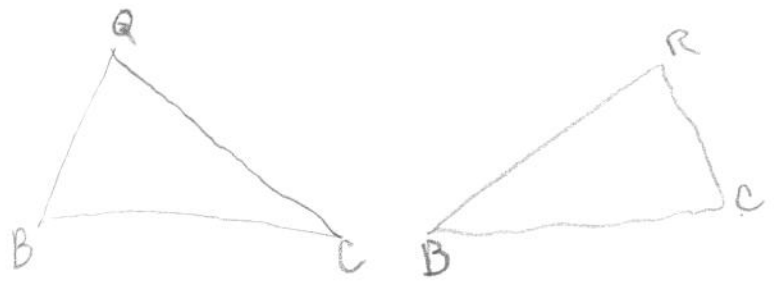

Statements	Reasons

After proving the next theorem, you can use it in your proof for #3.

2. **Given:** $\overline{AB}$ is a perpendicular bisector of $\overline{XY}$.
   Prove: Point A is equidistant from the ends of $\overline{XY}$.

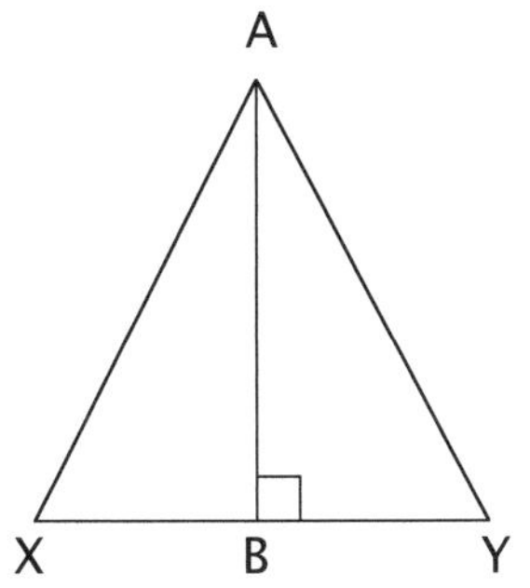

Statements	Reasons

3. **Given:** $\angle FEH$ and $\angle FGH$ are right angles.
$\overline{FH}$ is a perpendicular bisector of $\overline{EG}$.
Prove: $\overline{EH} \cong \overline{HG}$

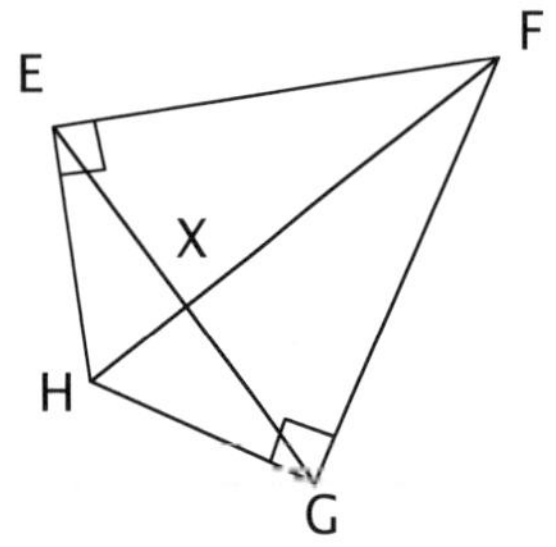

Statements	Reasons

Complete the following proofs using AA similarity.

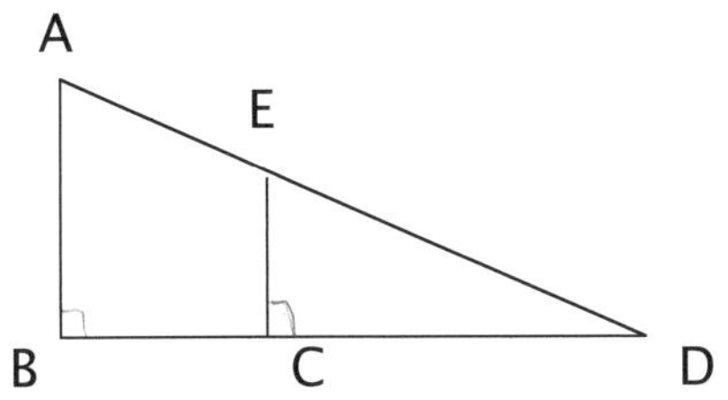

Given: $\overline{AB} \perp \overline{BD}$
$\overline{EC} \perp \overline{BD}$
Prove: $\Delta ABD \sim \Delta ECD$

STATEMENTS	***REASONS***
1. ________	given
2. ________	given
3. ___ ≅ ___	4. ________
5. ___ ≅ ___	6. ________
7. ___ ~ ___	8. ________

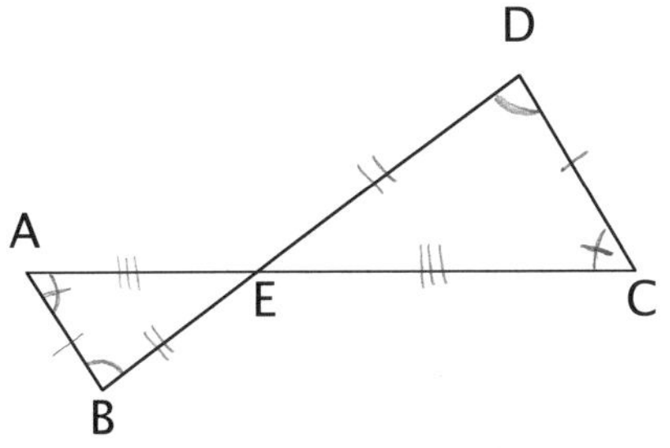

Given: $\overline{AB} \parallel \overline{CD}$
Prove: $\Delta ABE \sim \Delta CDE$

STATEMENTS	***REASONS***
9. ________	given
10. ___ ≅ ___	11. ________
12. ___ ≅ ___	13. ________
14. ___ ~ ___	15. ________

Find X using "corresponding parts of similar figures are proportional."

16. 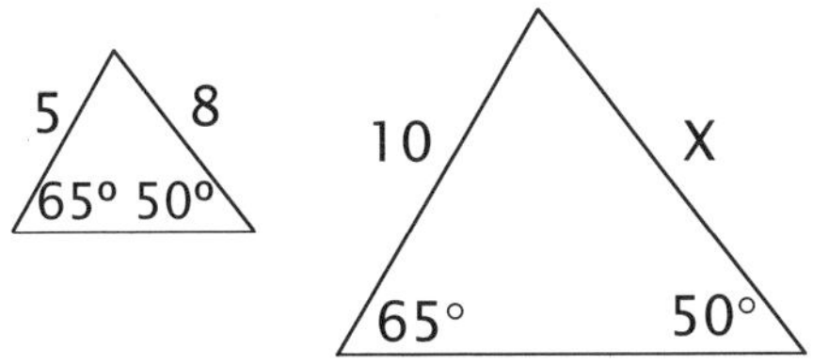

Find X using "corresponding parts of similar figures are proportional."

17.

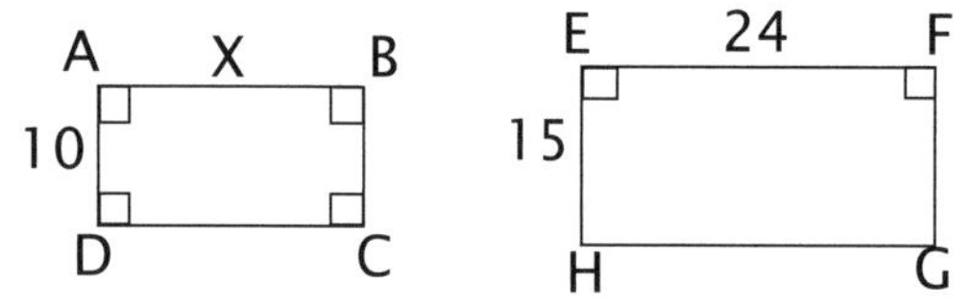

rectangle ABCD is similar to rectangle EFGH

18.

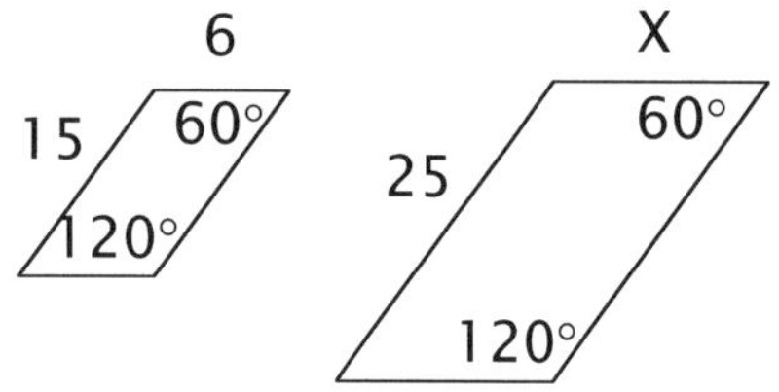

19.

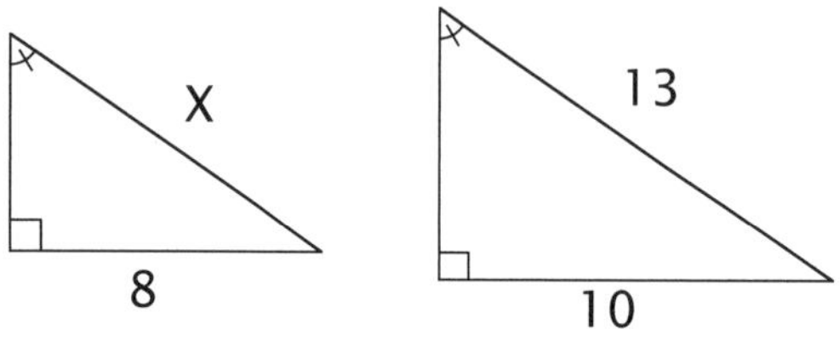

20.

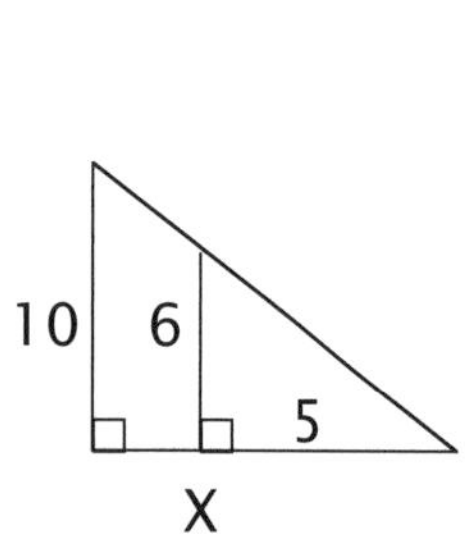

X is total base of the larger triangle.

Complete the following proofs using AA similarity.

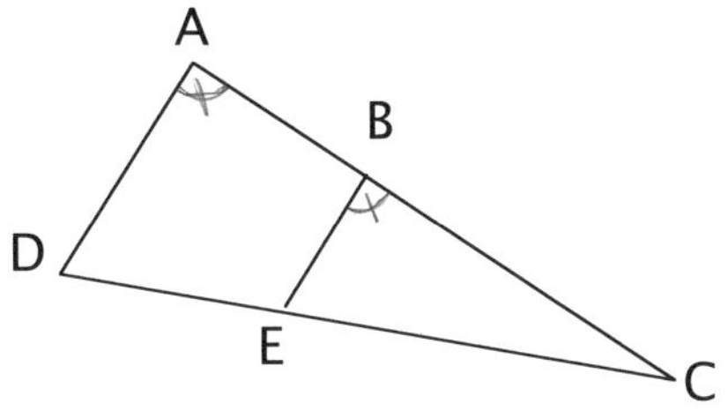

Given: ∠DAB ≅ ∠EBC
Prove: ΔDAC ~ ΔEBC

STATEMENTS	*REASONS*
1. ________	given
2. ___ ≅ ___	3. ________
4. ___ ~ ___	5. ________

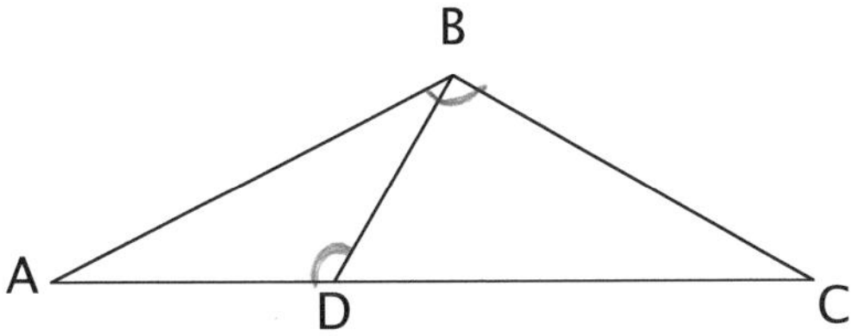

Given: ∠ABC ≅ ∠ADB
Prove: ΔABC ~ ΔADB

STATEMENTS	*REASONS*
6. ________	7. ________
8. ________	9. ________
10. ________	11. ________

Find X using "corresponding parts of similar figures are proportional."

12.

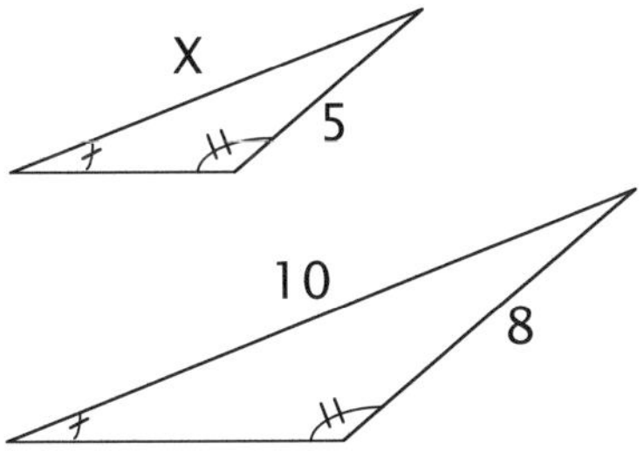

13.

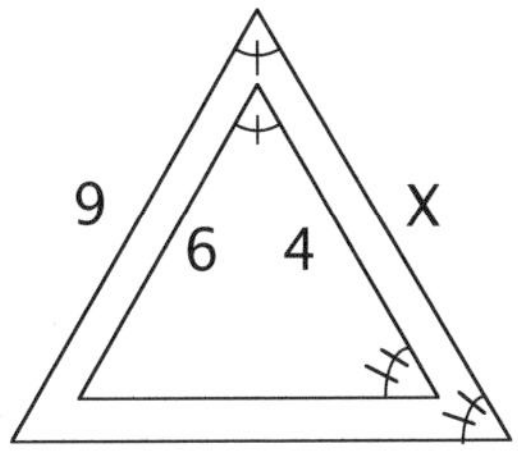

Find X using "corresponding parts of similar figures are proportional."

14.

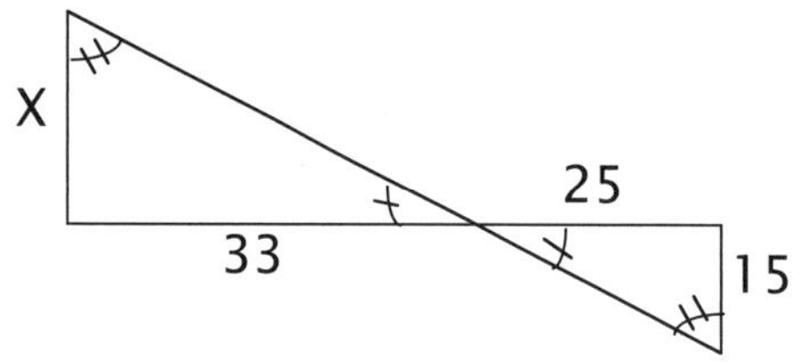

15.

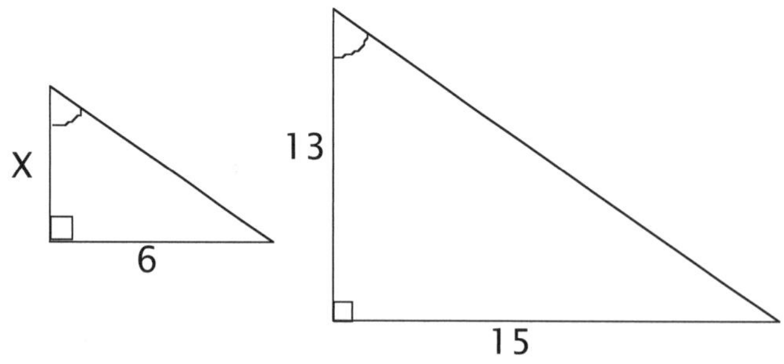

16.

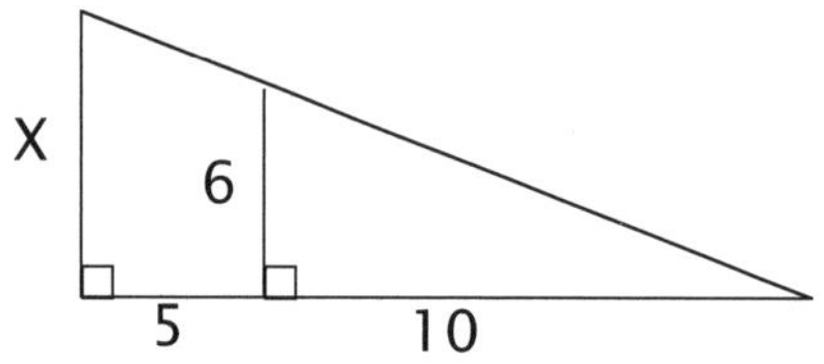

17.

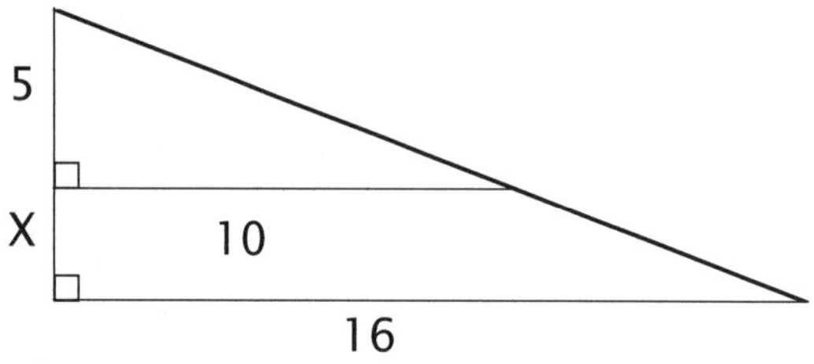

Complete the following proofs.

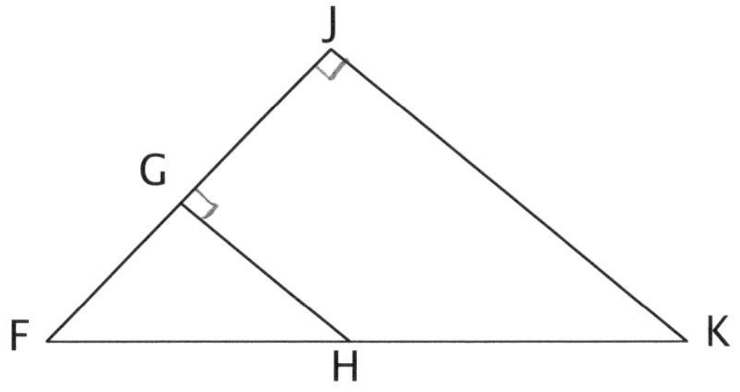

Given: $\overline{GH} \perp \overline{FJ}$, and $\overline{JK} \perp \overline{FJ}$
Prove: $\Delta FGH \sim \Delta FJK$

STATEMENTS	*REASONS*
$\overline{GH} \perp \overline{FJ}$ and $\overline{JK} \perp \overline{FJ}$	Given
1. ________	2. ________
3. ________	4. ________
5. ________	6. ________

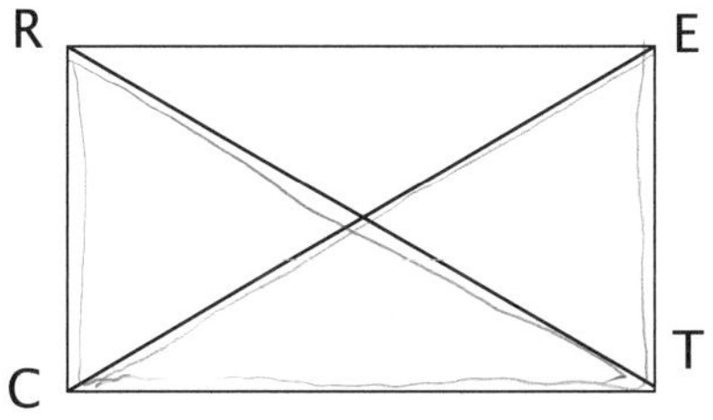

Given: ▭ RETC is a rectangle
Prove: $\Delta ECT \cong \Delta RTC$

STATEMENTS	*REASONS*
▭ RETC is a rectangle	Given
7. ________	8. ________
9. ________	10. ________
11. ________	12. ________
13. ________	14. ________

15. Is $RT \cong EC$? Why?

Follow the directions.

16. Find X if the triangles are similar.

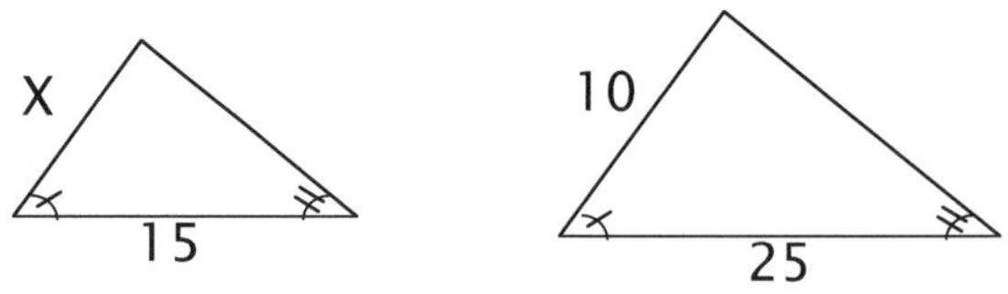

17. If the exterior angles of a regular polygon each measure 36°, how many sides are there?
What is the name of the polygon?

18. If the apothem of the polygon in #17 is $3\sqrt{2}$ cm and the length of each side is 5 cm, find the area. (Remember that the apothem is a segment drawn from the center perpendicular to one side.)

19. What is the measure of $\angle\beta$?

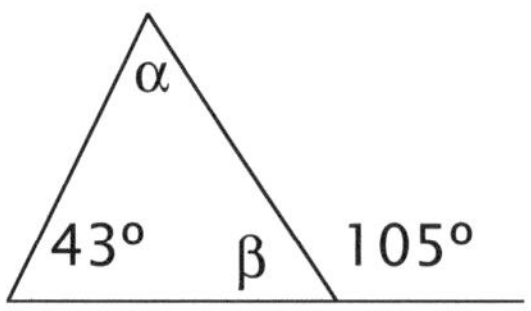

20. What is the measure of $\angle\alpha$?

27D

Complete the following proofs.

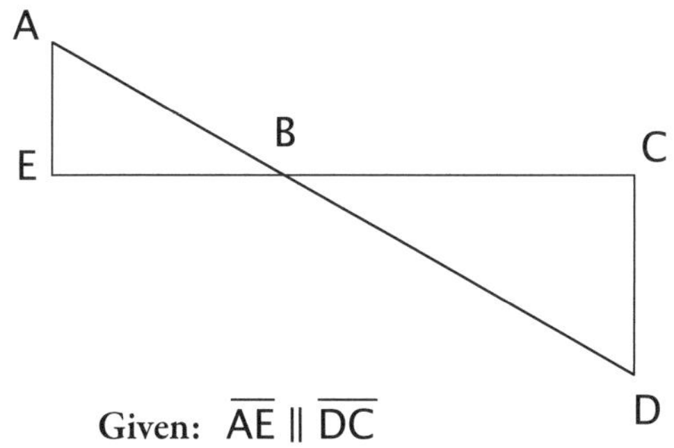

Given: $\overline{AE} \parallel \overline{DC}$
Prove: $\Delta AEB \sim \Delta DCB$

STATEMENTS	*REASONS*
$\overline{AE} \parallel \overline{DC}$	given
1. ________	2. ________
3. ________	4. ________
5. ________	6. ________

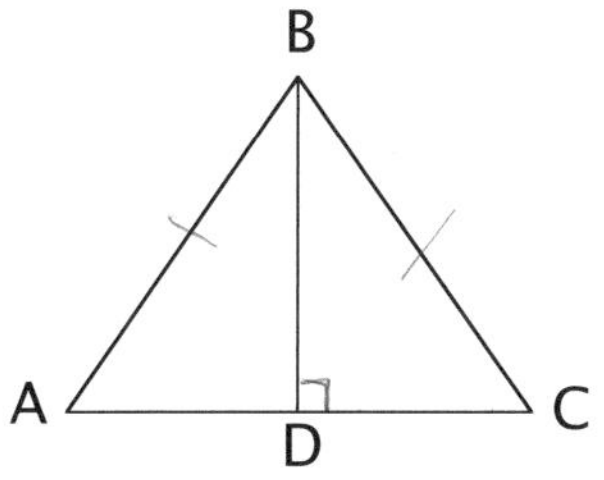

Given: $\overline{BD} \perp \overline{AC}$
$\overline{AB} \cong \overline{CB}$
Prove: $\overline{AD} \cong \overline{CD}$ using HL.

STATEMENTS	*REASONS*
$\overline{BD} \perp \overline{AC}$	given
$\angle BDA$ and $\angle BDC$ are right angles.	def. of $\perp$ lines
ΔBDA and ΔBDC are right triangles.	def. of right triangles
7. ________	8. ________
9. ________	10.________
11. ________	12.________
13. ________	14.________

Follow the directions.

15. Find X if the triangles are similar.

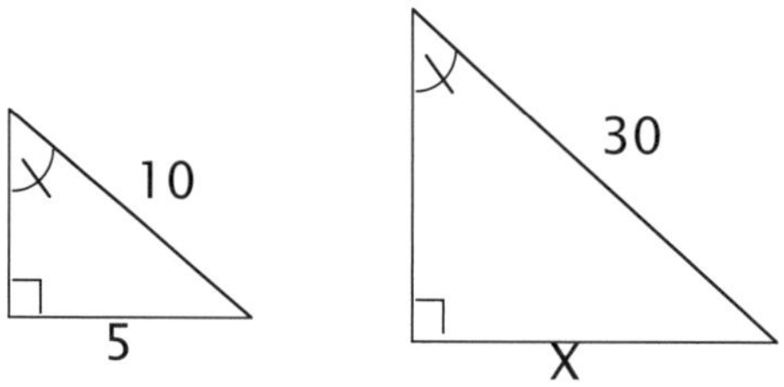

16. If the exterior angles of a regular polygon each measure 45°, how many sides are there?
What is the name of the polygon?

17. If the apothem of the polygon in #16 is 12 m and the length of each side is 10 m, find the area.

18. Find the the perimeter of the polygon described in #16 and #17.

19. What is the measure of $\angle\beta$?

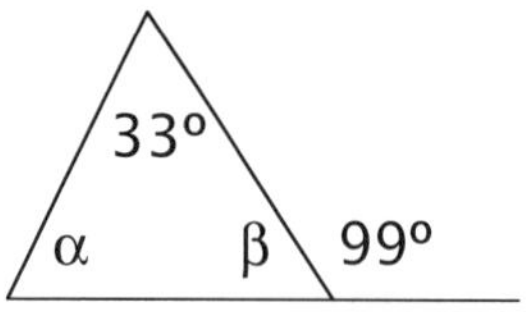

20. What is the measure of $\angle\alpha$?

Complete the following proofs.

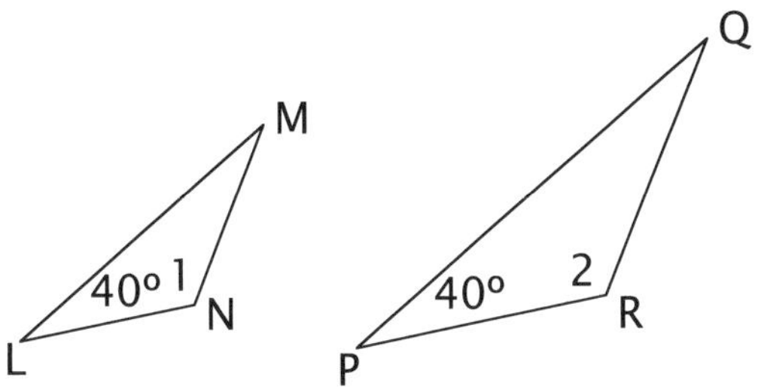

Given: ∠1 ≅ ∠2
Prove: ΔLMN ~ ΔPQR

STATEMENTS	*REASONS*
1. ________	2. ________
3. ________	4. ________
5. ________	6. ________

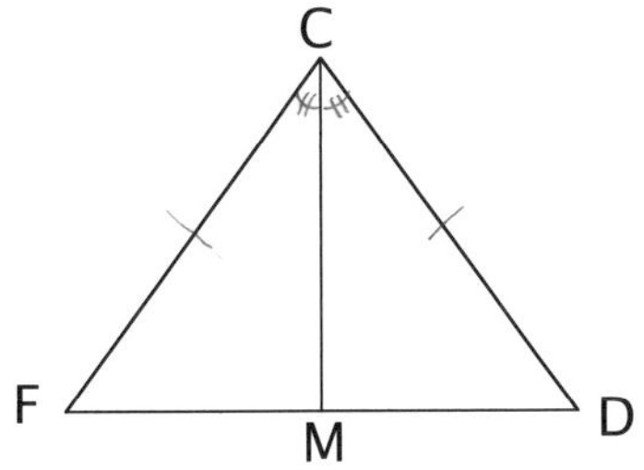

Given: ΔCDF is an isosceles triangle with long side $\overline{FD}$.
$\overline{CM}$ bisects ∠FCD.
Prove: ΔCDM ≅ ΔCFM

STATEMENTS	*REASONS*
ΔCDF is an isosceles triangle.	given
$\overline{CM}$ bisects ∠FCD.	given
7. ________	8. ________
9. ________	10. ________
11. ________	12. ________
13. ________	14. ________

Follow the directions.

15. Find X if the triangles are similar.

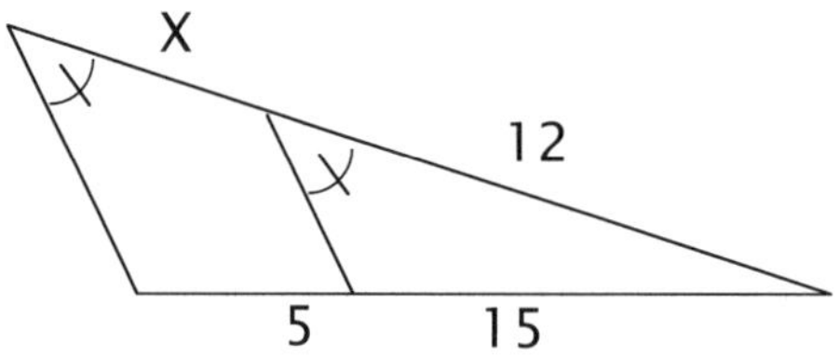

16. Find the area of a sector with a radius of 6' and a measure of 330°.

17. Find the volume of a section of a cylinder with a radius of 6', a height of 4.5', and a measure of 330°.

Sharpen your algebra skills!

Sometimes you can use what you know about geometry to write an equation and solve for X.

EXAMPLE 1 Solve for X

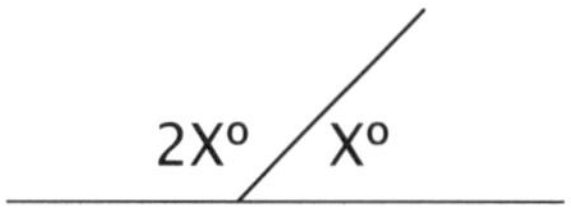

The angles are supplementary.

$2X + X = 180°$

$3X = 180°$ $X = 60°$

Solve for X.

18.

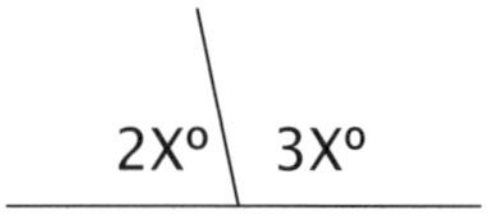

19.

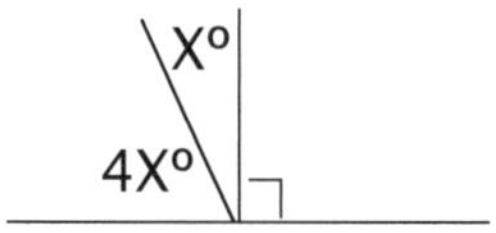

20. perimeter = 12

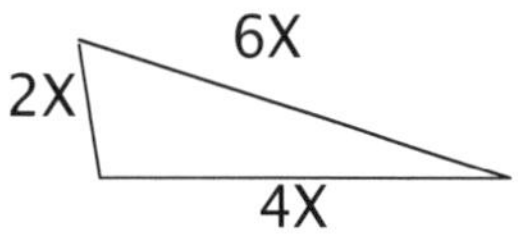

Some proofs involve circles. You may want to review the information in lesson 12 in your text before you try these proofs.

Prove each theorem using any postulates or theorems you have learned so far in this course.

1. **Given:** The lines are tangent to the circle at points X and Y.
C is the center of the circle.

Prove: $\overline{PX} \cong \overline{PY}$

Hint: Start by drawing the radii from the center to points X and Y.
You will also need to draw another line.

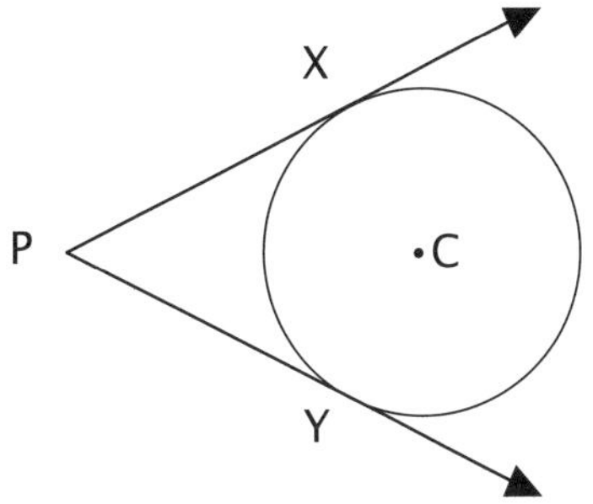

Statements	Reasons

Remember that the measure of any arc is the same as the measure of the central angle that defines it.

2. **Given:** $\overline{DE} \perp \overline{AB}$
C is the center of the circle.

Prove: A diameter perpendicular to a chord bisects the chord and its arc.

Hint: Start by drawing the radii from the center to points A and B.

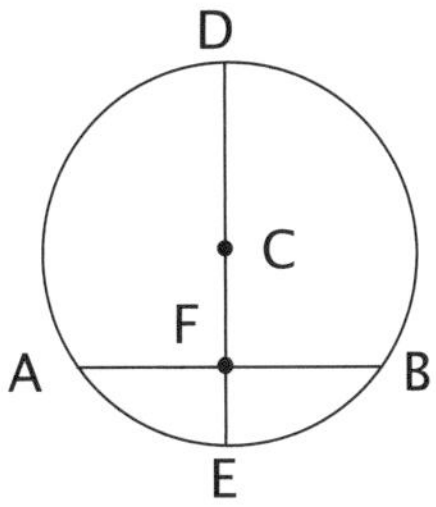

Statements	Reasons

3. **Given:** $\overline{OP} \cong \overline{LM}$

C is the center of the circle.

Prove: The perpendicular bisectors drawn from each chord to the center of the circle have the same measure.

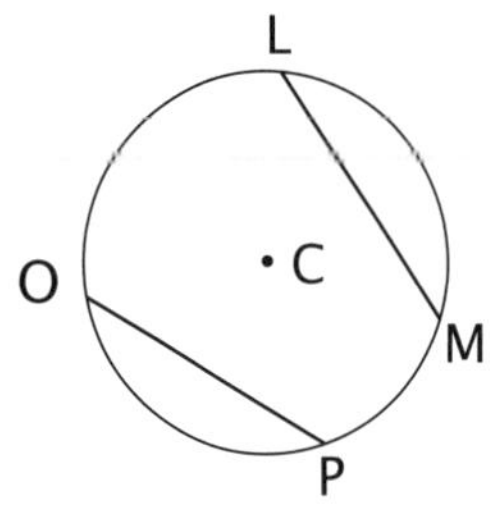

Statements	Reasons

Complete the following transformations.

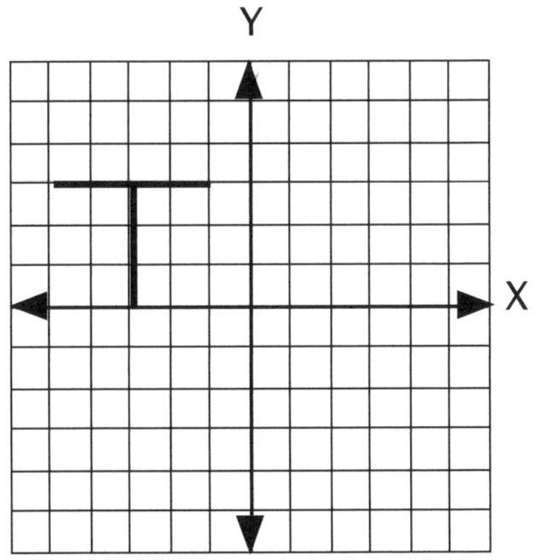

1. A translation (slide) of the figure over +3 and down 5.

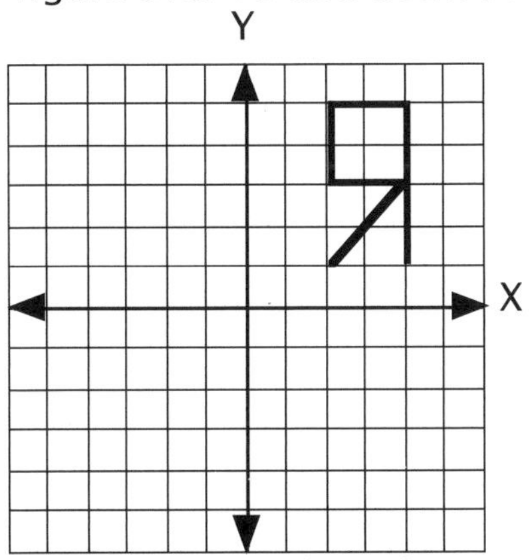

2. A translation of the figure over –6 and down 7.

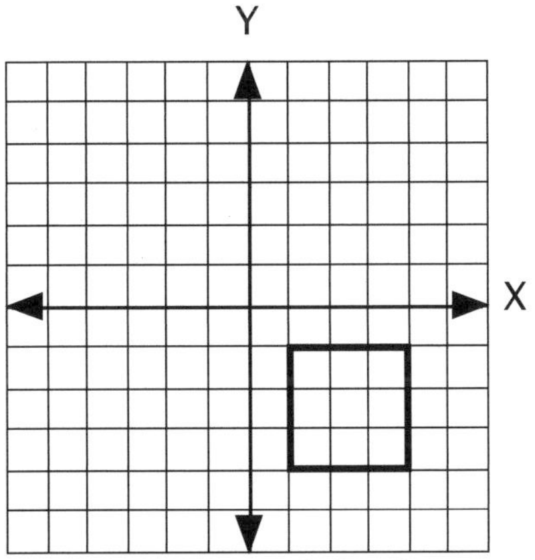

3. A translation of the figure over –5 and up 7.

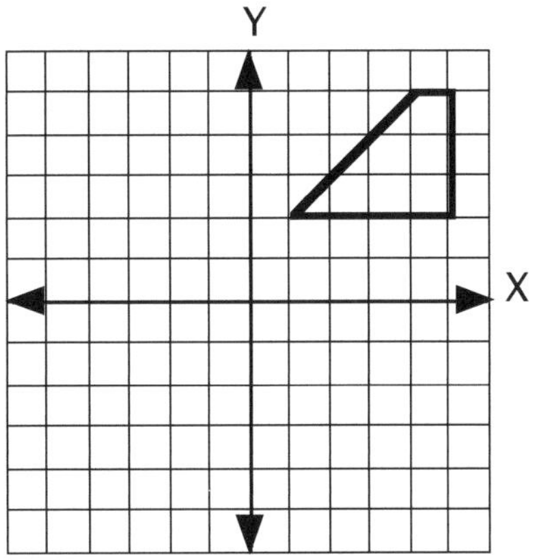

4. A reflection (flip) of the figure in the X-axis.

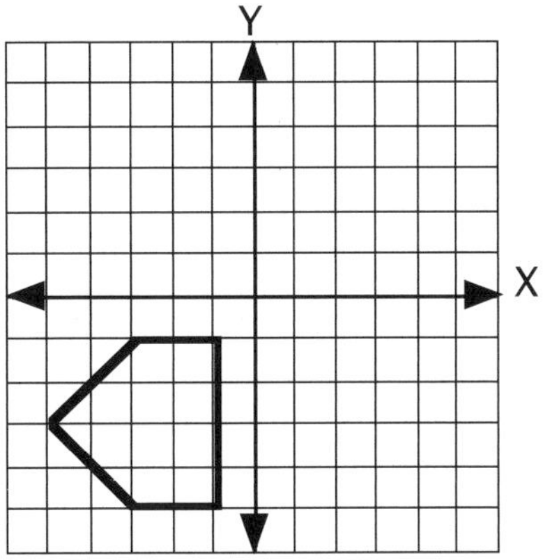

5. A reflection of the figure in the Y-axis.

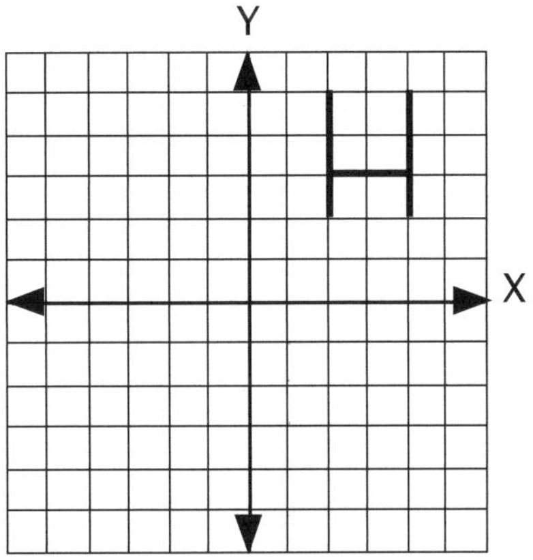

6. A rotation 90° around the origin (0, 0).

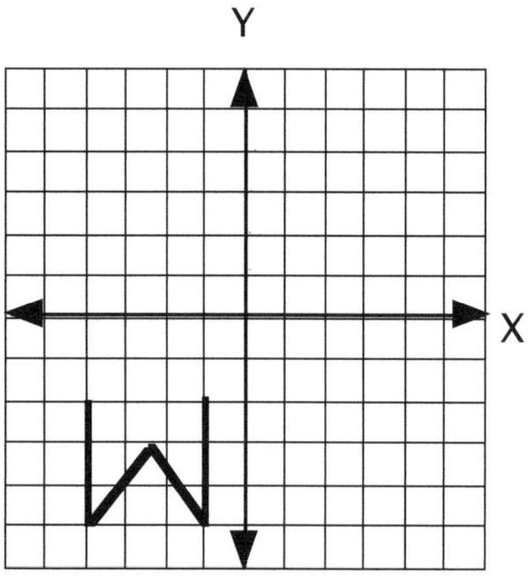

7. A rotation of the figure 270° around the origin (0, 0).

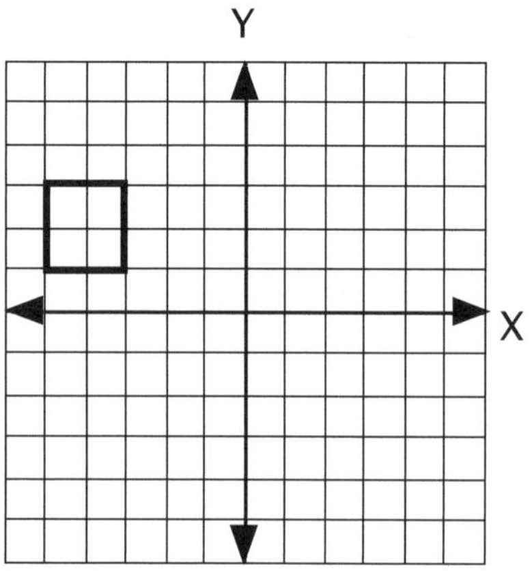

8. A dilation (stretch) two times around point (-4, 2).

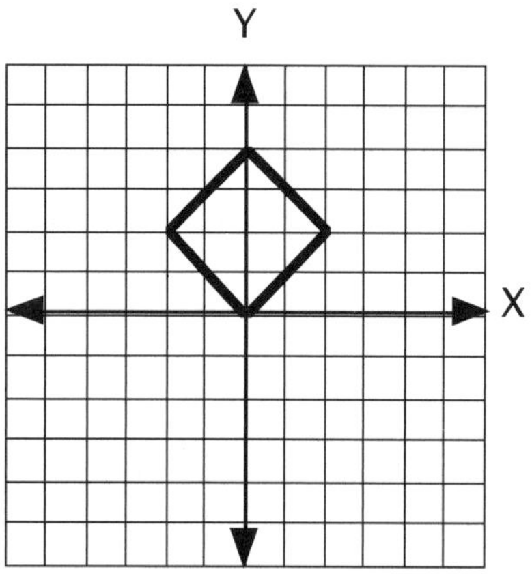

9. A dilation two times around point (0, 2).

Complete the following transformations.

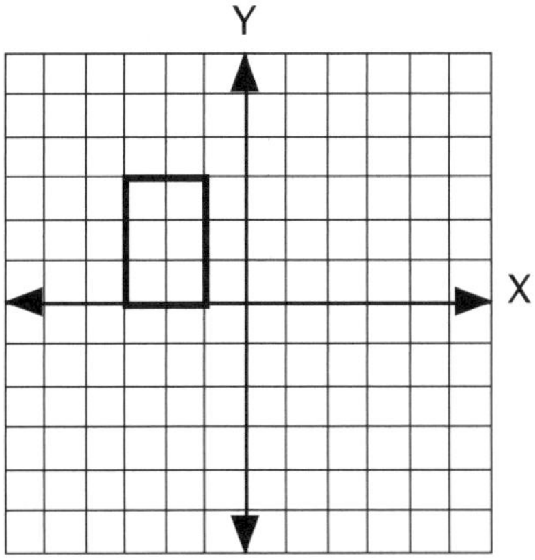

1. A translation (slide) of the figure over +5 and down 2.

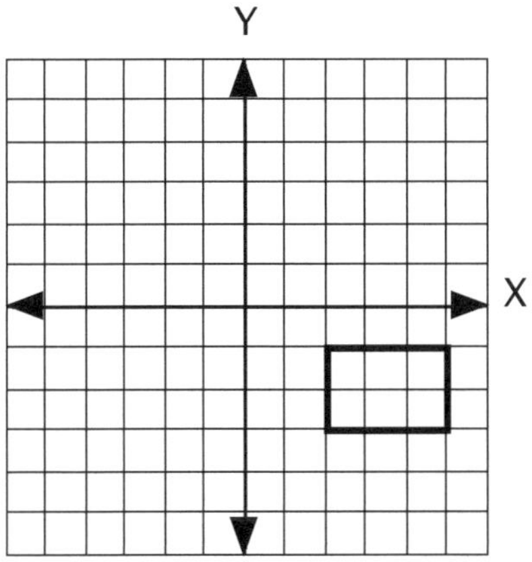

2. A translation of the figure over −3 and up 3.

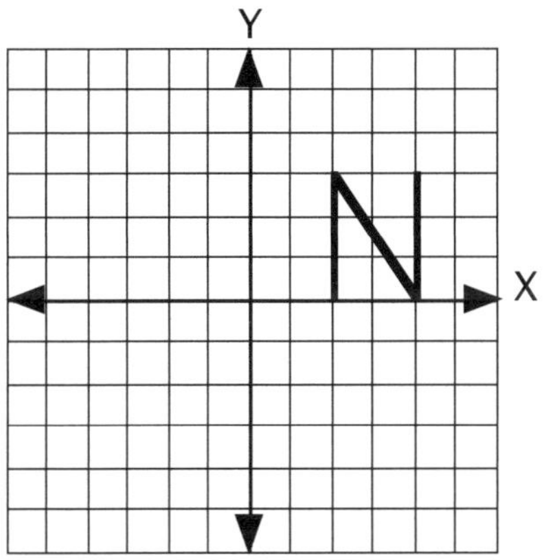

3. A translation of the figure over −2 and down 3.

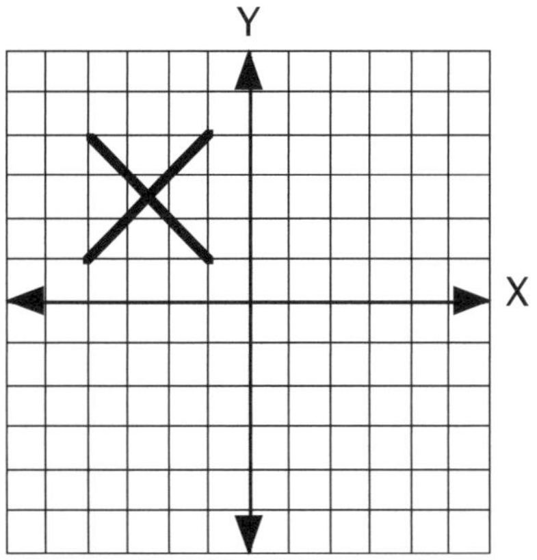

4. A reflection (flip) of the figure in the X-axis.

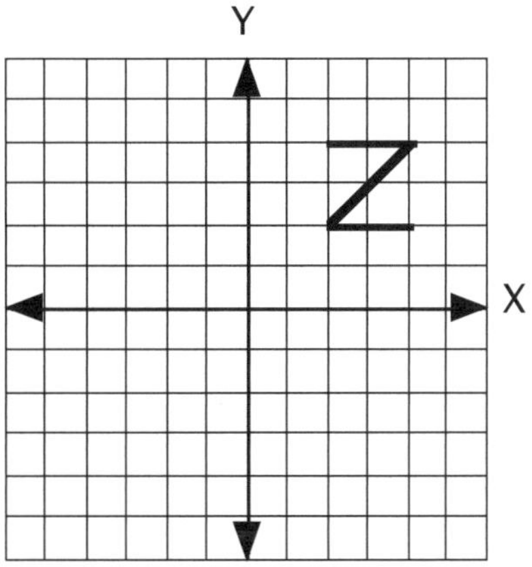

5. A reflection of the figure in the Y-axis.

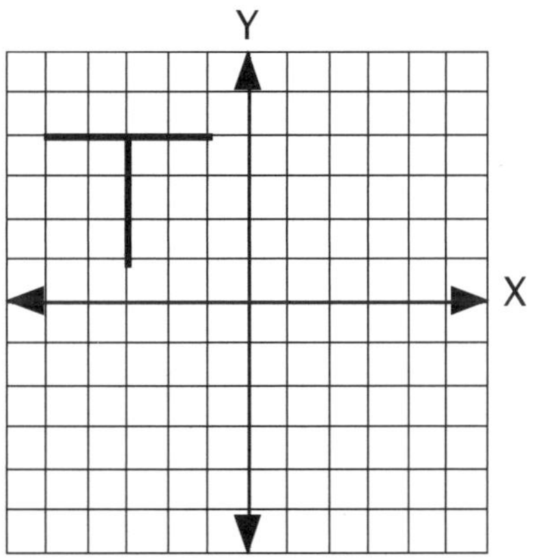

6. A rotation 180° around point (−3, −1).

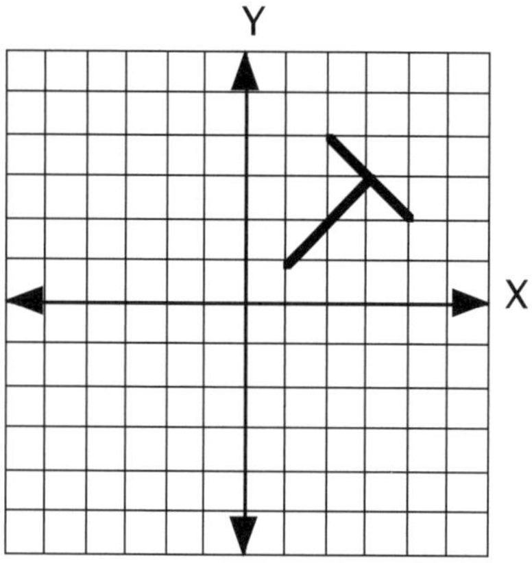

7. A rotation 270° around point (-1, -1).

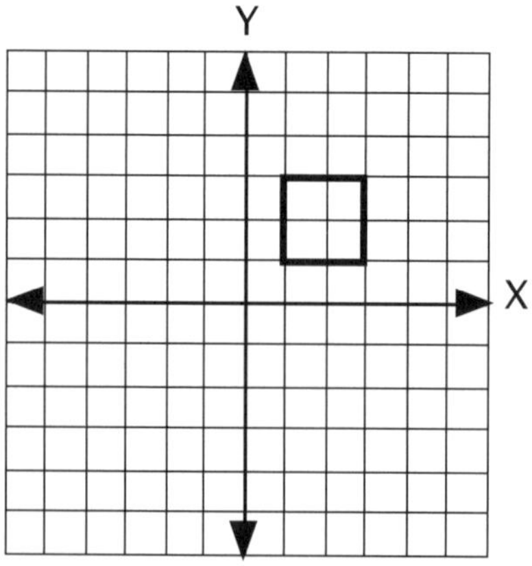

8. A dilation (stretch) two times around point (2, 2).

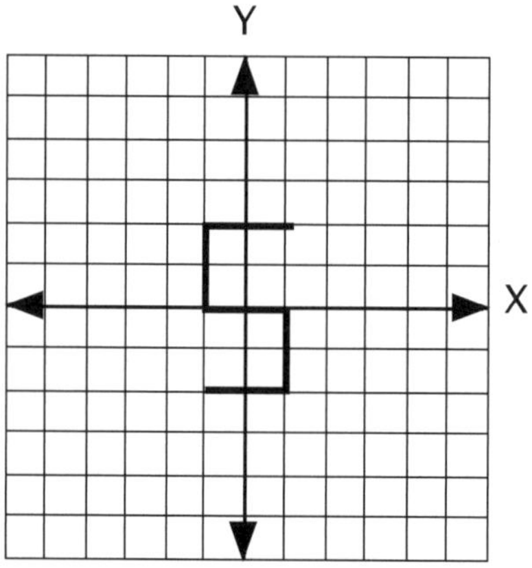

9. A dilation three times around point (0, 0).

Complete the transformations as directed.

A translation (slide) of the figure over +3 and down 4.

1. Plot the new points by translating each one over 3 and down 4.

2. Graph the result of #1.

For #1–4

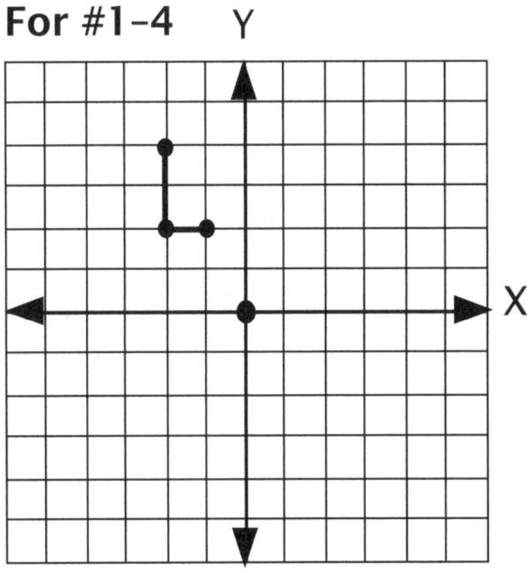

A reflection (flip) of the original figure in the Y-axis.

3. Plot the new points by reflecting each in the Y-axis.

4. Graph the result of #3.

For #5–8

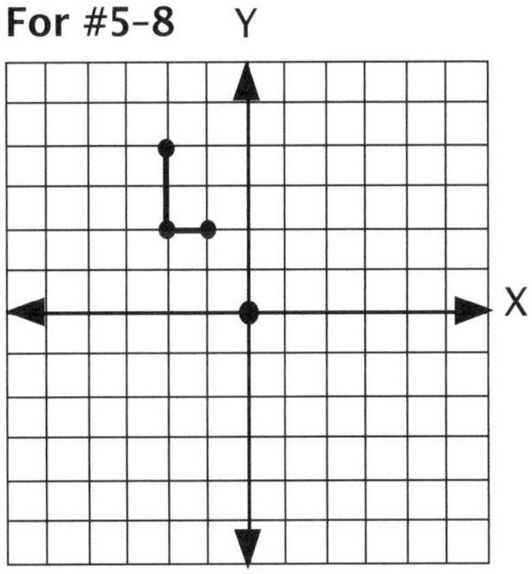

A reflection (flip) of the figure in the X-axis.

5. Plot the new points by reflecting each in the X-axis.

6. Graph the result of #5.

A rotation of the original figure around the origin.

7. Plot the new points by rotating the figure 180° around the origin.

8. Graph the result of #7.

Follow the directions.

9. Use the drawing to complete the equation.

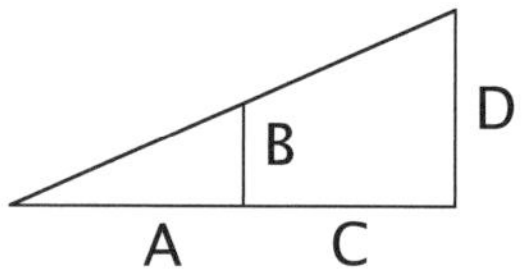

$$\frac{A}{B}=\frac{A+C}{?}$$

10. If A = 5', B = 3', and C = 10', then A + C = _____.

11. If A = 5', B = 3', and C = 10', then D = _____.

12. How tall is the tree if the man is 6' tall?

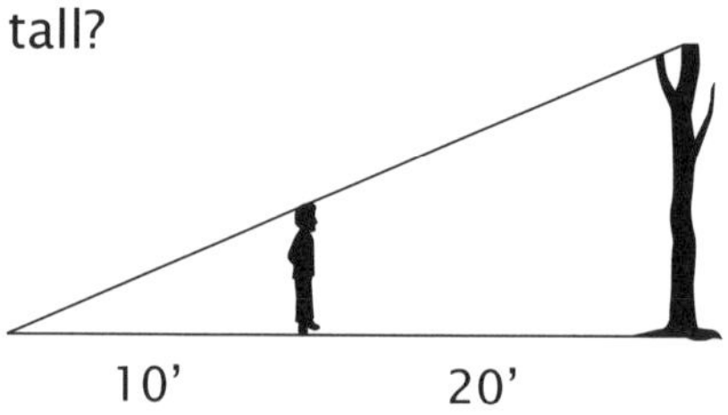

13. Give the name for an angle greater than 180° and less than 360°.

14. Simplify $6\sqrt{200}$.

Complete the following proof.

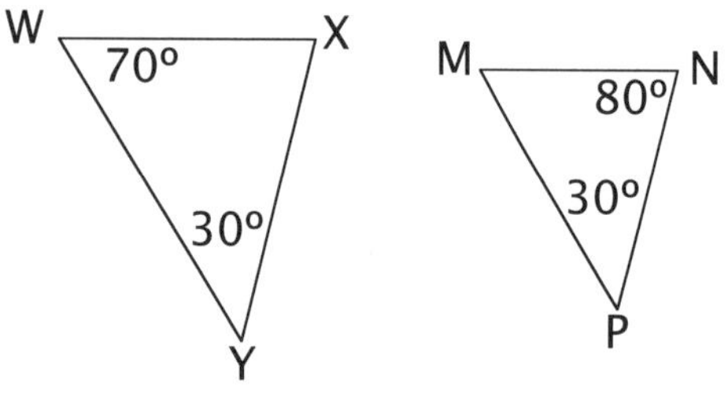

Prove: $\Delta WXY \sim \Delta MNP$

STATEMENTS	*REASONS*
15. ________	16. ________
m∠X = 80°	The angles of a triangle add up to 180°.
17. ________	18. ________
19. ________	20. ________

Complete the transformations as directed.

A translation (slide) of the figure over –4 and up 3.

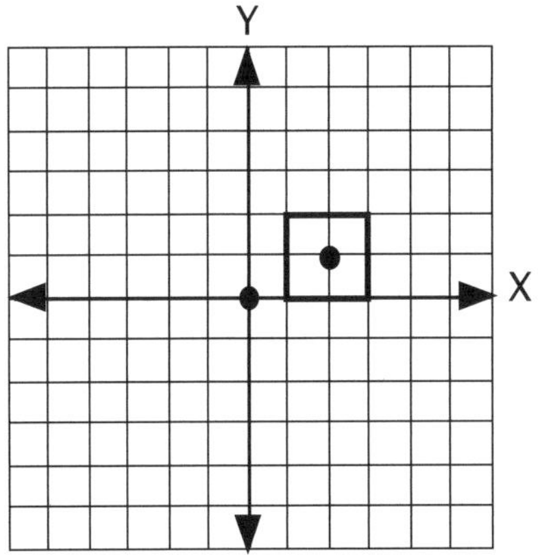

1. Plot the new points by translating each one over –4 and up 3.

2. Graph the result of #1.

A reflection (flip) of the original figure in line Y = –1.

3. Plot the new points by reflecting each in the line.

4. Graph the result of #3.

Follow the directions.

5. Joseph, 4' tall, is standing 15' from the front of the barn. If you were to lie down and look in such a way that your eye, the top of Joseph's head, and the top of the barn were in a straight line, the point where your eye is on the ground would be the vertex. Draw this.

6. From the vertex to Joseph's feet is 6'. How high is the barn?

7. If the distance from the vertex to Joseph's feet were 10', how high would the barn be?

8. Using the data in #7, how far is it from the vertex to the top of the barn?

9. What is the measure of $\angle\alpha$?

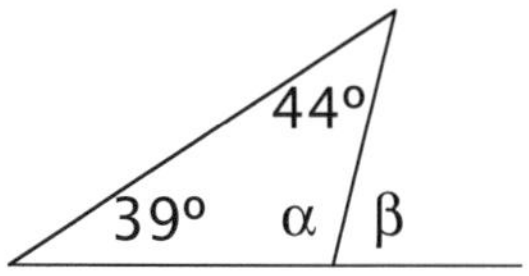

10. What is the measure of $\angle\beta$?

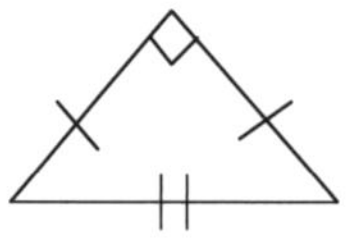

11. Describe the triangle above in terms of angles and in terms of sides.

12. The minor arc formed by a central angle is 79°.
What is the major arc?

13. What polygon has each interior angle measuring 120°?

14. If the apothem of the polygon in #13 is 5" and the length of each side is 7.5", what is the area of the polygon?

15. What is the perimeter of the polygon described above?

Complete the following proof.

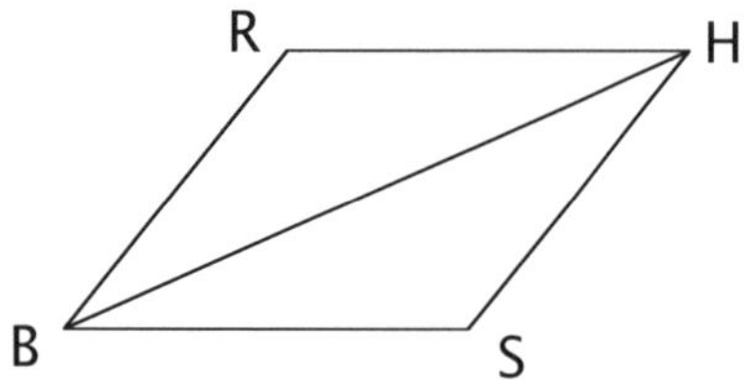

Given: ▭ RHSB is a rhombus.
Prove: $\Delta HSB \cong \Delta BRH$

	STATEMENTS	REASONS
16.	________	given
17.	________	________
18.	________	________
19.	________	________
20.	________	________

28E

Complete the transformations as directed.

A dilation (stretch) 3 times around the point (2, 1).

1. Plot the new points by dilating each around the point (2, 1).

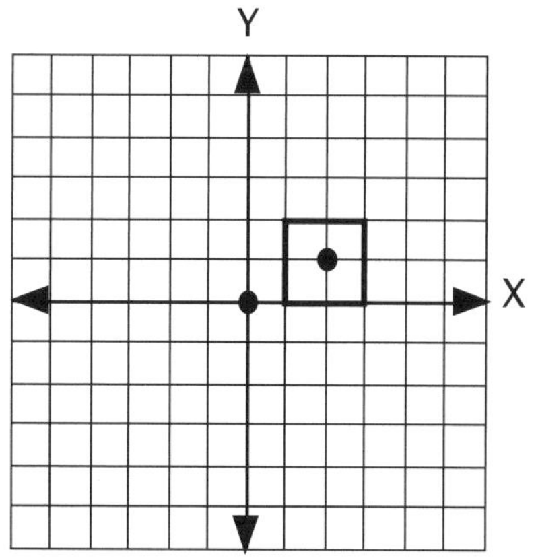

2. Graph the result of #1.

A rotation of the figure 180° around the point (-1, 0).

3. Plot the new points by rotating each around the point (-1, 0).

4. Graph the result of #3.

Follow the directions.

5. At a point 20 yards from the end of the shotgun, the pellets had spread three feet to the left and to the right when they hit the target. Draw a picture of this from a bird's eye view.

6. Assuming the same spread ratio, how much would pellets have spread in either direction 50 yards away?

7. Using the data in #6, how far is it from the vertex (end of the shotgun) to the edge of the spread?

8. What shape has each interior angle measuring 108°?

9. If the apothem of the polygon in #8 is 8 meters and the length of each side is 11 meters, what is its area?

10. What is the perimeter of the polygon described #9?

Complete the following proof.

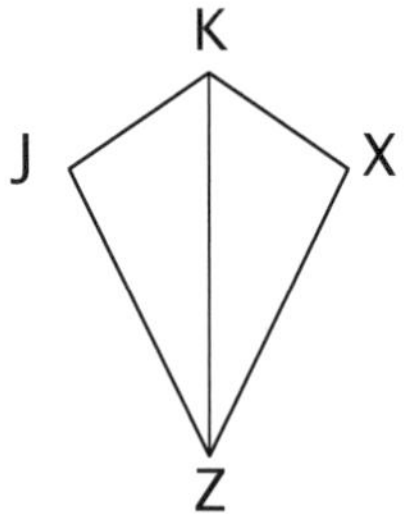

Given: $\overline{KZ}$ bisects ∠JKX and ∠JZX.
Prove: ΔJKZ ≅ ΔXKZ

STATEMENTS	*REASONS*
11. ______	given
12. ______	______
13. ______	______
14. ______	______
15. ______	______

Sharpen your algebra skills!

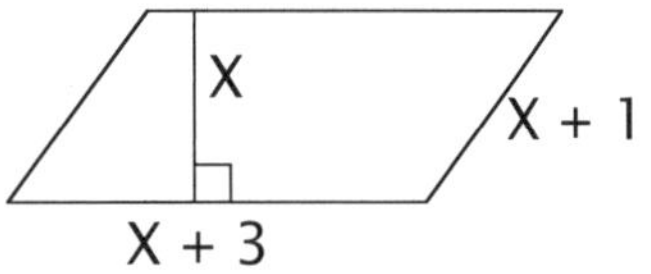

16. Perimeter = 36 feet, so X = _____.

17. Using your answer to #16, find the area of the parallelogram.

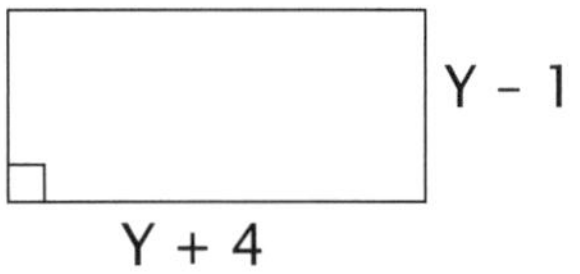

18. Perimeter = 98 inches, so Y = _____.

19. Using your answer to #18, find the area of the rectangle.

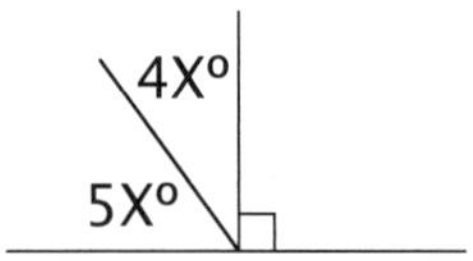

20. X = _____

There are a number of interesting things that can be done with inscribed angles, chords and tangents. We will not do the proofs for each of the following statements, but they all can be proved. There are four new rules below and three on the next page.

The measure of a central angle in a circle is the same as the measure of the intercepted arc.

The measure of an inscribed angle in a circle is one-half the measure of the intercepted arc.

If a quadrilateral is inscribed in a circle, the measures of each pair of opposite angles add up to 180°.

An angle inscribed in a semicircle is a right angle. (90° is one-half of 180°.)

Answer each question using what you know, the information given above, and your algebra skills if needed.

1. Find the measures of the intercepted arcs in terms of X, Y, and Z.

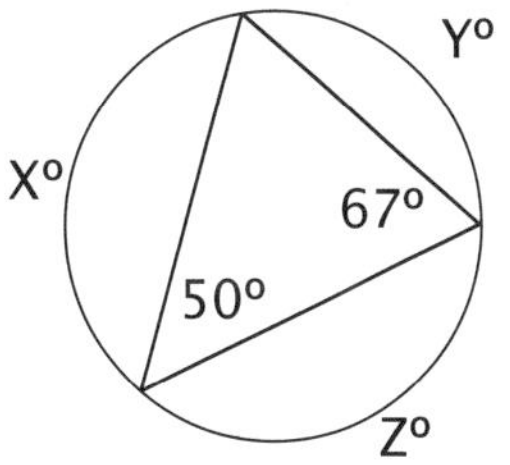

2. Find the measures of angles A and B. What is the measure of arc Cº that lies between A and the 84º angle?

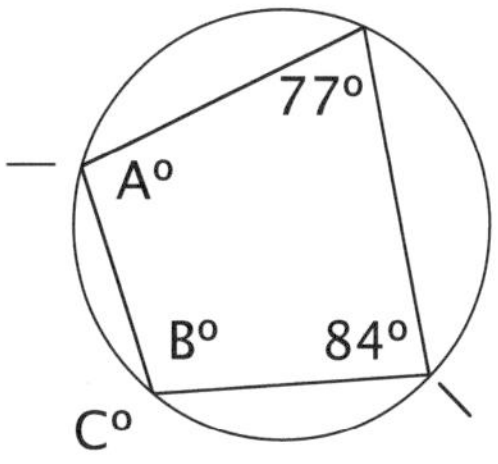

The angle formed by a chord and a tangent intercepts an arc whose measure is twice that of the angle.

3. RS is tangent to the circle whose center is C. m∠QRS = 63° What is the measure of ∠QCR?

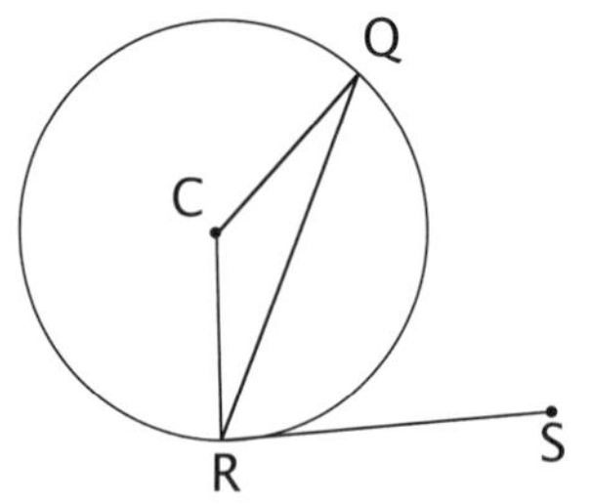

Each vertical angle formed by intersecting chords of a circle has a measure equal to one-half the sum of the intercepted arcs.

4. $m\overset{\frown}{AC} = 40°$ and $m\overset{\frown}{DB} = 30°$
What is the measure of each of the vertical angles formed at E?

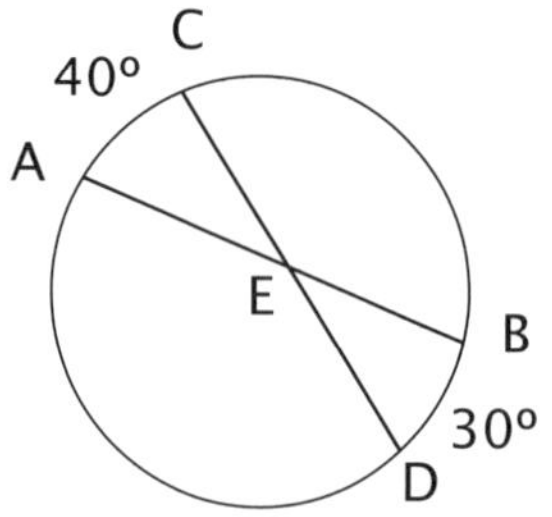

If two rays start outside a circle and cut the circle, the measure of the angle at the point, or origin, of the rays is one-half the difference of the two intercepted arcs on the circle.

5. $m\overset{\frown}{HJ} = 116°$ and $m\overset{\frown}{KL} = 36°$
What is the measure of ∠KPL?

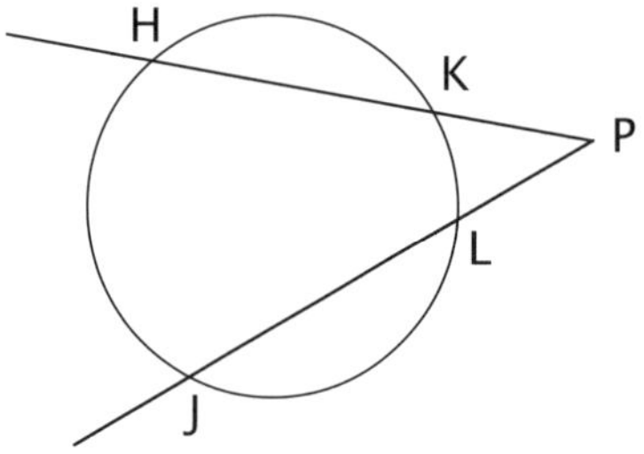

29A

Find the sine, cosine, and tangent of θ and α and express the ratios in fraction form. Reduce and simplify if possible.

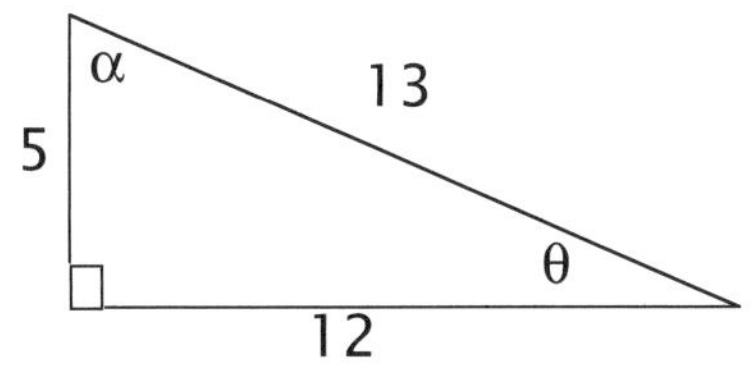

1. $\sin \theta =$
2. $\cos \theta =$
3. $\tan \theta =$
4. $\sin \alpha =$
5. $\cos \alpha =$
6. $\tan \alpha =$

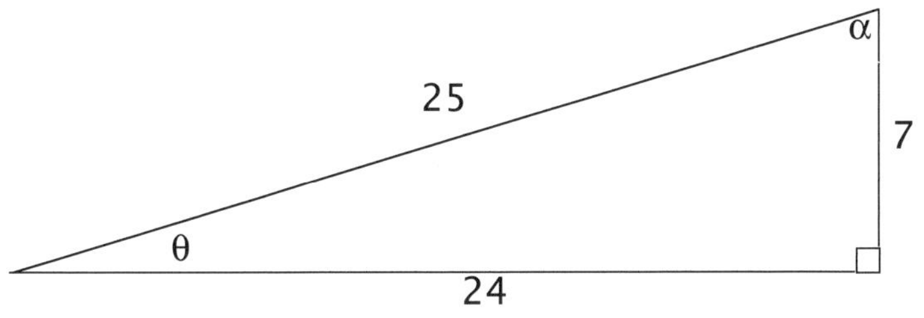

7. $\sin \theta =$
8. $\cos \theta =$
9. $\tan \theta =$
10. $\sin \alpha =$
11. $\cos \alpha =$
12. $\tan \alpha =$

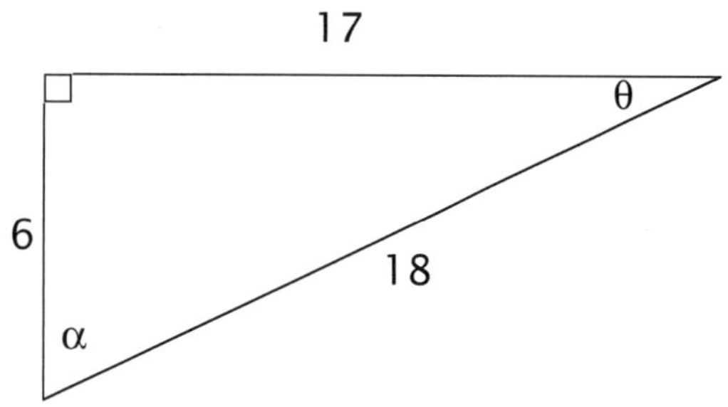

13. $\sin\theta =$

14. $\cos\theta =$

15. $\tan\theta =$

16. $\sin\alpha =$

17. $\cos\alpha =$

18. $\tan\alpha =$

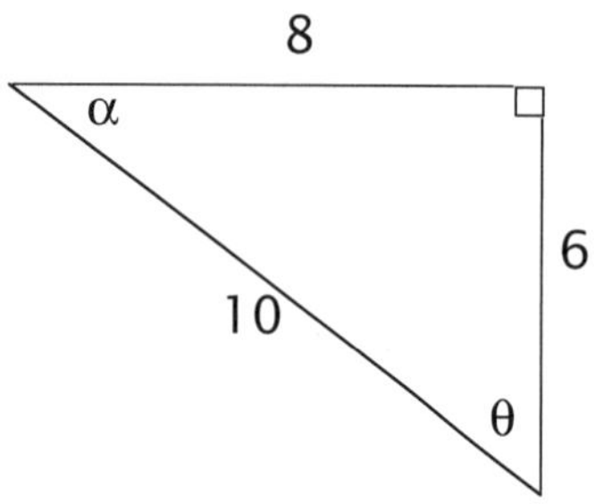

19. $\sin\theta =$

20. $\cos\theta =$

21. $\tan\theta =$

22. $\sin\alpha =$

23. $\cos\alpha =$

24. $\tan\alpha =$

LESSON PRACTICE 29B

Find the sine, cosine, and tangent of θ and α and express the ratios in fraction form. Reduce and simplify if possible.

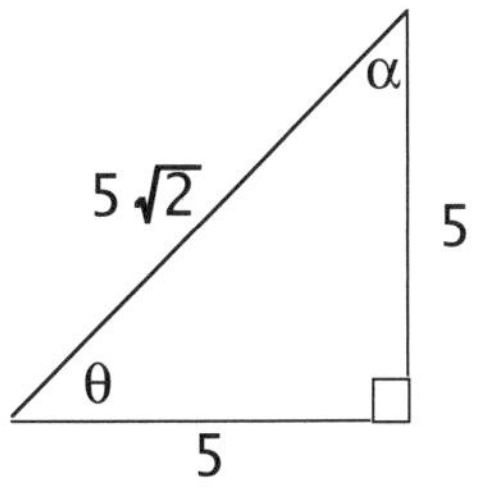

1. $\sin\theta =$

2. $\cos\theta =$

3. $\tan\theta =$

4. $\sin\alpha =$

5. $\cos\alpha =$

6. $\tan\alpha =$

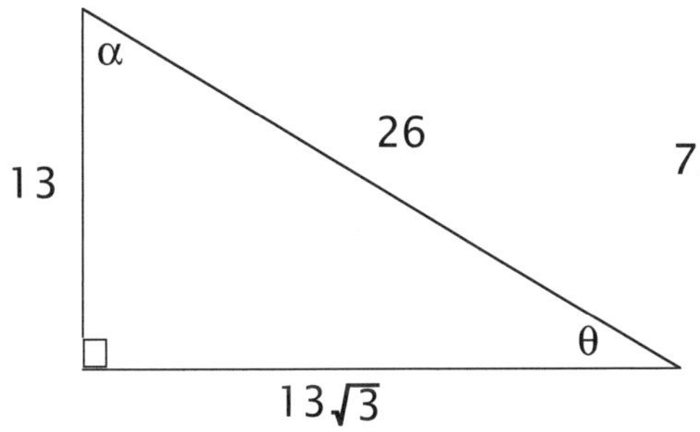

7. $\sin\theta =$

8. $\cos\theta =$

9. $\tan\theta =$

10. $\sin\alpha =$

11. $\cos\alpha =$

12. $\tan\alpha =$

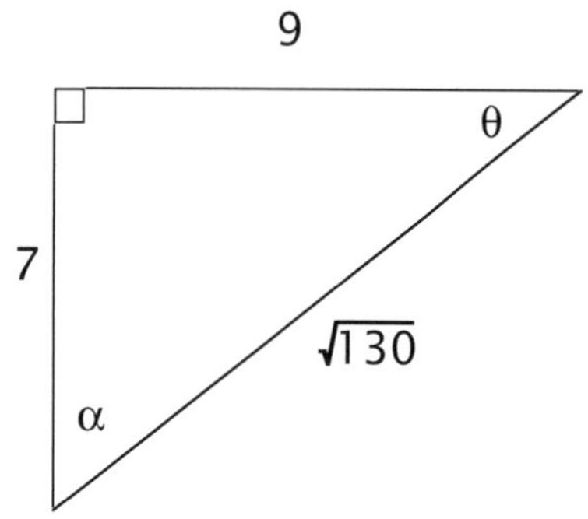

13. $\sin\theta =$

14. $\cos\theta =$

15. $\tan\theta =$

16. $\sin\alpha =$

17. $\cos\alpha =$

18. $\tan\alpha =$

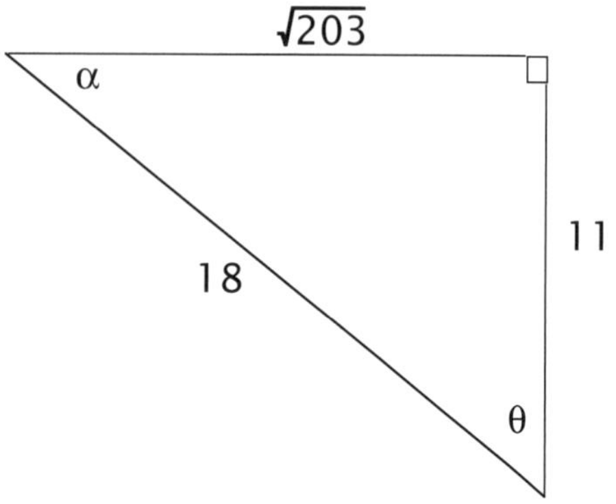

19. $\sin\theta =$

20. $\cos\theta =$

21. $\tan\theta =$

22. $\sin\alpha =$

23. $\cos\alpha =$

24. $\tan\alpha =$

29C

Find the sine, cosine, and tangent of θ and α and express the ratios in fraction form. Reduce and simplify if possible.

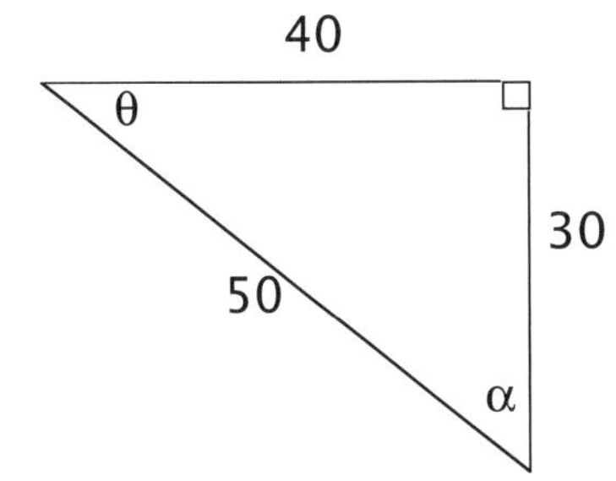

1. sin θ =
2. cos θ =
3. tan θ =
4. sin α =
5. cos α =
6. tan α =

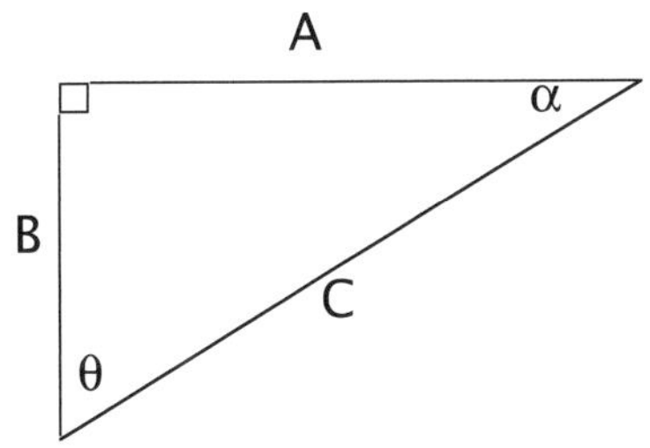

7. sin θ =
8. cos θ =
9. tan θ =
10. sin α =
11. cos α =
12. tan α =

Complete the transformations as directed.

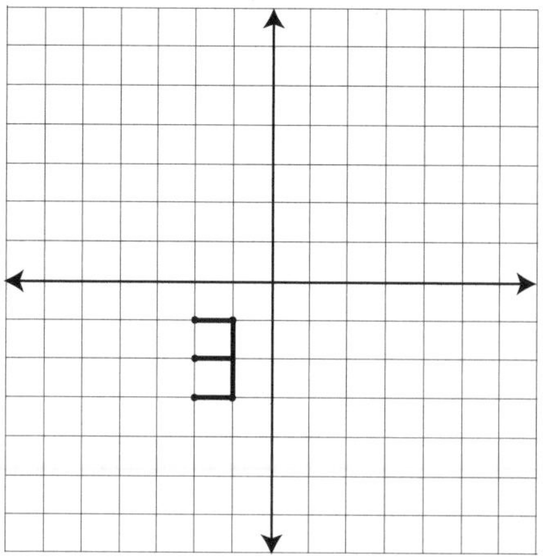

A translation (slide) of the figure over + 5.

13. Plot the new points.

14. Graph the result of #13.

A rotation 90° around the point (-1, -1).

15. Plot the new points.

16. Graph the result of #15.

Follow the directions.

17. At a point 10 feet from the end of a flashlight, the light had spread 24 inches to the left and 24 inches to the right. Draw a picture of this from a bird's eye view.

18. Assuming the same spread ratio, how much would the light spread in either direction 25 feet away?

19. How much would it spread 100 feet away?

20. How much would it spread four feet away?

29D

Find the sine, cosine, and tangent of θ and α and express the ratios in fraction form. Reduce and simplify if possible.

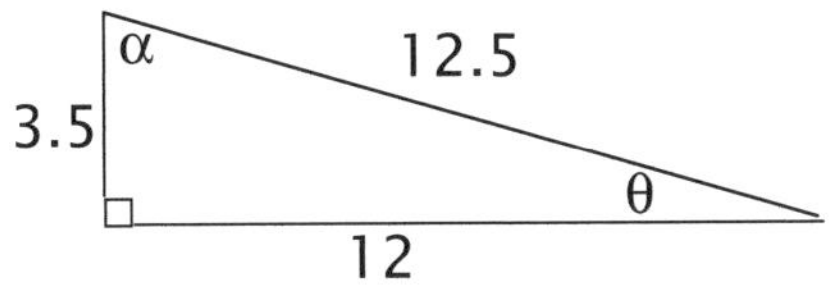

Hint: Multiply the ratios by 10/10 or some other fraction equal to 1, to eliminate the decimals before reducing the fractions.

1. $\sin\theta =$

2. $\cos\theta =$

3. $\tan\theta =$

4. $\sin\alpha =$

5. $\cos\alpha =$

6. $\tan\alpha =$

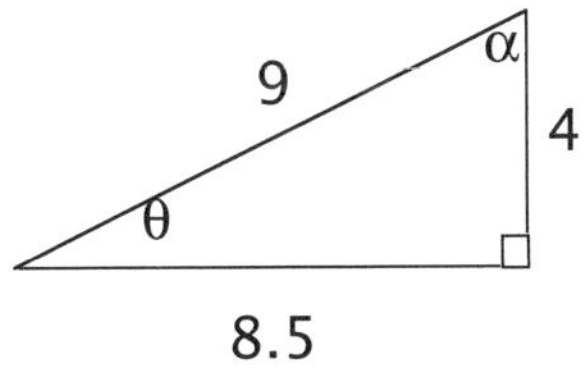

7. $\sin\theta =$

8. $\cos\theta =$

9. $\tan\theta =$

10. $\sin\alpha =$

11. $\cos\alpha =$

12. $\tan\alpha =$

Complete the transformations as directed.

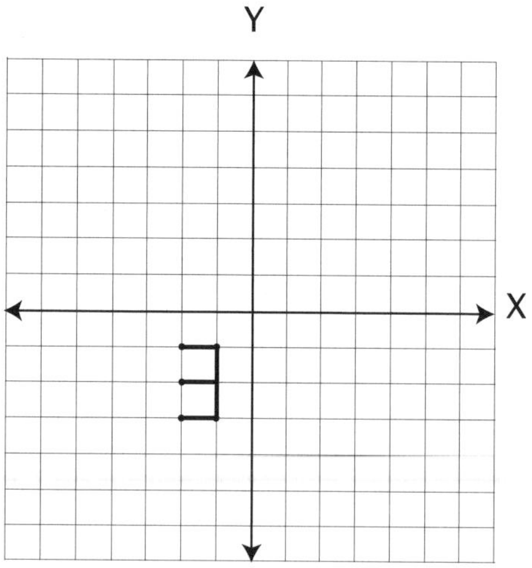

A reflection (flip) of the figure in Y = 1.

13. Plot the new points.

14. Graph the result of #13.

A reflection (flip) of the figure in X = 1.

15. Plot the new points.

16. Graph the result of #15.

Complete the following proof.

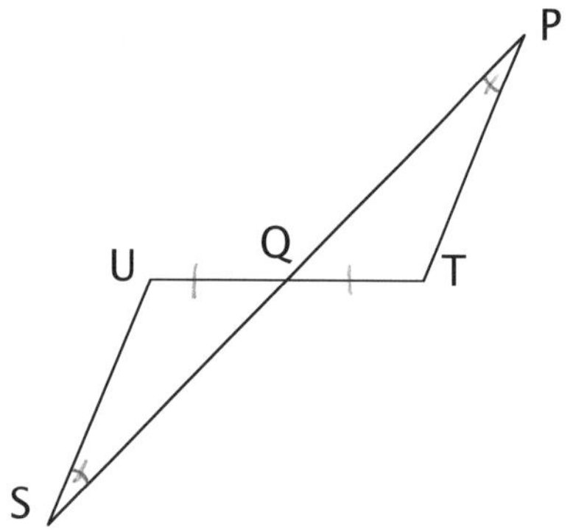

Given: ∠QSU ≅ ∠QPT
Q is the midpoint of $\overline{UT}$.
Prove: ΔQSU ≅ ΔQPT

STATEMENTS	***REASONS***
∠QSU ≅ ∠QPT	given
17. ________	________
18. ________	________
19. ________	________
20. ________	________

29E

Find the sine, cosine, and tangent of θ and α and express the ratios in fraction form. Reduce and simplify if possible.

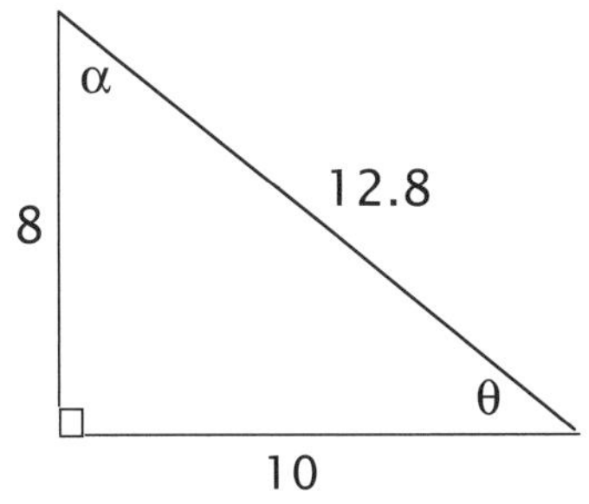

1. $\sin\theta =$
2. $\cos\theta =$
3. $\tan\theta =$
4. $\sin\alpha =$
5. $\cos\alpha =$
6. $\tan\alpha =$

Complete the transformations as directed.

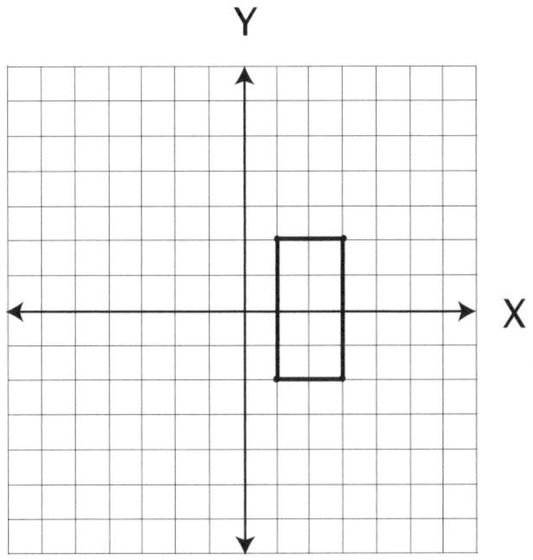

A translation (slide) of the figure over −6 and down 2.

7. Plot the new points.
8. Graph the result of #7.

A reflection (flip) of the figure on the X-axis.

9. Plot the new points.
10. Graph the result of #9.

Follow the directions.

11. Describe the triangle in terms of angles and of sides.

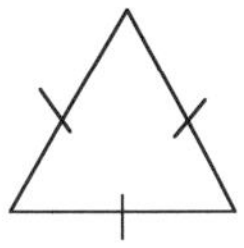

12. The long leg of a 30°–60°–90° triangle is $5\sqrt{6}$. What is the length of the short leg?
13. What is the length of the hypotenuse of the triangle in #12?
14. Give the term for a chord through the center of a circle.

Use the figure to find the measure of each of the following arcs.

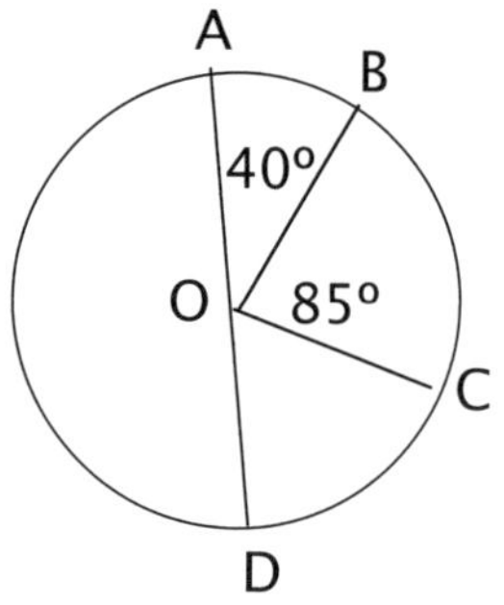

15. What is the measure of arc ABC?

16. What is the measure of minor arc DC?

17. What is the measure of arc ABCD?

Given: Line AD goes through the center of the circle.

Sharpen your algebra skills!

Find X. All lines that look parallel are parallel.

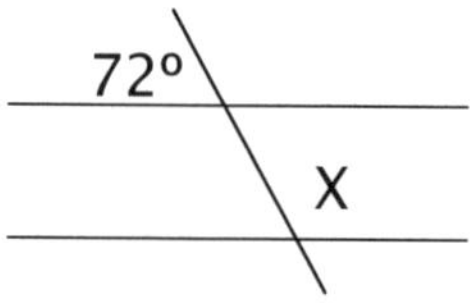

18. X = ________

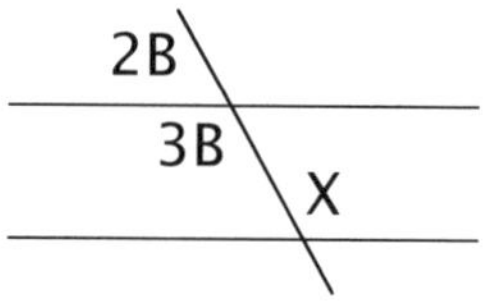

19. X = ________

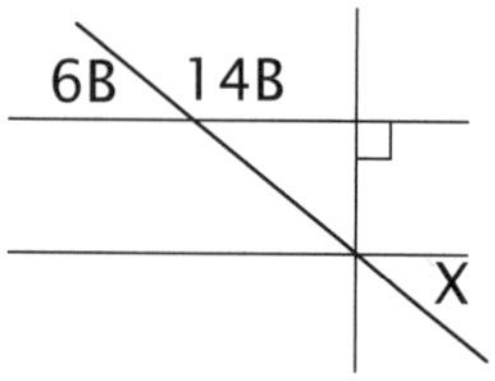

20. X = ________

29H

The Pythagorean theorem makes it possible to find the third side of a right triangle if the other two sides are known. Trigonometry uses ratios to find the other two sides of a right triangle if you know one side and an angle in addition to the right angle. In this lesson, we will explore solving problems using the tangent ratio.

A scientific calculator will give you the trig ratios in decimal form for any fraction. Before calculators were available, people used tables to find the needed values.

Follow the directions to make your own table for the tangents of certain angles.

1. Write the tangent ratio for each angle, and then divide to change the ratio to decimal form. Write your answers in the chart. The first one is done for you.

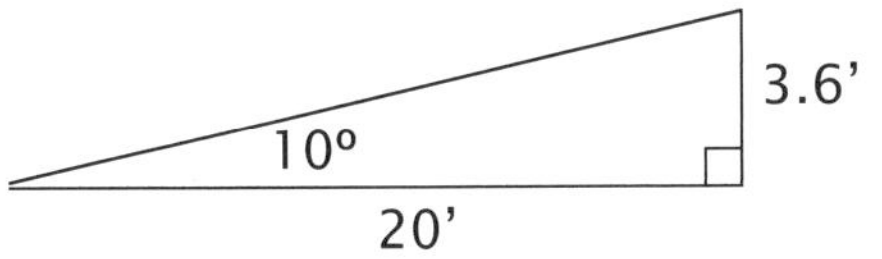

$\tan 10° = \frac{3.6}{20} = 0.18$

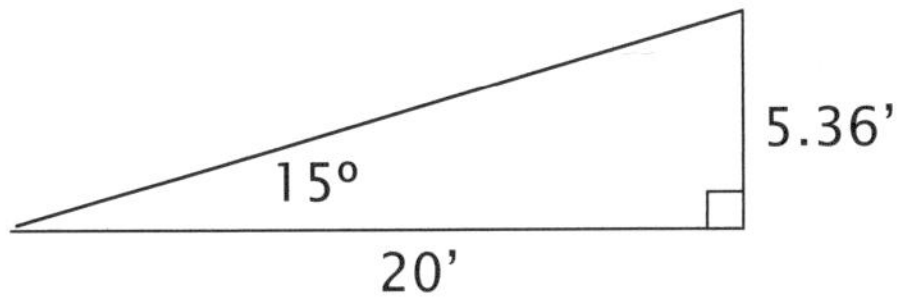

$\tan 15° = \frac{5.36}{20} =$ ______

angle	tan
10°	0.18
15°	
30°	
45°	
60°	

$\tan 30° = \frac{11.6}{20} =$ ______ $\tan 45° = \frac{20}{20} =$ ______ $\tan 60° = \frac{34.6}{20} =$ ______

Using a chart, we can find the decimal form of the tan ratio for any angle on the chart. Please note that any right triangle with a 10° angle will have a tan ratio for that angle of 0.18. All of the triangles with 90° and 10° angles will be similar by AA, so the *ratios* of their sides will be the same. Here is an example of a problem that can be solved using the tan ratio.

A man wants to know the distance across a river (a). He measures 50 ft along the stream bank from a point directly across from a tree on the opposite bank. He sights the tree from the new point and decides the angle from the stream bank is 60°. Using the tan ratio, he writes the following equation:

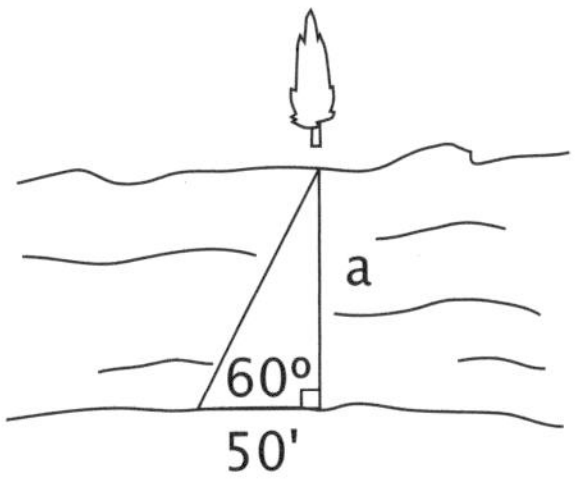

$\tan 60° = \frac{a}{50}$ Using the table, we rewrite tan 60° as 1.73, so we have $1.73 = \frac{a}{50}$

Solving for *a* gives 86.5 ft as the distance across the river.

2. Robin is 20 miles from a point directly below the summit of a mountain. The angle between the ground and the top of the mountain is 10°. How tall is the mountain?

3. Shane stood 150 feet from the base of a tall building and determined that the angle between the ground and the top of the building was 45° at that point. What was the height of the building?

LESSON PRACTICE

30A

Find all six trigonometric ratios for θ and write in fraction form. Always reduce if possible.

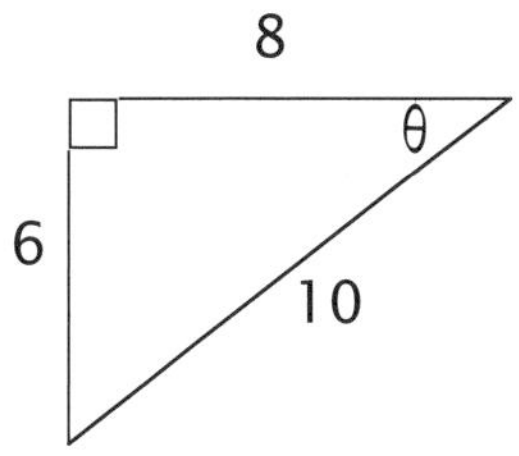

1. $\sin\theta =$

4. $\csc\theta =$

2. $\cos\theta =$

5. $\sec\theta =$

3. $\tan\theta =$

6. $\cot\theta =$

7. $\sin\theta =$

10. $\csc\theta =$

8. $\cos\theta =$

11. $\sec\theta =$

9. $\tan\theta =$

12. $\cot\theta =$

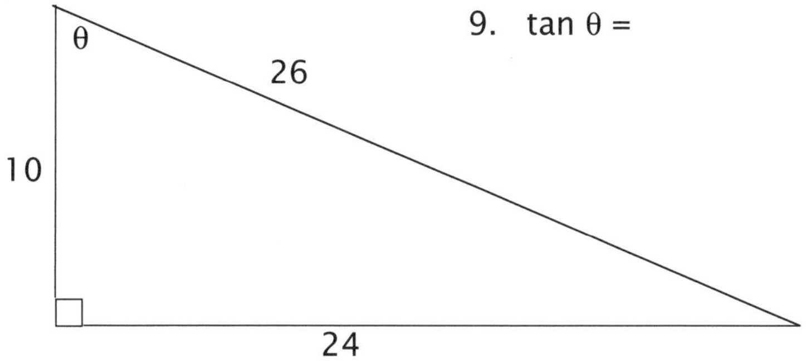

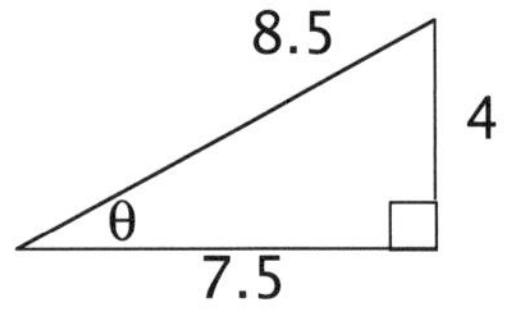

13. $\sin\theta =$

14. $\cos\theta =$

15. $\tan\theta =$

16. $\csc\theta =$

17. $\sec\theta =$

18. $\cot\theta =$

Fill in the blanks.

19. $\sin^2\theta + \cos^2\theta =$ __________ .

20. The formula above is the ______________ ______________
expressed with trig ratios.

LESSON PRACTICE

30B

Find all six trigonometric ratios for θ and write in fraction form.

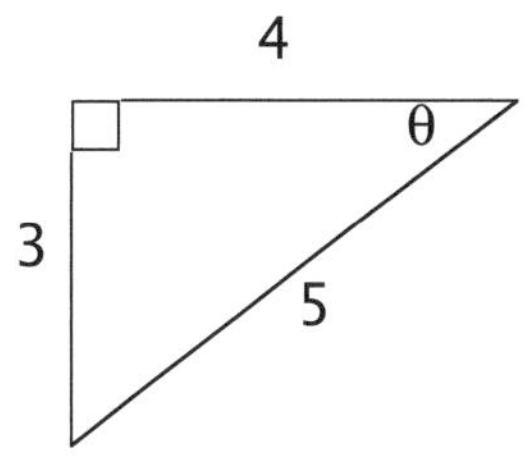

1. $\sin\theta =$

2. $\cos\theta =$

3. $\tan\theta =$

4. $\csc\theta =$

5. $\sec\theta =$

6. $\cot\theta =$

7. $\sin\theta =$

8. $\cos\theta =$

9. $\tan\theta =$

10. $\csc\theta =$

11. $\sec\theta =$

12. $\cot\theta =$

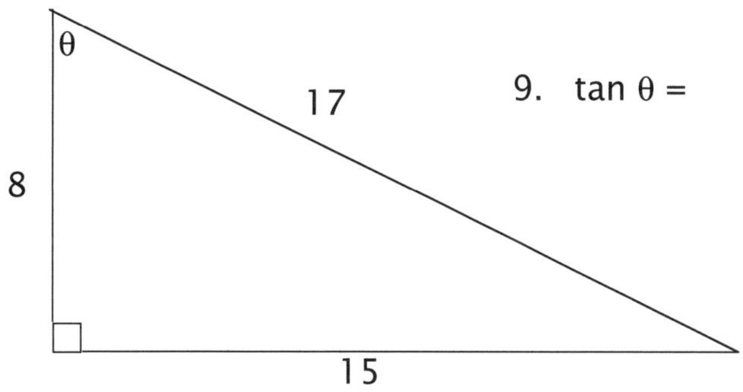

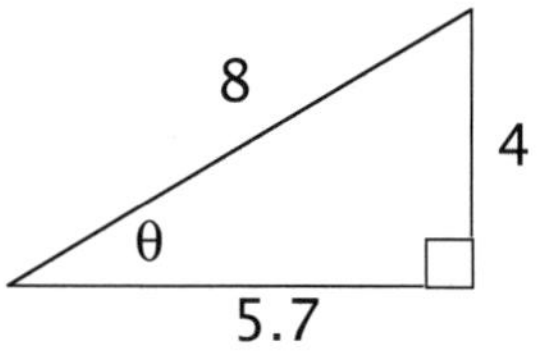

13. $\sin \theta =$

14. $\cos \theta =$

15. $\tan \theta =$

16. $\csc \theta =$

17. $\sec \theta =$

18. $\cot \theta =$

Fill in the blanks.

19. $\sin^2 \theta +$ __________ $= 1$

20. The formula above is the Pythagorean theorem expressed with

________________ ________________ .

30C

Find all six trigonometric ratios for θ and express the ratios in fraction form.

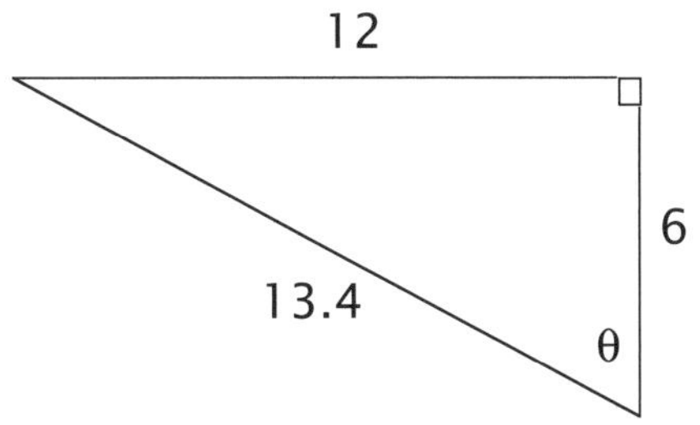

1. $\sin \theta =$

2. $\cos \theta =$

3. $\tan \theta =$

4. $\csc \theta =$

5. $\sec \theta =$

6. $\cot \theta =$

7. Write the Pythagorean theorem using trigonometric ratios.

Complete the transformations as directed.

A dilation (stretch) two times around point (2, 0).

8. Plot the new points.

9. Graph the result of #8.

A reflection (flip) in line X = –1.

10. Plot the new points.

11. Graph the result of #10.

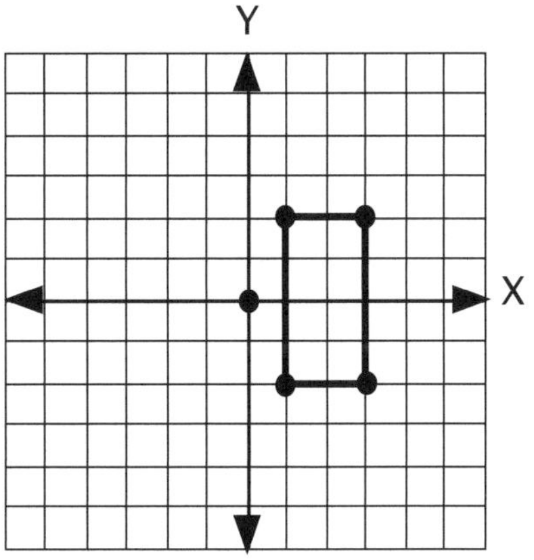

Complete the following proof.

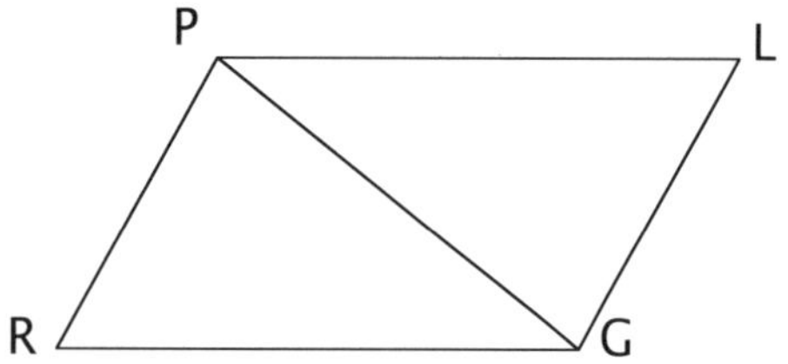

Given: ▱ PLGR is a parallelogram.

Prove: $\Delta PLG \cong \Delta GRP$

STATEMENTS	*REASONS*
▱ PLRG is a parallelogram.	given
12. ________	________
13. ________	________
14. ________	________
15. ________	________

Fill in the blanks.

16. A ten-sided figure is a(n) ________________ .

17. Vertical angles are ________________ .

18. Axioms and postulates are used to prove ________________ .

19. A piece of the circumference of a circle is a(n) ________________ .

20. In a 45°-45°-90° triangle, multiply ________________ by the length of a leg to find the length of the hypotenuse.

Find all six trigonometric ratios for θ and express the ratios in fraction form.

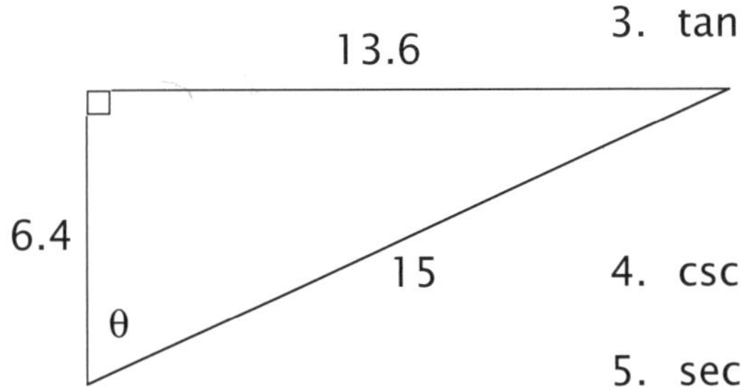

1. $\sin\theta =$
2. $\cos\theta =$
3. $\tan\theta =$
4. $\csc\theta =$
5. $\sec\theta =$
6. $\cot\theta =$

7. $(\sin\theta)^2 + (\cos\theta)^2 =$

Complete the transformation as directed.

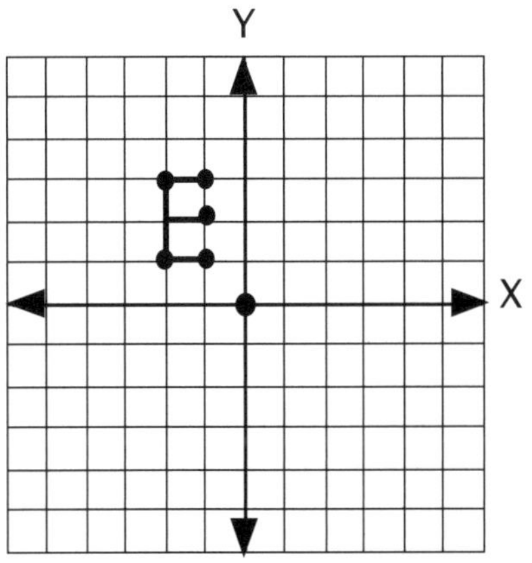

8. Plot the reflection of the three points in the line X = 1.

9. Draw the reflection of "E" on the line X = 1.

Complete the following proof.

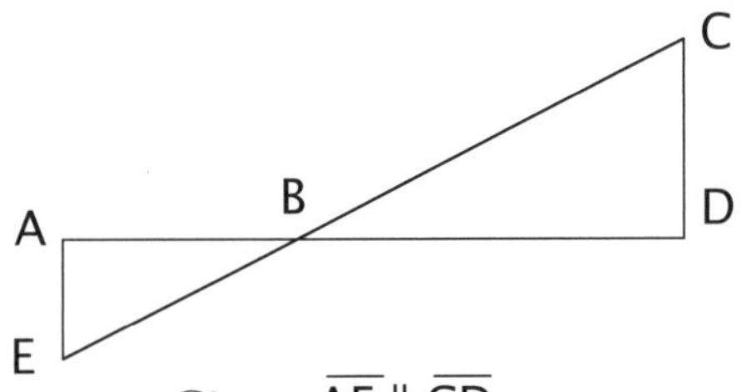

Given: $\overline{AE} \parallel \overline{CD}$
Prove: $\triangle ABE \sim \triangle DBC$

	STATEMENTS	***REASONS***
10.	______	______
11.	______	______
12.	______	______
13.	______	______

Fill in the blanks using the drawings as needed.

14. $\overline{AB}$ is a(n) _______________ .

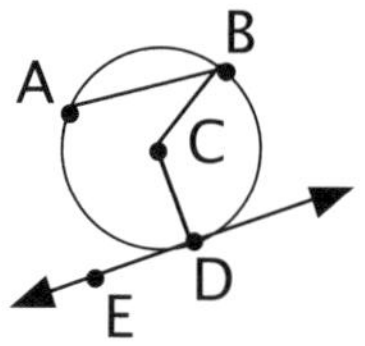

15. $\overleftrightarrow{ED}$ is a(n) _______________ .

16. In a 30°-60°-90° triangle, multiply _______________ by the length of the short leg to find the length of the long leg.

17. The sum of the interior angles of a triangle is _______________ .

18. The sum of the exterior angles of a regular polygon is

_______________ .

19. The volume of the pyramid is _______________ .

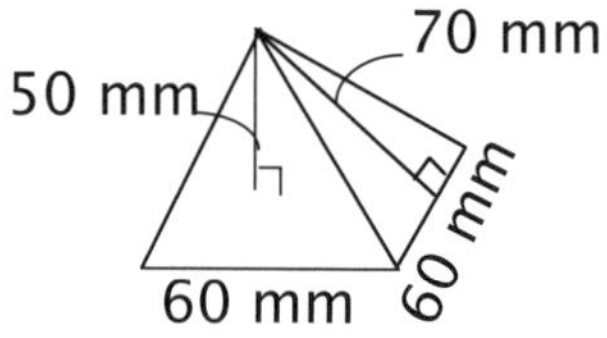

20. The surface area of the pyramid is _______________ .

Find all six trigonometric ratios for θ and express the ratios in fraction form.

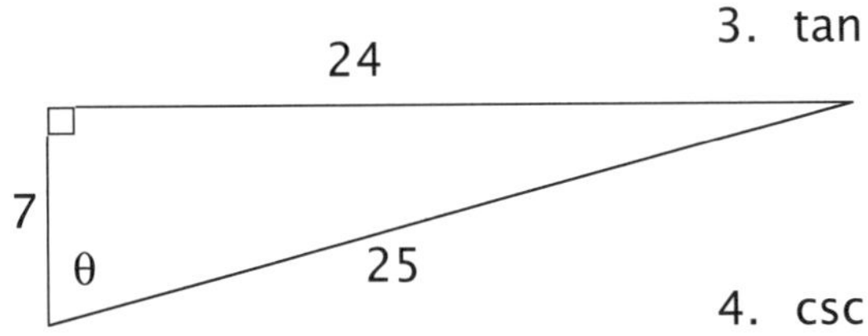

1. $\sin\theta =$
2. $\cos\theta =$
3. $\tan\theta =$
4. $\csc\theta =$
5. $\sec\theta =$
6. $\cot\theta =$

7. $\_\_\_\_\_\_^2 + (\cos\theta)^2 = 1$

Complete the transformation as directed.

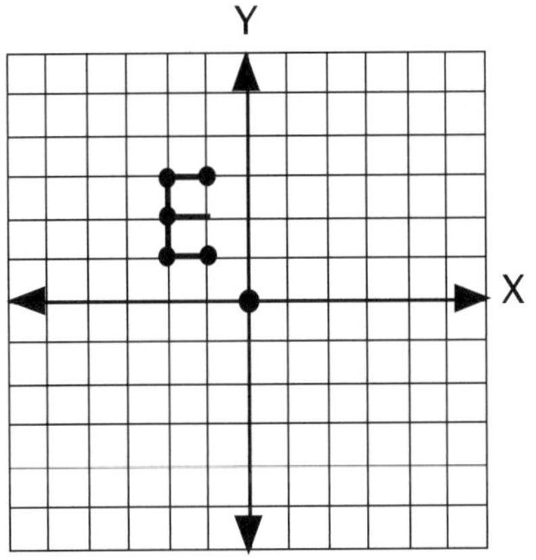

8. Plot the translation of the three points over -2 and down 3.

9. Draw the translation of "E" over -2 and down 3.

Fill in the blanks, using the drawings as needed.

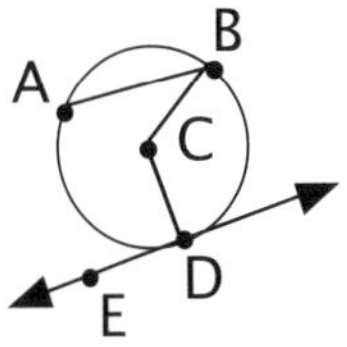

10. An eight-sided figure is a(n) ________________.

11. In the circle, $\overline{CD}$ is ________________ to $\overleftrightarrow{ED}$.

12. If the diameter is 20', the area of the circle is ________________.

Fill in the blanks, using the drawings as needed.

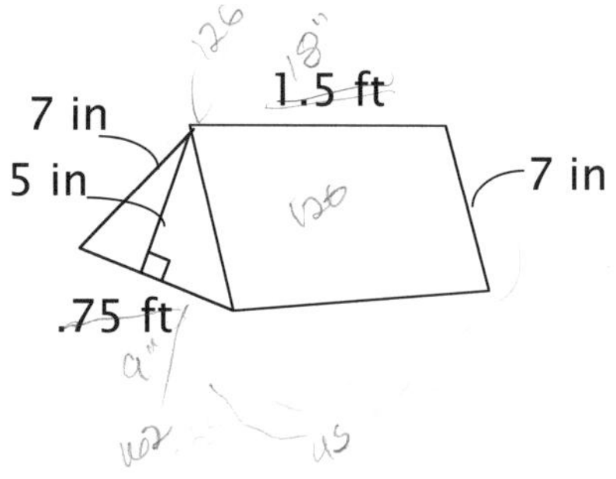

13. The volume of the prism is ________________ .

14. The surface area of the prism is ________________ .

15. In the figure below, a circle with center O is circumscribed about a square. What is the circumference of the circle?

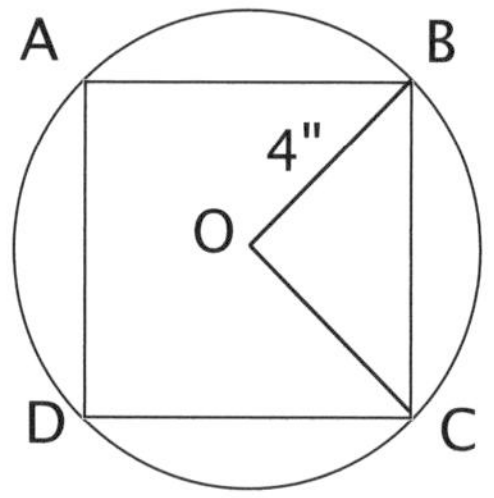

16. Given your answer for #15, find the length of minor arc BC.

Sharpen your algebra skills!

17. Average base = 14 inches, so X = _______.

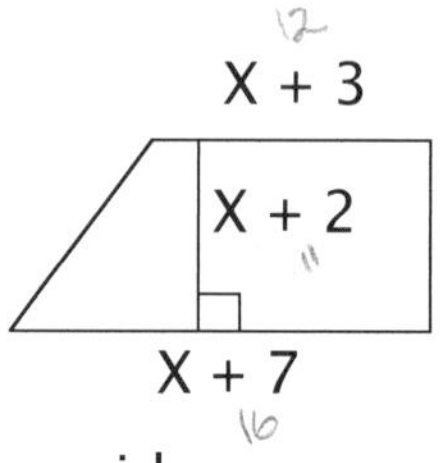

18. Using your answer to #17, find the area of the trapezoid.

19. Perimeter of the triangle = 36 feet, so A = _______.

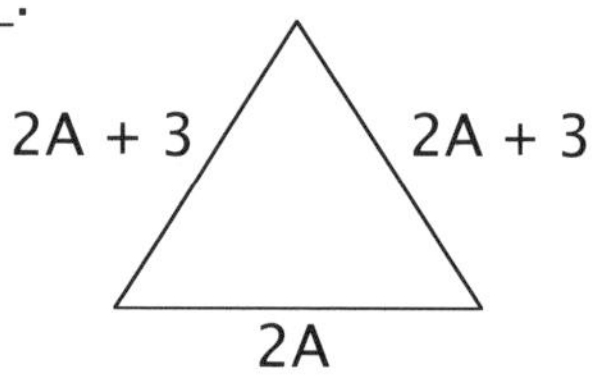

20. What is the value of A if the perimeter is 42 feet?

As we mentioned in the last lesson, calculators may be used to find the values of trigonometric ratios. If you have a calculator with sin, cos, and tan keys, try using it to check the values you put in the chart in lesson 29.

For most calculators, push the tan key, and then enter the measure of the angle. You will notice that some of the values are slightly different due to rounding. The trig charts found in math books usually round the value of each ratio to four decimal places.

The sine and cosine ratios may also be used to solve problems. If you have a calculator that can find trig ratios, try using it. Otherwise, you can find the values you need at the bottom of the next page.

Use the sin of the angle to help you find the missing information. Set up a ratio and solve for the unknown as you did for the problems in lesson 29. Draw a sketch of each problem.

1. A ladder 14 feet long is leaning against a wall. The bottom of the ladder forms a 55° angle with the ground. How high on the wall does the ladder reach? $\sin 55° = \frac{w}{14}$

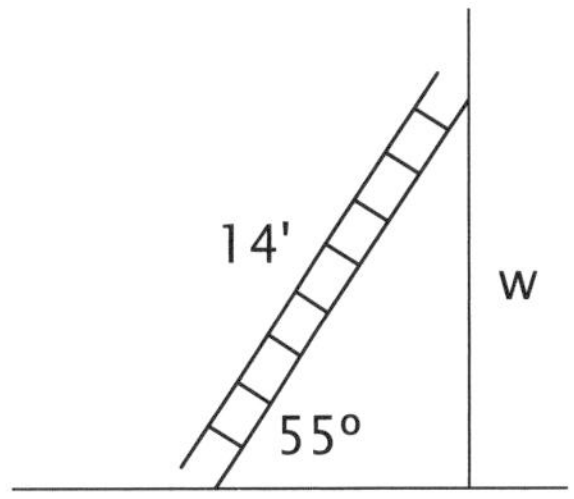

2. A road makes an angle of 4° with level ground. As a car moves three miles along the road, how many feet does the car climb?

3. A radar operator reported that a plane was detected at an angle of elevation of 34°. The direct distance between the radar screen and the plane was 4.5 miles. How high was the plane above the ground?

Use the cos of the angle to help you find the missing information. Set up a ratio, and solve for the unknown. Draw a sketch of each problem.

4. A ladder 14 feet long is leaning against a wall. The bottom of the ladder forms a 55° angle with the ground. How far from the building is the bottom of the ladder? $\cos 55° = \frac{g}{14}$

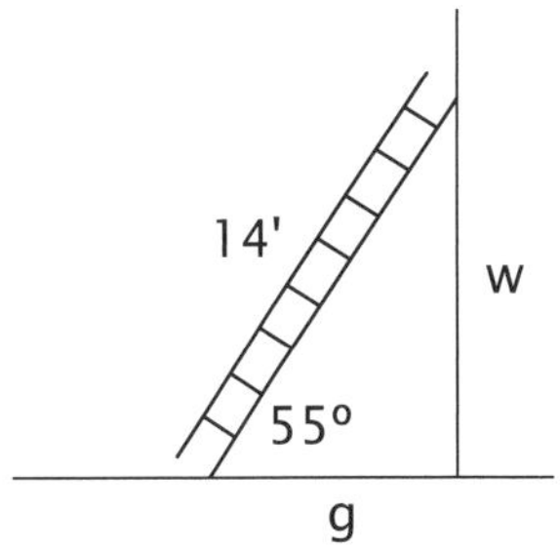

5. The ramp to a bridge has an angle of 7° with level ground. If a car traveled 500 feet up the slant of the ramp, how far ahead had it moved horizontally, from the beginning of the ramp?

6. Nolan put a support cable from the top of a telephone pole to a point 30 feet from the base of the pole. If the angle between the cable and the ground is 60 , how long is the cable?

Here are the sine and cosine ratios for these problems if you need them.

angle	sin
4°	0.0698
34°	0.5592
55°	0.8192

angle	cos
7°	0.9925
55°	0.5736
60°	0.5000

Symbols & Tables

SYMBOLS

$<$	less than
$>$	greater than
$\leq$	less than or equal to
$\geq$	greater than or equal to
$=$	equal in numerical value
$\neq$	not equal
$\approx$	approximately equal
$\cong$	congruent
$\sim$	similar
$\sqrt{\ }$	square root (radical sign)
π	pi (≈ 3.14 or $\approx \frac{22}{7}$)
α	alpha
β	beta
γ	gamma
δ	delta
θ	theta
$\{\ \}$	set
$\subset$	subset
$\cap$	intersection
$\cup$	union
$\varnothing$	empty set
∞	infinity
$\leftrightarrow$	line
$\rightarrow$	ray
—	line segment
$\frown$	arc
$\angle$	angle
$m\angle$	measure of angle
$\perp$	perpendicular
$\parallel$	parallel
∟	right angle

VOLUME

Measure of inscribed angle =
$1/2$ measure of intercepted arc

Perimeter: add the length of each side

Circumference of a circle = $2\pi r$ or πd

Area

rectangle = bh (base x height)
triangle = ½ bh
square = bh or s^2
parallelogram or rhombus = bh
trapezoid = $\frac{base_1 + base_2}{2}(h)$
circle = πr^2
ellipse = ½ short axis x ½ long axis x π

Surface Area

rectangular solid, cube, prism, pyramid: add the area of each face
cylinder: $2\pi r^2 + 2\pi rh$
sphere: $4\pi r^2$

Volume

rectangular solid, prism = area of base (B) x h
cylinder = area of base (B) x h
pyramid and cone = $1/3$ area of base (B) x h
sphere: $\frac{4}{3}\pi r^3$

MISCELLANEOUS

Number of degrees

sum of interior angles of a regular polygon

$(N - 2) \times 180^0$ $(N = \text{number of sides})$

sum of interior angles of a quadrilateral: 360^0

sum of interior angles of a triangle: 180^0

sum of eterior angles of a regular polygon: 360^0

Measure of central angle = measure of intercepted arc

Pythagorean Theorem

$L^2 + L^2 = H^2$

$\sin^2 + \cos^2 = 1$

Special Triangles

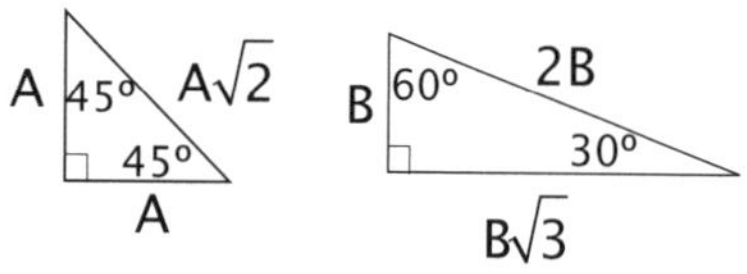

Trigonometry functions

$$\text{sine}(\sin) = \frac{\text{opposite}}{\text{hypotenuse}}$$

$$\text{cosine}(\cos) = \frac{\text{adjacent}}{\text{hypotenuse}}$$

$$\text{tangent}(\tan) = \frac{\text{opposite}}{\text{adjacent}}$$

$$\text{cosecant}(\csc) = \frac{\text{hypotenuse}}{\text{opposite}}$$

$$\text{secant}(\sec) = \frac{\text{hypotenuse}}{\text{adjacent}}$$

$$\text{cotangent}(\cot) = \frac{\text{adjacent}}{\text{opposite}}$$

Glossary

A–B

Acute angle - has a measure greater than 0° and less than 90°

Acute triangle - each angle is less than 90°

Adjacent angles - share common side and have the same origin

Apothem - perpendicular line from side to center of a regular polygon

Arc - a piece of the circumference of a circle

Area - the number of square units in a two-dimensional figure

Associative property - the way terms are grouped does not affect the answer; true for addition and multiplication

Axiom - same as a postulate, known to be true but cannot be proven

Bearing - the compass direction or angle used to navigate a ship or plane in the desired direction

Bisect - to cut into two equal parts

Bisector - a line or line segment that divides another line segment or an angle into two equal parts

C

Carroll diagram - a chart used to organize what is known and discover what is unknown in simple logic problems

Cartesian coordinate system - the X-Y graphing system named for René Descartes

Chord - line drawn between two points on the circumference of a circle

Circumference - the distance around the outside of a circle

Collinear - refers to two or more points on the same line

Commutative property - the order of terms does not affect the answer; true for addition and multiplication

Compass rose - a design used on maps to indicate directions

Complementary angles - any two angles whose measures add up to 90°

Conclusion - in formal logic, the final statement based on the major and minor premises

Conditional - the major premise of a logical argument or syllogism

Converse - in formal logic, a statement formed by reversing the order of the major premise

Cone - a three dimensional figure rising to a point from a circular base, as in ice cream cone

Congruent - having the same size and shape

Converse - the reverse of a postulate or theorem

Coplanar - refers to two or more lines lying in the same plane

Cosecant - in trigonometry, the inverse of the sine

Cosine - trigonometric function defined as adjacent angle over the hypotenuse

Cotangent - in trigonometry, the inverse of the tangent

CPCTRC - corresponding parts of congruent triangles are congruent

Cube - a rectangular solid with all the edges having the same length

Cylinder - three dimensional figure with a circular base and top, and perpendicular sides, as in a can

D–E

Decagon - regular polygon with ten sides and angles

Deductive reasoning - starts with a known fact and reaches a conclusion using the rules of logic

Diameter - a line drawn from one side of a circle to another that goes through the center of the circle

Dilation - a figure is enlarged or reduced without changing its shape

Dodecagon - regular polygon with twelve sides and angles

Ellipse - a "stretched" circle with two centers or foci

Empty set - no possible answer; same as the null set

Equiangular triangle - all angles are congruent, angular means angle

Equilateral triangle - all sides are congruent, lateral means side

Exterior angles - the angles on the outside formed by a transversal intersecting parallel lines, or the outside angles formed by extending the sides of a polygon

F–H

Face - the flat surface of a three dimensional figure or solid

Factors - the numbers being multiplied to find the product; in the geometric illustration, the dimensions of a rectangle

Formal logic - uses deductive reasoning and predetermined rules to reach a conclusion

Golden rectangle - a rectangle whose proportions are thought to be particularly pleasing; ratio between the sides is the golden ratio

Hexagon - regular polygon with six sides and angles

Hypotenuse - the side opposite the right angle in a right triangle

I–L

Inductive reasoning - comes to a specific conclusion based on general observations

Inscribed polygon - a polygon drawn inside another figure, so that each vertex of the inscribed polygon touches the outer figure

Intersection - where two or more figures or sets overlap

Interior angles - the angles on the inside formed by a transversal intersecting parallel lines, or inside angles of a polygon

Intersection - where two or more lines or planes meet, where two lines share a common point or two planes share a common line, or where two sets overlap

Irrational numbers - cannot be written as a rational number; if changed to a decimal the numbers continue ...

Isosceles triangle - a triangle with two congruent sides

Latitude - horizontal lines that measure the north-south distance from the equator

Line - an infinite number of connected points

Line segment - a finite or measurable piece of a line

Longitude - vertical lines extending from pole to pole that measure the east-west distance from the prime meridian

M–O

Major premise - the first statement in a syllogism; also called the conditional

Minor premise - the second statement in a syllogism

Mobius strip - a strip of paper joined in such a way that one continuous line can be drawn on both sides

Midpoint - marks the center of a line segment

Null set - set with no members; empty set

Oblique prism - a prism whose sides are not at right angles to the bases

Obtuse angle - has a measure greater than 90° and less than 180°

Obtuse triangle - one angle greater than 90°

Octagon - regular polygon with eight sides and angles

Origin - the point where the X and Y axis intersect on a graph, or the starting point of a ray

P

Parallel lines - two straight lines in the same plane that don't intersect

Parallelogram - a four-sided figure with opposite sides parallel and of equal length; angles may or may not be right angles

Pentagon - regular polygon with five sides and angles

Perimeter - the distance around the outside of a two-dimensional figure

Perpendicular bisector - a line or line segment that is perpendicular to another line segment through its midpoint

Perpendicular lines - two lines that form right angles where they intersect

Pi - Greek letter π, the relationship between the diameter and circumference of a circle, equals 22/7, approximately 3.14

Plane - infinite number of connected lines lying in the same flat surface; has length and width; two-dimensional

Plane geometry - study of two-dimensional figures

Point - in geometry, the smallest possible unit of measure; has position but no dimension

Polygon - a two-dimensional shape with three or more sides; a regular polygon has all sides equal

Polynomial - an algebraic expression with more than one term

Postulate - assumed to be true, but cannot be proven; an observation

Prism - a solid with two parallel bases and lateral surfaces that are parallelograms

Protractor - device used to measure number of degrees in an angle

Pyramid - has a square base and four triangular faces, or a triangular base and three triangular faces

Pythagorean theorem - describes the relationship between the legs and the hypotenuse of a right triangle

$(L^2 + L^2 = H^2)$

Q–R

Quadrilateral - a four sided polygon

Radical - a numeral written with a square root sign

Radius - a line from the center of a circle to the edge; plural is radii

Rational number - the result of dividing two whole numbers; can be a whole number, decimal or fraction

Ratio - relationship between two numbers expressed as a fraction

Rectangle - means "right angle" - a four sided polygon with four right angles and opposite sides the same length

Ray - part of a line having a definite starting point and proceeding in one direction only

Rectangular solid - has six faces and all the angles are 90°

Reflection - a figure is flipped in a line to form a mirror image

Reflex angle - has a measure between 180° and 360°

Reflexive property - A = A

Regular polygon - a polygon with all sides and all angles congruent

Remote interior angle - interior angle farthest from the one under discussion

Rhombus - a quadrilateral with four sides congruent

Right angle - an angle with a measure of 90°

Right triangle - a triangle with one 90° angle

Rotation - a geometric figure is rotated around a given point

S

Scalene triangle - has no congruent sides

Secant - a line intersecting the circumference of a circle in two places, or in trigonometry, the inverse of the cosine

Sector - pie-shaped section of a circle

Set - a collection of numbers or things

Similar - two geometric figures whose angles are congruent, and whose sides have the same ratio

Sine - trigonometric function defined as opposite angle over the hypotenuse

Solid geometry - study of three-dimensional figures

Sphere - a three dimensional circle; "ball"

Square - a quadrilateral with four congruent sides and four right angles (also congruent); a four-sided regular polygon

Square roots - the factors of a square, 3 is the square root of 9

Straight angle - 180° angle

Subset - a part of a given set

Supplementary angles - any two angles whose measures add up to 180°

Surface area - the sum of the areas of all the faces of a solid

Syllogism - the reasoning process in formal logic

Symmetry - if A = B, then B = A

T–U

Tangent - (geometry) a line that intersects the circumference of a circle at exactly one point

Tangent - (trigonometry) the function defined as opposite side over the adjacent side

Theorem - a statement that can be proven true by the use of postulates

Transformational geometry - concerned with moving and changing figures on a graph

Transitive property - If A = B and B = C, then A = C

Translation - a figure is moved, but not changed

Transversal - a line that intersects two or more lines

Trapezoid - a four-sided polygon with two parallel sides and two sides that are not parallel

Triangle - polygon with three sides

Trigonometry - study of the measurements of triangles and their relationships

Union - two or more sets combined

V–Z

Vector - a measurement involving both direction and speed or force

Venn diagram - two or three overlapping circles or ovals; used to illustrate intersection and union of sets

Vertex - the point of an angle where the lines, segments, or rays intersect

Vertical angles - opposite angles formed by the intersection of two lines

Volume - the number of cubic units in a three-dimensional figure